MARRIAGE WITH GENIUS

MARRIAGE
WITH GENIUS

by

FREDA STRINDBERG

JONATHAN CAPE
THIRTY BEDFORD SQUARE
LONDON

FIRST PUBLISHED 1937

JONATHAN CAPE LTD.   30 BEDFORD SQUARE, LONDON
AND 91 WELLINGTON STREET WEST, TORONTO

PRINTED IN GREAT BRITAIN IN THE CITY OF OXFORD
AT THE ALDEN PRESS
PAPER MADE BY JOHN DICKINSON & CO., LTD.
BOUND BY A. W. BAIN & CO., LTD.

CONTENTS

FOREWORD

In his preface to the first of his autobiographical volumes, August Strindberg makes an interviewer put the question: 'What sort of a book is it that you are about to give us — novel, memoirs, biography — or what?' Whereupon the author makes answer: 'The title page tells you, it is the story of the growth of a soul.'

This book, too, is neither a novel, nor a biography, nor memoirs, it is simply the story of my marriage. I wrote it down as life itself dictated it, because it belongs above all to my mate, to August Strindberg, who has willed:
'I want no other monument than a cross of wood upon my grave, my story and my letters.'

Four decades have gone by since Sweden's great poet, August Strindberg, married me on the Isle of Heligoland — the Holy Land. He, the pioneer, the iconoclast, the fighter and thinker, the poet-seer — I, a simple girl, nothing but youth, thirsting for life, with a warm heart beneath the hindering cuirass of an artificial education. He, the 'Unknown' out of *Toward Damascus*, I, 'The Lady' in it. We were an unequal pair, partly complementing each other, partly divided by our unlikeness. The union was rich in joy and sorrow. We took both as they came, not chaffering, draining sweetness and bitterness to the last drop.
'A Spring Love, bewitching and pitiless; storm-clouded, but full of radiance and power. Now happiness, now sorrow' — he called those days, his Second Spring —
Then we parted for a while.

One more May was in the land when I did pilgrimage — to a grave.

Believing in a resurrection.

Hail, Stockholm, thou city of his birth! He speaks to me in every stone of thine. I feel him in thy diaphanous azure, in thy scented sea breeze.

Here I must find him. The Past rises.

'They have erected a beautiful statue to August Strindberg on one of our finest spots, in front of the City Hall,' a friend tells me. 'Would you like to see it?'

Would I! . . .

It is already dark. As in a dream I walk through solemn portals over a stony courtyard, step out into the garden of the City Hall and — stand transfixed. The moon glimmers ghostly white on the water. Beyond it, the old quarter of the town rears sombre peaks into the night.

But my eyes do not dwell upon the picture in all its beauty and greatness. They seek the man who was my husband and find him — never again to forget this meeting.

The tall figure stands white before me in the white glare, delivered up to wind and weather, sun and moon, day and night, and to everybody's eyes. No pitying shadow covers him, no mantle.

Am I bewitched, is it a phantom?

No. It is August Strindberg's monument. It is my man, who held me warm against his heart, to whom I bore a child.

Day by day I am drawn to him. Night after night his glory and his misery haunt me. I want to shelter him in my heart, to give back earth to earth. I want to tear him down from that pedestal. Yes, that is what I would like to do.

'That is what you always wanted. I was pulled upward, you were held fast below, woman!'

You have spoken — I was woman! I saw you suffer. I suffered with you and could not help you, could only make free your path to the heights. You were destined for the peaks. You were chosen and doomed to be a prophet.

But I witnessed your martyrdom.

You saw what others did not see, and heard what others did not hear. You overcame time and space. You were a wonderfully subtle instrument, and the first to receive the message on its way to mankind. You paid, and I saw you tremble and throb like a bundle of wires, when the air was charged with electric tension.

You were a ruler by grace of your art. It broke through the confines of our limited reality and gave you the creator's power. You paid, and I saw it oppress you and force you to seek and see Truth always, with mistrust in your soul. Tolstoy, grown old and living a lie, lied also when he said that Truth could never be hideous. The truth about mankind is frightful. You fled from Art to Science and to Research — but you remained a poet. You brought down the Light to earth, but, more hapless than Prometheus, you brought it to the blind. When I read again now the attacks levelled against you in those days, then I do not wonder that your nerves should have given way, then I wonder only how you found it possible to keep alive. I still see the wounds on your weary feet, I hear your cry of pain. But you never turned back, however rough the road.

Not even when it was Love, that stood pale and bleeding on the wayside where you must needs pass by.

It led you to your triumph. On a peak and in loneliness you have become immortal and turned to stone.

Let it be so. Here is the story of our marriage. Here are the letters which he wrote to me, the sweetest and the bitterest of them. Here is, in documents, the picture of the world and of the time which went to make up our destiny. In no other period would his way have been so hard as in this age of barren dogma and of vainglorious intellect.

Here is Amelia out of *Advent*, Jeanne out of *Crimes and Crimes*, Victoria out of the *Dreamplay*. Here is Ingeborg, the Lady out of *Toward Damascus*. When she set out on the pilgrimage with the Unknown, she was only a young girl, full of joy, with faults and weaknesses, one with the green earth. She could not bear to see men suffer, but it came about that she must suffer, she as well.

'An apology? A confession?' the inquisitive interviewer goes on to ask in that Preface.

And August Strindberg replies to him what I would still add:

'No. No self-defence and no confession. I want no excuse and no pardon. I begin — mind that I say, I begin — to believe that we are not responsible, since apparently it is not we who direct our destinies.'

MARRIAGE WITH GENIUS

by

FREDA STRINDBERG

assisted by
ETHEL TALBOT SCHEFFAUER

edited by
FREDERIC WHYTE

INTRODUCTION

THE TALLOW DIP

(August Strindberg's Story) [1]

PLACED between the two alternatives, either to kill a woman or be killed by her, I took a third one. I left her — and my first marriage was dissolved . . .

The beginning of 1893 finds me in Berlin, living as a bachelor in a furnished room.

The tortures of divorce have crushed me. The affection of my children has been alienated from me. Sunk in misery, I have lost all hope, all energy, all wish to live. The only faith which still remains with me is the belief that Evil governs the world. In spite of my bankruptcy, I continue, however, to bear the burden of life, not because I shrink from a sudden death, but out of curiosity. I want to see how far infuriate Destiny will carry its persecution. Whenever a new misfortune befalls me, I say to myself with malicious joy: 'Aha! I guessed as much. See how right I was!'

This belief in the inevitability of misfortune and in the victory of evil paralyses me. My literary talent has deserted me, and with it the possibility of supporting myself and my children. Letters full of reproach, threats, insults, pile up and crush me beneath a remorse which turns into blasphemies against the unseen powers who, not satisfied with punishing the guilty one, lay their avenging hand also upon the innocent. I have grown sour and rejoice in the misfortune of others as much as in my own.

---

[1] Both this fragment and Freda Strindberg's fragment *The Sun* were written in Heligoland, 1893, as the beginning of a novel which Life alone continued.

My work has been struck with barrenness. The lash is driving me on and commands: Work! — as the coachman whips on his horse, when it is already dead-beat.

I begin to look upon myself as a corpse and in order to give myself the illusion of life, I bury the shreds of my soul underneath the roots of a young tree, which starts to grow, to bear foliage and finally to blossom. My friend, Popoffsky[1] is heir to my relics and no sooner has he attained maturity than he takes care to introduce me to the world as a kind of dunghill. And right he is: only he ought to have confessed that he, himself, was the mushroom, not the first and not the last that grew from it.

The famous inn, the Schwarze Ferkel[2], close to the Linden, is the meeting-place of artists and men of letters; a trysting place for the souls of the damned, if ever there was one.

For there is not one among them who does not drag behind him the ball and chain of ill-luck. Curses shower and blasphemies hail here. Often the passer-by stops in the street in the night hours. Out of the shop-window, with its barrier of bottles, a wailing and gnashing of teeth penetrates the stillness. Then the listeners hasten on, exclaiming: 'What a murderous den!'

Popoffsky, a student of medicine and the editor of a socialist paper, lived with a girl and with their child. He loved her and idolized his son, but pride and ambition made him reluctant to bow beneath the yoke of matrimony; he feared the chain and considered woman as a genius of evil, a microcosm, an earth-spirit which mates with dust and clay. As far as that goes, his ideas and mine meet, but there is the difference that I desire the clay to mould a picture or at least a semblance of it and that I have decided to mate once more as soon as my means will permit. And I am not devoid of hope, since several of my plays have been accepted.

---

[1] Stanislaus Przybyszewski, the Polish poet.
[2] The Black Porker, August Strindberg's favourite tavern.

However, everyone must await his time and until then I eschew easy conquests and street-adventures, which, thanks to a sound and well-found instinct, are abhorrent to me. If you want to know, there is a beacon guiding me from afar, out of the dark night of drink, a flame which sheds light and warmth upon me — the thought of my children.

On January 7th, 1893, my name-day, I had been invited to dinner by a rich patron of literature and the fine arts in the Tiergarten viertel. . . .

THE SUN

(*Freda Uhl's Story*)

MY life always has run smoothly, in a most harmonious consistency. Nothing has ever turned out according to expectation. I always reacted to everything differently from the way other people reacted and the results, too, were always different.

Furiously the April storms had lashed precocious flowers, the sun flamed laughingly down upon belated snow, when I was born — in April, in the gay and optimistic sign of the Ram.

Before my very birth, I was hasty and self-willed. I did not wait until the house which my father built should stand ready, the spruce Renaissance mansion of red brick on the shores of the lovely Mondsee (Lake of the Moon), near Salzburg. In an inn on the roadside, I boldly uttered my first cry, more like a gipsy babe than the daughter of a man who had risen to influence and prestige through his literary talent and personality. It was unseemly.

But actually I was right — even at that time. That mansion, properly speaking, did not concern me at all. It had not been constructed in my honour, but had come to be only because father had some time previously found in a large farmhouse an antique Renaissance cupboard of most noble structure. His collector's heart had glowed at the first sight of it. Since the cupboard was as spacious as the epoch in which it was made, it would not fit in with modern proportions; that is why the new villa of Friedrich Uhl was built. It was difficult for me to nourish any illusions; if I played any part at all in the affair, it was a very secondary one.

Nor did the cupboard long remain alone. It quickly multiplied. Many another cupboard and many a casket, many a chest and many a table, many a chair and many beds, many looking-glasses, many clocks, many statues, many paintings, pewter, porcelain, jewels of the craftsmanship of past times, all poured in. They were so numerous and so exquisite that already a few years later the house was, much to my father's despair, mentioned in the tourist guide as a notable 'sight', and he was thereby compelled to spend the entire holiday season in relentlessly driving out tourists, for he guarded his treasures with the green eye of jealousy. It was not long before the infuriated Herr Hofrat was himself looked upon as one of the sights. But the house was really beautiful, behind its dark yew-trees and its velvety roses. No passer-by would fail to stop and look. Then it might happen that from the wide balconies there would come down to him the newest opera air. Great artists were father's frequent and cherished guests. It was painful for the loiterer to tear himself away from the scene and he would exclaim enviously: 'What a Paradise!'

But no more children came after me. I had not come into the world because my father loved my mother, but because he loved another woman whom he wanted to forget. As a remedy, however, I had failed. My parents separated soon after my birth. They wrote to each other almost every day, with mutual high respect, and out of regard for each other, avoided meeting unnecessarily. Mother returned to her family. They were rich landowners on the Danube with no interest in life except its creature comforts. We called them the Phaecians. My father settled down in Vienna and became editor-in-chief of the *R. K. Wiener Zeitung*. He lived in the Hofburg in a tiny apartment of his choice, which looked much like a prison. It terrified all his visitors, but suited his own tastes. To tell the truth, neither of my parents ever quite forgave me my failure. My nurse, old Resi, was promoted to the position of caretaker of the villa, and I remained in her charge with the cupboard and the rest of the collection. Those were my happiest days.

The first thing I can remember is the Sun. If it smiled on me I was happy. It must have smiled continuously, for I cannot remember anything in those early days except its smile. Now it glistened on the lake, now it rocked to and fro on the apple blossoms, now it danced all around me in a race with the butterflies. Then again it hid in the golden-brown oak of the panelled room in which father's books were kept. For hours and hours it hid there, as I did, quite still and lost to the world. And before I had even attained the age of ten, I had read the classics and understood them in my way.

But it was most beautiful of all when the mountains and the lake and the blue sky joined in the laughter of the sun and when I could abandon myself unreservedly to its warm kiss.

'You do not live, you vegetate!' says father with a frown. And I retort: 'Isn't that much finer . . . like the lilies of the field?' He shrugs his shoulders as do all fathers of his generation when youth gets close to the truth in spite of the lies of the nursery.

My parents put me into one convent school after another. They did not want to live a family life together. I myself begged to spend every year in a different school, to make the acquaintance of a new country each time. The *Wanderlust* flamed in my blood as did the sun. And, although I only came to see the world from behind convent walls and out of convent eyes, yet I saw and felt the sun of Italy, the sun of Germany, the sun of England, and the sun of Paris, until I was grown up and had come to be eighteen and a half. Then I took a profession, and overnight became a critic like my father. Now I was self-supporting and free.

I lived at first in Munich. But Munich was too small for me after all those many convent schools, so I went to Berlin.

Berlin in those days resembled a gold-mining camp. A young emperor was building unto himself a new capital. From far and wide adventurous young folk streamed in to take their share in the venture. There was much noise and shouting. I did not mind. Life beat high and the Sun shone — the Sun.

The day came when it veiled itself for me. I fell in love with a married man. Confronted with the choice of making his wife unhappy or growing unhappy myself, I chose a third alternative: I left him — and the affair, which had never developed into a real affair, came to a close.

There was no other way for me. Compromise was against my nature. Nor could I bear the thought of sharing. I was born as the only woman of one man. But was I right?

The conflict arose because I stood alone with my law in the midst of a sickly hot-house Society. The marital triangle was an opiate which a great majority took clandestinely, for pleasure or relief.

My heart was heavy and the ground under my feet seemed to be falling away. Suddenly a liberator appeared who gave back to me the faith in my own self.

The great poet, August Strindberg, had recently been divorced in Sweden. The echo of this divorce had also reached Berlin. It had resounded like a battle cry.

He too would not believe in sharing. He gave his utmost —

and he demanded all. There and only there was the fullness of Life. He showed the way back to the Sun.

I read, nay, I devoured him.

On January 7th the first night of Sudermann's *Magda* took place. As a critic I had to attend. It was not an easy hour for me, this very author and this very drama had played the great part in my young life.

But after the production I was to go to the house of a rich patron of literature and fine arts in the Tiergarten district. It was an important occasion.

I had been invited to meet August Strindberg.

I

BERLIN

January — February, 1893

THE FIRST MEETING

I NEED only close my eyes, and I live that evening again.
I hear every voice, scene after scene comes back, one dim
and fugitive, dream-like, effaced, the other distinct, poignant
like the living hour.

Eleven o'clock at night. I have left the theatre. Snow-
flakes drift slowly across a night without moon or stars.

Only a few steps from the hubbub of the Potsdamer Strasse
there opens the lonely Matthaikirch Platz. Stately homes of
the well-to-do form a pleasant crescent, which the brick
church on bright days gaily cuts in two. Now it projects
sober and black into the night. Buried in snow, the green
close around it seems like a cemetery. Tall lilac trees, which
in spring lure the passer-by and scent the air, lift thin grey
arms up to a cold and invisible sky.

The first floor of a distinguished-looking mansion at the
end of the square glows with light. There the E—— family
live.

Dr. E—— is — say, rather, what is he not? — a writer, a
connoisseur and an art critic. He is an art-collector. He
edits Björnson and Ibsen, he buys canvases of French
impressionists. He is on the rush all day long, keenly interested in some new art and eagerly looking out for one still
newer. He is — Berlin. The emblem of this super-modern,
hectic, eclectic new Berlin, that is what he is.

23

A long corridor. At its end, three men taking leave of the hostess. They excuse their hasty departure: 'Gala night at the Ferkel Tavern (The Porker), dear lady! We are expected. One of our circle departs, the others have sworn that he shall not leave sober.' Two of them I know are painters.

But behind them in the shadow emerges a startling new figure. He wears what seems a loose great storm-coat. Stands there like a rugged grey rock. Stone grey the coat, stone grey the hair, hewn of grey stone the powerful head, of a flickering grey the iris of the eyes, grey are the hollows of his cheeks. Melancholy and romantic he stands there, a picture of the Flying Dutchman. I cannot turn my eyes away.

Frau E—— introduces him to me:

'Herr August Strindberg.'

So that is he, the lover of Truth who unmasks the Lie. He who adores woman and lashes her for not being divine.

'Herr August Strindberg,' repeats my hostess, slightly embarrassed by my silence, 'Fräulein Uhl of Vienna'.

Fräulein Uhl of Vienna has, in spite of her select convent education, no self-control whatever. She stares at Herr August Strindberg like a starved orphan child who all of a sudden in the midst of emptiness has come across the keys to the doors of life.

He returns the fixed glance, then he steps out of the shadow.

Seen now in the full light, he is most reassuringly real. The storm cloak reveals itself as an ulster — as they are called; and he wears a soft low collar, a well-knotted black silk tie, and a slightly antiquated frock-coat, the cut of which makes him look like an official rather than the fashionable lion of a modern drawing-room. He is altogether a surprise. His hair is not grey, but blond. As he passes his hand lightly over it, it rises and ripples in yellow locks. His eyes shine and dart rays of blue, and the severity of the cheeks is softened by the gentleness of the mouth and a coquettish little moustache. He is just the same man as before and yet another. He carries his head high; there is power and dignity in his poise, his glance grows more searching and questioning and is riveted on mine as mine on his.

All of a sudden I wake up. I essay a hasty awkward bow and allow my startled hostess to take me to the dining-room, where supper has been reserved for the stragglers. A bright lamp sheds golden tints upon white damask and green foliage, roses, silver and crystal. Here Literature is walking on the broad way.

'Are you coming, Strindberg?' I can hear one of the two friends slyly ask. I throw a furtive glance behind me. 'Heigh Ho!' The Flying Dutchman overcoat has abruptly gone on to the wall. The folded cape droops like a pair of sleepy pinions.

'No. You two may go ahead without me. I shall be with you in another half hour.'

Strindberg stays!

From the table to which I am taken I can overlook the drawing-room. There is a black human surge pushing forward and rolling back, like the ebb and flow of the tide. The Salon E—— is at one and the same time a literary exchange and mart, a gourmet's favourite resort and a fashionable place of entertainment, a harbour for many a ship. Here buyer and seller meet, author, critic, artist, manager and editor. Often one disposes here of the cargo of the last trip and gently provides for the next one.

Legend does report how the Flying Dutchman fared on his quest for a true love. But how he fared as merchant — that the legend does not say.

What is a Strindberg doing here?

A jovial voice cuts short my reverie.

'Would you like to meet Strindberg? Let me arrange it for you.'

A reporter, a young giant, is bending over me. He laughs. He will take no refusal. He has a cheerful round face, covered with scars of his numberless *mensuren*, as German students call their duelling trials of skill.

We move together to the next room. Is the whole world flocking round the light to-night? They have knotted themselves into a coil beneath the dazzling chandelier. At first I can make out nothing except backs. About a hundred backs and more, men's black coats and women's white shoulders. But then . . .

At last I see him. Quite near.

He stands right in the centre bathed in light. His hair flames like a yellow sun. The eyes are like doors of eternity. They are a deep sapphire blue, like the distant skies above my native mountains. I never knew or imagined that so much light could radiate from a human being.

For the second time within an hour we now face each other, he who knows all secrets and the young girl ignorant of her own self. No wonder that she stands there tongue-tied and would give worlds to have one word to say.

Suddenly I break into a gay and happy laugh. I have looked up defiantly and discovered that August Strindberg is still more embarrassed than I myself.

This laughter is like a signal, brother and sister have met in the wilderness, where they had each taken the other for the wolf.

Now the blue eyes beam at me. He smiles. 'You have come late! And to-day is my name-day!'

I do not know what witchcraft was worked that night upon the hundred guests of Madame E——; they vanished for him and me.

At first our conversation had drifted automatically to the play from which I had just come, and I had clung to the subject. Had not the problem of Suderman's *Magda* threatened to become my own? Had I not, scene after scene, as each was written, put to the author the question:

'Has the unusual, the artist woman, really the right to unusual morals, has the self-supporting woman the right to the child without a father's name?' And the author, despondently, had avoided my glance and had replied: 'We live in a time of compromise.'

Compromise did not exist for me. Did the thing called free love exist? Or was it only a mirage in the barren deserts of Passion?

I am putting these questions to August Strindberg now. He is the freest of the free . . . he will certainly tell me that the price does not matter where the heart dictates.

But he only smiles gently. He looks at me indulgently, almost tenderly; as a father would, at the prattle of his child, so smiles August Strindberg, affectionately, but unconcerned.

'Free Love is always a drawback for the mother and the child. No soprano can replace a father and a mate.'

With this he declines a thing too remote from him, to count.

He delivers me from an obsession; if he thinks thus, then I was right.

I was right.

I give a sigh of relief . . . I expand. My eager words slacken . . . go astray . . . I allow them to roam and pay no attention to them any longer. Words — do words mean much, do they ever express the real ultimate truth?

We have slowly retreated to a little side table, we are alone. I feel light as if I were high up on my mountain . . . under a blue sky — And there is the Sun.

He is telling me, in answer to my question, of his beloved Skaren islands, of the translucent Baltic Sea, the green pine

27

forests . . . Especially of one glorious bright summer which, in his young student days, he and friends had spent in a holiday camp. They were all very poor, but everyone had felt himself master of the world. His companions called him the Eagle in those days. . . .

Now, too, it is as though gigantic wings were swiftly carrying me up to the heights.

It is a wonderful, a marvellous thing about such flights; never will she, who has shared them with genius, lose her deep longing for the skies.

Time flies, half an hour, an hour has passed. We have gradually returned to the earth. He is explaining now how it happened that he had already been at the dress rehearsal of *Magda* although generally he did not go to the theatre. They had held him to a promise which he had given in an unguarded moment, after an opulent dinner party.

'I had to keep my word. But what was expected of me there — and what is socially expected of me further — I do not know.' He smiled wistfully.

But he knew it only too well. Free wine comes dear. He was expected to pay with his personality, to be there for the entertainment of celebrity hunters and snobs.

All around us the crowd surged. Everyone bent on their own advantage and everyone satisfied and in their element. The instincts of the gold-miner raged all around. August Strindberg was a rock, but the banal flood would sooner or later draw him into its whirlpool and submerge him.

'Ah, there you are, my dear Strindberg!' an officious voice breaks in on us. And Dr. E. smiles amiably but with an offensive absent-mindedness at me, 'Excuse us, my dear lady, business, you know — ' and in a moment he has forgotten my existence, pushes his arm under Strindberg's and proceeds to draw him away.

Around us the crowd surges. This is not the place for August Strindberg.

I do not hear why he is wanted, but I see how he dislikes the touch of the compelling arm. An expression of helplessness creeps over his face, and I only just prevent myself from crying out: 'My dear good man, do leave him alone!'

Alas, Strindberg alone would have understood.

I have fled into an empty side-room. It houses the library of Dr. E., famous all over the city. A quiet, almost solemn room. There is little furniture, but it is very fine. A large desk, the bookcases with their treasures, a tabouret for ash-trays and two deep English armchairs. The overheated reception-room blazed with brilliant lights which hurt the eyes; here only a single, hermit-like student's lamp is burning, its green silk shade poised like a lost oleander butterfly. Usually for me things are never lively enough. No crowd, no pleasure is too mad for me as a rule. To-day I am anxious for quiet. I have met a man whose like I shall not see again. Invisible threads are woven from him to me, my nerves seem to lie exposed and bare. They tremble at every strange touch — Strindberg's whole life is just such a torture for him and has been for a long time past. I know his history. Everyone here knows it, the newspapers were full of it. It is because everyone knows it, that it is so hard for him.

Two of the guests now stop at the door without noticing me. They talk, as everybody here does to-night, of Strindberg.

'How do you explain his extreme nervousness?' asks one of them.

The other man shrugs his shoulders. 'He pays. To be in advance of one's time is an expensive thing. Have you any idea how fatiguing it must be to concentrate one's entire strength on a Truth and to find that this Truth is not understood? To be consumed with love for it and to be unable to render it tangible to men? Imagine yourself compelled to stop after every word you say to explain its meaning, while your mind is rushing on, dragging you forward? Fighting? That is nothing. Pain? You can endure it. But to meet mockery and derision when you are persuaded that you have at last approached the meaning of Life for which you have sought, that is unbearable. Strindberg has as good manners as any man in the world, but he preaches in the desert and that in the end renders any voice shrill and hoarse.'

'What does he preach?'

'Life, just Life! But he has disciples. There was a whole crowd waiting for him, as for a redeemer, when he arrived in Germany. We are in the deadlock which the age of mechanization and "intellect" has landed us. We are thirsting for one divine spark, let us call it intuition or genius — or, as he does, the Unknown. The best minds in the land are once more seeking the Soul in things.'

'And does it happen to be the Soul that you are seeking in the Ferkel which you all so assiduously attend and where Strindberg is known to preside?' There is a sarcastic ring in the questioner's voice.

'That is the one place where he is understood, if anywhere,' comes the reply. 'His friends there even understand him so well that they steal his ideas before he can write them down himself. He does not notice it. He suffers from a spiritual congestion. He squanders the treasures of his genius at these meetings. Whoever wants to do so can at any time get from Strindberg a ready-conceived drama or a well-constructed novel. I know several men who have done so without mentioning the source of their inspiration. — Come along. We are sure to find him there by now. It is worth while. Strindberg at the Ferkel has become an attraction. Seats are much in demand.'

They have gone again. Deeply stirred I push back the curtains and lean against the window. The hands of the clock point to five minutes before midnight. Strindberg's name-day draws to its close. The church and the square are resting under the snow, silent and motionless; black spots on the white, like crosses on a grave. The naked trees are shivering.

*

'It was hard work to shake him off. But here I am!'

With a smile on his lips, August Strindberg stands in the doorway, stands there as a matter of course. His chest expands with satisfaction. He has accomplished an unpleasant duty and now he dismisses it from his mind.

'You . . . How do you come here . . . ?'

'Did you not want me to? How strange, I even fancied you were calling me . . .'

'Of course, I wished you would come. But I only wished it, I would not have dared to hope for it.' I laugh gaily and turn my back to the graves and crosses.

He has seated himself in the armchair facing me. The green lampshade like an oleander butterfly gives an illusion of green foliage around us. The room, which a moment ago looked bare, has become cheerful and warm.

'To tell the truth, madame, I wanted to ask you how you got here, to this country and in this company? I have been looking for you, oh, such a long while, but I never dreamed that I should meet you here!'

'You have been looking for me?'

'For you — or her whom you recall to me. We are all in quest of her, our mother. I imagine I shall always remain tied to mine. She died too early, and even while she lived, she did not give me my full share of love. I have something owing to me.'

'Tell me more about yourself — please!' I beg softly.

He hesitates. At first his limited German affects him like a torture. But by and by he conquers the hindrance. And as he does so, he reveals that he not only talks about himself willingly, but that it is an urge and a command to him. His thoughts rush upon him while he is striving for words. Now they gush forth.

To talk about himself with him means to talk of the things which of late are dominating him like an obsession — Nature and her Mystery. August Strindberg, the poet, wants henceforth to be only a scientist.

After he had at last succeeded in casting off the shackles of his miserable marriage, he had left Stockholm. On a little island near the city he had lived in seclusion during summer and autumn. After the last leaves had fallen he stayed on throughout the desolate winter-time. There, in the solitude of the snow desert of Brevick, beside a shoreless sea, beneath an unbroken dome of clouds, Nature, herself, had risen commandingly before his eyes, a Goddess of Death. Compared with her immensity all human matters had appeared to him infinitely minute, far off and colourless. Since that day his only thought had been to discover Nature's innermost mystery. He wanted to tear away the thousand masks she wears, to defy the thousand aspects behind which she hides. Literature in his eyes had shrunk to a child's toy. He was not willing to vivisect poor tortured little souls any longer. Nor to write plays for living marionettes. Nature stood before his vision — she alone, who held Life and Death in her hands. Just as he, the dramatist, had played with puppets, so did She. But her stage has the vastness of the Universe. It was a new, a tremendous, a fascinating task. There was the lure and there the reward.

New horizons open before me. Startling cohesions between things that seemed remote. Darkness turns into light.

'Who is to solve the riddle of the universe?'

He touches its problems one by one. He bends down every twig of the Tree of Knowledge.

It is quite silent in the room. We are alone.

At first one or another of the guests had stepped in and had cast a surprised glance at us. But we paid them no attention and they walked away with a shrug, a laugh. He has become voluble by now, continuing to speak without waiting for a reply, goes on speaking as though talking aloud to himself. Yet his eyes do not leave mine, his gaze pierces into me. It almost seems as if he were drawing out of me the words that rush from his lips.

Suddenly the spell is broken. Down from a church tower sound the hard, metal beats of the clock. They make us start up, stare at the window. I had neglected to close the curtains. The night is gleaming, serene and cold. It is no longer snowing, the sky has grown diaphanous, the naked lilac bushes have dressed up in white and silver like Christmas trees. The black hand on the dial plate of the church points to two.

He turns toward me a shy, absent-minded smile. 'I have fatigued you, I dare say? It happens now and then to me that I go on talking for hours. That is inconsiderate. But you must not forget that I have been condemned to three years of silence; for three long years I have had no opportunity of sharing my thoughts. My solitude has been complete.'

He nervously strokes the hair back from his forehead. No more than a moment ago it had been shining, curly and light, now it clings, damp and colourless, to his temples.

Once he had had a wife, a home and three lovely children. They lay buried under the wreckage of his divorce.

'And for what sin, exactly, did the windmill wings lash you and wound you, most noble Knight, Don Quixote?' I try to jest, to hide my shy emotion.

'For the strange sin that I took them for enemies of equal birth at least — if not for friends; and for my blunder in mistaking a cattle wench for my Dame Dulcinea.'

'You ought not to speak like that of the woman who has been your wife.'

'Ought I not? But you are a woman, too, of course!' he flames up, 'Quite so, *la Sainte Vierge aux Fleurs du Mal!* My divorced wife has already her congregation; she will be venerated as a holy martyr soon. One ought to add a chapter to botany about this new variety.'

He is no longer aware that an unknown girl or any human being at all is present. A kind of trance has seized him. What had been an experience in the past is now transforming itself, as he looks back upon it, into food for the creative process. He dissects it with scalpel now. He probes into his most intimate marital recollections, drags out the most aching, most hidden secrets. On each of them there still twitches some bleeding shred of his heart. But the more it bleeds, the more it quivers, the more triumphant grow the eye and the voice of the surgeon artist. There! Now he holds Truth at last!

I feel my own heart contract. I feel as though by stealth I had obtained entrance to the sanctuary of a temple watching some tragic sacrifice. I do not try to hear, nor to comprehend. I would like to start up and take to flight. But I do not even dare to move. At every one of his gestures tall hasty grey shadows flit across the chalk-white walls. The weatherworn head of a giant is thrown upon them in sinister outline, and heavy black arms jerk spasmodically up and down.

'Why, is it possible to hate while one loves?'

He looks at me wonderingly. 'Say rather, can one love and not hate?'

The black arms on the wall descend like an executioner's axe.

He grows silent and draws himself up. He shakes off a bad dream. He has magically become a new man. He looks around him composedly, awake and with keen eyes. His chest expands, he draws a deep breath and smiles, well-satisfied. 'Yes, I have been through Hell. But I have lived life to the full.'

It sounds as unconcerned and detached as though until now he had not been talking about himself at all, but of some stranger, as though he now enjoyed the subject as an artist.

'Have you been joking with me? Was it not true, then, what you said?' I stammer, disconcerted.

He pityingly looks me up and down. 'Not true? . . . You forget that I am a poet.'

That would be difficult to forget.

The third hour of the morning has passed. Most of the guests have taken leave, only a few intimate friends have lingered.

Our hostess has come in to hint to us that it is getting late. She cannot entirely hide the slight uneasiness which our unending *tête-à-tête* has caused her. She had thought of my father, and the thought cannot have been exactly reassuring. Father is a notorious stickler for etiquette where his daughters are concerned and he has a highly original method of punishing innocent third parties if ever this code is infringed. She feels relieved that the evening is over.

Out in the open, the moon, the stars and the street lamps are sparkling on the dazzling snow. Strindberg is wrapped in his Flying Dutchman cloak. On his lion's mane balances a small bowler hat which lacks the necessary greatness for this honour.

Two men offer to take me home. They, like myself, are living in the west of Berlin, while Strindberg's way leads in the opposite direction through the Linden, past the Ferkel! The conversation I overheard recurs to my mind. Audible to him alone, I beg:

35

'Don't go down there . . . don't go to them . . . don't . . . not to-night!'

And he, with a radiant glance, replies, 'No! . . . Not to-night!'

At the next turning I look back. Strindberg is marching vigorously, rocking a little in his gait like a mariner ashore. A brisk wind is blowing and swells out his great cape.

*

In my stove at home the embers still glow. A good *bourgeois* atmosphere again envelops me. A strong wave of fragrance greets me. An enormous bunch of violets stands on my desk. It must have come here during my absence. Against the desk leans a laurel wreath.

It takes me a moment to recollect — good Heavens, a souvenir from *Magda*!

How kind of Hermann Sudermann! So he has thought of me in the midst of his triumph!

It has come too late, however, the message could reach me no longer. I have started on a new path to-night. I do not yet know where it leads, but I do believe it is mine.

I am tired. Soon I have fallen asleep and dream.

I fly as one flies in dreams, without a body and without a care, across the sunny azure over my native mountains. Far down below the merry lake, the green billowing hills, the white rocks and above me — the Sun.

All of a sudden a huge dark form descends between us. Is it the giant wings of an eagle? Is it a storm cloud? Or a grey storm cloak? It lashes me in the face. I cry out. Is it a cry of joy or of pain or of both?

I awake. I am cold. My pillow is wet. Wet from tears, or from the snow which blows in through the open door of the balcony, or from both, perhaps? I know no longer. I know nothing more. I only know — I dreamt of August Strindberg.

BERLIN

Shall I not be satisfied with life? I am its care-free and spoilt child. I have chosen my father well, that seems to suffice in our present order of things. I chose a good father, he takes care of me, moves every stone out of my way, his very existence suffices to do it. The editor of the *Imperial Viennese Gazette* is an important personage, whose daughter has smooth sailing under his name and flag. I have a delightful apartment here in Berlin; drawing-room, dining-room, bedroom and library, quite close to the distinguished Lützow Platz. One cannot call it sumptuous, perhaps, but it is original and has a strong personal note — be it only that the four rooms form but one. This one is a Proteus and well assisted, especially on moonlight nights, by a most impressive glass balcony door. It occupies almost the entire background and creates the right atmosphere for every change of scenery. The walls are of soft olive; a big oaken desk looks solemn underneath a fine reproduction of Rembrandt's 'Man with the Golden Helmet'. A large rare leopard-skin, a soft wide wrap which Father sent to me not long ago, spreads at day-time over the couch, which no one suspects of being at night the severe chaste bed of a maiden. Father has friends all over the world. One of them went hunting in Africa, this leopard has died for me. A sumptuous oriental drapery veils a door which leads in well-bred fashion into the general dining-room. A painter, who could not pay his bill, left it behind. During the daytime it hides in tactful and discreet fashion the puzzling roundness of my washstand, nicknamed 'Mystery of the Harem'.

*

Dr. Otto Neumann-Hofer, the dramatic critic and editor, is an old friend of my family. I feel at home in his hospitable house. He had married an American. She was a pianist, Annie Bock, the *protégée* of the American critic James G.

37

Huneker, now she too is writing. No one can help that in Berlin.

This morning Otto comes to see me in my own quarters. His steps are not guided merely by personal concern, the nature of his call is of a higher order.

It seems that I had been missed at the party after Sudermann's success. They had been growing anxious as to where I could be, when, about two o'clock, a telephone message reassured them that Fräulein Uhl was industriously and successfully at work converting August Strindberg from his woman-hatred. That is at least what Otto now laughingly pretends. — 'Tell me, have you been flirting with him or was he flirting with you?' he hastens to inquire, eager to pin down a biographically important fact.

'Flirting! The word "flirt" applies to a lieutenant of the Guards, but not to August Strindberg!'

Otto's mirth increases. 'Well, well, then you spent three hours talking with him about literature.'

I look down on him from supreme heights. 'Does one talk with a Strindberg? He spoke to me. About philosophy, psychology, biology, geometry, chemistry, botany, astronomy and a few more subjects. — Also about himself.'

'How interesting! And he carefully selected the youngest girl present for this instructive talk?'

'I must admit, I feel rather surprised myself — did he credit me with so much importance or did he simply forget that I existed? Was I by chance merely interposing air, across which he talked to himself? I had that feeling now and then.'

Otto laughs. 'Your feeling is likely to be right. Most probably this sudden friendship of August Strindberg is due to it.'

August Strindberg's friendship? How proud and happy I would be if I possessed it.

I hear about him every day. The whole town is telling anecdotes of him. He sounds through Berlin like a clarion. Wherever his steps lead him, sleep is chased away. Whether he kindles sympathy or the reverse of it, life flames up. Alas, he himself is the Flying Dutchman, restless and homeless, welcome everywhere, and nowhere at ease; tortured by the unfamiliar language, the unfamiliar people, the unfamiliar city, the unfamiliar food, or by the lack of food.

'That "Scandinavian Night" of the "Literary Society" next week will be an event. Strindberg, also, will be in the show,' Otto informs me. 'He is bound to read badly, but what people want is to see the great mysogynist in flesh and blood.'

I flare up: 'I see, they don't want his work, it's to be an exhibition. Don't you think the man's too good for that? You others are putting him in the pillory. You must not do it!'

'How can I prevent it?'

'It was wrong of you all to force him into it. Sudermann must interfere.'

Otto absent-mindedly plays with a manuscript on my desk, he does not look at me.

'Sudermann has left for Italy. Didn't you know?'

August Strindberg fills a burning need in my life.

Ten years of incense! Mute pious candles on golden Gothic altars, the song of the organ to vows of an ecstatic, eternal love, an adoration of the Power which keeps the world in the hollow of its hands, highest perfection, sublime beauty, wisdom, mercy! Ten years of foretaste of Heaven with the body of the Saviour on the lips at Holy Communion! Ten years among the brides of God.

Those ten years I had spent in my convent schools. It is hard to resign yourself to poor mortals when you have grown used to God. But still harder is it to give up worship after it has become a part of your flesh and blood. Once you have, from childhood up, tasted the divine rapture of the cathedral, can you ever again forego the longing to look up and humbly offer your heart and soul? Can anything less than godliness ever content you after all that?

And now! Had Otto not told me that all literary Berlin envied me this sudden friendship of Strindberg's. . . .

I am dreaming, dreaming. . . .

A first-night at the Deutsches Theater. Ibsen's *Master-Builder*. I must attend and I join the Neumann-Hofers. The weather is cold and wet. The wind bites as we get out of the tram. We must cross the bridge. It is no easy matter. Annie and I both shiver and hold our coats pressed to our chins. On the bridge we meet two men. One of them, tall, stately and in a flying storm-cloak, I joyously recognize from a distance. The other, shorter, has a military walk.

'That is He!' I whisper to Annie, glowing with delight, and I drop my wrap, disdaining the cold, in my enthusiasm ready to stop in the middle of the street amid wind and snow, in order to shake his hand and to expand the pleasure of this meeting.

But the storm-cloak flutters by. His hat does not rise more than an inch and that exclusively in Annie's honour; over me his eyes pass approvingly but without the slightest recognition or memory. Only his short companion includes me, too, in his polite recognition.

'Good evening, gentlemen!' Annie returns the greeting.

'I happened to meet them the other night,' she explains.

'Quite so . . . quite so . . . Most likely poets are always talking only to themselves.'

CUT OFF

My life has darkened overnight. Instead of the careful advice by which Father has been guiding my steps from afar, there drops out of the clear sky a short, senseless, aggressive letter for which there is no explanation. He commands me to leave Berlin at once and to return either to mother or go back to Munich. That is bad enough, but still worse is the tone! My greatest treasure, my father's friendship, seems lost.

What have I done? I am too full of spirit, I am terribly thoughtless, I do not mind the world and its opinions, I have adopted the motto of Christina of Sweden: '*Il y a des gens auxquelles tout est permis et tout sied.*' But if I want to live like an author and not like a schoolgirl, it is only because I respect our profession, father of mine. What can I say to the world, if I must listen first to what the world says about me?

Father hints that the Berlin air is poisoned. Magda is the murderess of her father, he says, and in his paternal over-estimation he naively enough believes that Sudermann had seen me when he portrayed that enfranchised super-woman.

I adore my father. What shall I tell him? That he is behind the times? That Sudermann left for Italy more than a week ago and that I took no notice of it, Strindberg being now in Berlin? That Strindberg, moreover, is not really present either, as far as I am concerned, that he talks to me all night long and does not even see me? Will that soothe Father, or maybe it won't? Who has upset him against me?

Was it my landlady by any chance? The dignified dame in whose boarding-house I stay, is the perfect symbol of what woman was thirty years ago and what we no longer want her to be. She is admirable, but detestable. We have nicknamed her 'The Iron Virgin'. She wears a heavy, flaxen plait around her head like a crown; it is fastened with heavy pins, a true forest of spears. Whatever bosom her eight children have left to her she compresses in a kind of iron cuirass which makes her waist-line shrink and her hips protrude. I do believe she thinks it proper to go to bed in this cuirass and to get up in it. This cuirass is a creed.

41

I find out that it is not the Iron Virgin who has interfered with my destiny. She is highly indignant that I should have suspected her. Never would she give a woman away to any man. This does not prevent her from siding with my father on the subject of my departure from Berlin. She disapproves of Berlin and she disapproves of a single life for me.

'I mean well by you, believe me. You will have to marry anyhow sooner or later. A well-bred young lady like yourself cannot live by writing. And how do you expect to find a husband if so many gentlemen are after you? Those people whom you meet are no good for marrying.'

'They are the best people in the world!'

'They can tell you that, but they are not. Do as your father wishes. Go to your mother. She will find you a husband. That is what mothers are there for.'

The worst is, that she does not stand alone with this idea.

*

'Do you want to see Strindberg on his own plane?' Otto asks one night this same week. 'Come with me to the Schwarze Ferkel.'

It is 1 a.m.

I hesitate but overcome my reluctance. . . . After all, why not?

The cab rolls through the Brandenburger Tor and at the very beginning of the Linden turns into the Neue Wilhelm Strasse. Four houses to the right and four to the left have all the same old-fashioned architecture. The second on the left harbours a wine restaurant on the ground floor. A black monster hangs above the entrance — it looks like a great swollen black pig. In reality it is a Bessarabian wine skin with little strings dangling down. Bottles brighten the windows as flowers would.

Before I enter I covertly survey the narrow room. A bar stands opposite the entrance. Behind it is a pretty blonde

woman, the proprietress, Frau Türke. Bottles hide the walls.
Herr Türke declares that he has one hundred liqueurs to
choose from.

Tables and again tables. Thick cigarette smoke and loud
voices. Then suddenly, silence. I see Strindberg sitting in a
corner behind a big table and talking. I cannot catch his
words, his voice is low and quiet. He holds himself erect,
his head high, sitting squarely and heavily, almost majestic
in his ponderousness; he speaks slowly, chooses his words,
then abruptly drives them in, forcibly as with a hammer.

I see no sign of a woman. A dark slim young man jumps
up.

'That's the insurance agent, Richard Dehmel,' Otto
smiles. 'He does accounts in the morning and composes
poems at night.'

He does not think of accounts now! His cane lashes
through the air, cuts off the golden neck of a green bottle.
The guests are jubilant. Champagne sparkles in the glasses,
champagne streams across the floor. Some Maecenas must
be near. Strindberg is presiding over this Witches' Sabbath
as calmly as if it were a committee meeting.

The handsome young Pole, Stanislaus Przybyszewski, is
sitting to his right in the attitude of the favourite disciple
at the Last Supper. He is the only one who has not a wine-
glass but a water glass standing in front of him. This large
glass is full to the brim with cognac. He is bent forward,
his eyes riveted on the glass; greyish-bluish, slanted, half-
closed eyes, a greyish skin, a thin blond Henry IV beard:
on his blood-red, finely chiselled lips, is a voluptuous and
tortured smile. Now he comes closer and slowly kisses the
two hands of August Strindberg, who, surprised, and with a
blush, withdraws them.

'What do we want here?' I ask and turn away sad and
depressed.

'You are right, the crowd is too big already!' Otto agrees. As unnoticed as we entered, we are about to leave the place. We stand already close to the exit when a full voice reaches us. Richard Dehmel, the poet, with his beaming dark eyes enveloping August Strindberg, absorbing him with his glance — is improvising.

Verses!

> An Immortal!
> I lay in a dusky thicket of yews
> And was afraid . . .
> In the shadows before me sat a man,
> Like unto a great and misty cavern,
> In which a gigantic badger of eld
> Dreamed of new worlds; . . .
>
> .   .   .   .   .
>
> STRINDBERG

*

'Strindberg! Strindberg!'

A confusion of voices, an exploding of corks.

Then silence. The sounds of a piano. Stanislaus is playing Chopin.

In the dim recess of the tavern, to which no ray of light penetrates, a land of longing is now singing its song. Fields with ripe grain are rocking in the sunlight; the forest whispers a secret; the flowers in the garden are luring; glowing colours are melting into each other — love-drunk creation celebrates its mating.

Knightly castles with marble stairs — old times arise. Proud men with clinking swords; beautiful dames in rustling silks. Peasant cottages throw open their doors to liberty. Fair children, happy mothers, peasants behind the plough, scented bushes, dipped in night; meadows lit by the moon —

The heated faces of the Round Table radiate all at once

in delight; each of them hears his own homeland sing —
the Chopin that he loves.

August Strindberg looks as though in a trance. He is in
Sweden now — better than that, in a Sweden of his dreams
where there are no dragons in front of the doors of Science,
no marriage fights and no divorce.

Otto gently guides me out into the street. I cannot help
it, I throw a most affectionate glance at the dangling monster above the entrance door. There is no doubt, it gains
at a closer view. 'I am quite sure the dear thing only looks
like a swine, it is not one, it is a most respectable wine-skin,
one that comes from Bessarabia . . .' I plead with a dreamy
sigh — 'the most noble vine grows there and the sun ripens
those luscious, delicious grapes. . . .'

'I think I had better take you home now, Miss Freda,'
Otto interrupts my dithyramb, as eagerly as though he saw
the Porker already swallowing me too.

'I know, of course, the little girl ought to be in bed! But
do say something nice about that dangling darling before
we go away,' I plead. 'We have been misjudging it.'

'All right then . . . wine-skin or not . . . its like may be
dangerous for us. It is not for a Strindberg. I was present
at a bout, a few nights ago. It was six in the morning when
I took three of the guests home, dead drunk. Strindberg
had stayed behind and I felt uneasy about him. I am not
exactly a Samaritan, but one knows what a man like him
means to the world, so I called on him after I had had a
little sleep. I was ready to fetch a doctor. Do you know
what I found out? He had not even been to bed. He sat at
his writing-desk in his grey flannel jacket with his velvet
cap on his head — he says his brains need warmth — and
was busy noting down some fresh mathematical dogmas
which had occurred to him, just accidentally, on his way
home. His hand was firm and his writing stood out like an

45

etching on the parchment paper he is using. Quite close to
him on the floor rested his famous "Green Bag" — ready for
a new conception.'

*

Is it an accident, no, it is a decree of fate, that August
Strindberg should have been born on January 22nd, the
same day on which, in 1561, Francis Bacon was born, the
greatest scientist of the golden age of Elizabeth; in 1788,
Lord Byron; and exactly seven days prior, in 1688 — the
Swedish seer, Emanuel Swedenborg, whose *Opera philo-
sophica et mineralogica* has built the bridge of the organic
system between the world of matter and the world of
spirit.

Is it an accident, or is it a decree of fate, that the production of Strindberg's *Creditors* is on January 22nd, in the
Residenz Theater in Berlin, as a Literary *matinée*? On its
success or failure depends — for the immediate future at
least — the author's fate.

Let it be said at once: *Creditors* was an uproarious success.

The spicy little Residenz Theater in the east of Berlin
is about the last stage upon which one could have hoped to
hear the voice of Strindberg. Usually they serve you up
adultery, French *cuisine*, adding to it lots of '*Paprika*', red
pepper. (The manager, Herr Lautenburg, comes from the
Danube shores.) The poor cuckold of a husband raises
storms of laughter.

This time, too, adultery occurred, but this time it was the
cuckold husband who did the laughing. The seducer died
when he gazed into Medusa's face. The woman wept over
her victim. The audience, at other times impious, to-night
scarcely dared to breathe.

What was it that had worked this abrupt change from
farce into tragedy? Suddenly abysmal seas have flung open

their depths. Domesticity is unmasked as only a thin and crackling crust of ice over the sex urge of woman.

And I? I sat motionless, shuddering at the horrid truth, at love, the destroyer, and at the misery it caused, forgetful of the world. Otto tells me I stammered, 'Strindberg is ill. I must help him . . .' But even of this I was unaware.

All I remember is that when we were back in the street again I had asked Otto, almost imploringly: 'Tell me only this one thing, from whence comes this murdering shadow, this hatred?' And that he had replied, quietly, 'Strindberg himself says, from Light, from Love itself'.

We were already in the cab when I still heard the audience clamouring 'Author! Author!'

But Strindberg had left the theatre long before. He was not born for the crowd.

OUR SECOND FIRST MEETING

The fates have secretively conspired to make us meet again.

Annie Neumann-Hofer has invited me, nothing big she said, just a little dinner, only a few nice people would be present.

My simple white gown is out of place, though. When I arrive — the few nice people are the flower of intellectual Berlin. Even a most pretentious stage star is present. Behind Annie is an elegant young man, probably an officer in mufti.

And close to him — Strindberg.

He is not the restless Flying Dutchman this time, rather a dignified, correctly-clad gentleman, a scientist or some high official with a benignant smile. To see him look happy makes me feel happy. I stretch out my hand impulsively.

He has politely risen to welcome me. Now he takes my exuberant hand into his, most amiably but visibly surprised and looks at me with interest and friendliness, but void of every recollection.

Annie laughs and everybody else laughs at my speechless embarrassment. It is quite clear that he does not remember me at all.

Well, well, it is not exactly flattering, but it has a certain piquancy. There sits a gentleman who happens to be a great man and does not even suspect that he ever set eyes on me. If one considers closely, it is magnificent to be so little chained to one's past as he is; to forget things as soon as one has experienced them; to meet people anew day after day. Life's voyage would be so much gayer without luggage. This man, here, carefully picks from life exactly what he needs and nothing else. So he remembers quite well that he talked to a young lady, the other night; the young lady was necessary for the purpose of expansion; it did not really matter who the young lady was. He simply effaces the detail from the picture. That is exactly how one ought to write or paint. The chief law in that, too, probably, is to efface and to forget.

The guests sip their coffee, they smoke, they chat. Everyone who starts to speak instinctively addresses Strindberg. Strindberg listens as a man of the world, rapidly picks up every subject. But no sooner does he enter into it thoroughly than a wave of embarrassment and almost torture darkens his high forehead. His thoughts come rushing, but the foreign language only obeys reluctantly and often it does not obey him at all. Then it lames him.

Once more I feel the current which I felt on that first night. It supplies me with the words which he seeks in vain. I snatch up his thought in its flight and I complete his sentence for him.

Now the conversation dances and whirls from one topic to another. The young supposed officer, Herr von Treskow, leads at first. But he is not an officer after all, only the son of an officer and he is a police commissioner. That makes him interesting. He reaches in his official capacity as high as the throne (he seems to hold more or less the threads of the most distinguished love-affairs in his hands) and down to the mob (where they often end). Treskow's post is a new one; it has been founded only recently and his chiefs do not yet take it seriously, it is barely tolerated. His own interest in it, therefore, is less that of the policeman than that of the sociologist and of the psychologist. Treskow is the police authority on . . .

Otto cuts him short. He does not like to hear this word spoken in his wife's drawing-room. He looks over at us ladies and then significantly at the gentlemen.

'On . . . You know what I mean!'

One knows. It has happened shockingly often of late that men who occupied a high position either by birth or work had been detected in the practice of perversity. It is said, for instance, that not only a close relative of the Kaiser, but also the best-known architect in the city revels in a most unplatonic platonicism; the latter, a charming man, but his heart only throbs with love when he perceives the epaulettes on the shoulders of the cuirassiers.

The discreet Herr Treskow possesses a trustworthy file containing hundreds of such names. No one would ever have dreamt of finding such names there. They are names without which no exclusive list at Court would be complete. 'It almost seems a flaw not to be amongst them!' he remarks. The file had been compiled by a devoted officer for the Kaiser in the illusory hope that His Majesty would graciously order the air to be purified. But William II had indignantly refused to listen to one single word about the matter and nobody had dared to be more explicit. In the meantime the compiler had died.

'It is not good for a Sovereign,' remarks von Treskow, 'to be surrounded all day long by a chorus of gentlemen who dance at night dressed up in women's skirts with coachmen in "The King of Portugal" or who treat poor soldiers to champagne behind the back of the respectable Berolina.'[1]

'How terrible, when your strongest instinct continually brings you into conflict with the criminal law. These men are to be pitied,' I say in a low voice.

'Kindhearted child! She has even sympathy for sins against nature and for the pathological!' Otto is trying to apologize for my unmaidenly utterance.

All the others laugh. Strindberg alone does not.

'The problem cannot be solved by the moralist nor by the alienist,' he remarks thoughtfully. 'And one cannot very well call anything unnatural which Nature has made — although it must be admitted that Nature's ways are often intricate. But just for the very reason that the whole thing is completely unexplained, one cannot talk of it as a disease. Biology may possibly . . . In the meantime there is another question, quite important, what attitude we should adopt from the angle of the preservation of the species.'

Otto now beams eagerly.

'Since we are discussing the subject, how do you define the manly woman?'

'The manly woman is a product and a victim of our false civilization. Love is a mask which nature uses to bend us to her aims. But we have surrounded it with so many twigs and garlands that we have confounded woman in the end with a divinity. She is not even the equal of man.'

'Who is no god!' Annie chimes in.

'And where woman assumes the part of man, she loses her privileges. The manly woman has existed throughout the ages, but the woman-man has pushed to the front of late. She is not a good species, she is not vital. Unfortunately, however, she and all her misery continue to reproduce. Effeminate men instinctively select them, so that they

---

[1] The allusion is to the well-known statue symbolizing Berlin.

multiply and put into the world beings of an indefinite sex for whom life is cruel. If we want to progress, or want at least to recover our health, we must make as clean a sweep of the manly woman as the manly woman has made of romance. Man must learn anew to approach love without the wine of false sentiment. He must once more grow virile. Must look upon love as the source of strength and must not let it weaken him. Then only shall we be advancing toward a new age.'

Only a little later and Strindberg and I are once more together — just as on that first evening. Once more we have become unaware of our surroundings. But to-day we are in a happy comrade-like mood.

At last the party breaks up. 'Who is taking Fräulein Uhl home?' Annie asks, slightly amused.

'Strindberg knows what is proper!' — the words come from behind me, they sound correct and stiff, truly Swedish.

Annie's face reveals that she has been convinced of it from the beginning.

Before we separate, Treskow has drawn Strindberg aside and has offered his services as a 'bear's guide'. That is what the police call it when famous visitors are shown around the hidden nests of vice. Treskow intends, in the near future, to take Strindberg and with him the poet-surgeon, Schleich, and one other man, to a ball and to a café — 'which Socrates and Sappho would frequent if they should happen to be guests in Berlin in 1893', he says with a meaning smile.

Then Strindberg and I are under the open sky. We have taken leave of the others. The fresh air cools our foreheads. Good smells of earth and water arise. Berlin is far off and has never existed, still less Greece.

He has offered me his arm. We walk along the canal up

to the Friedrich-Wilhelm Bridge. The reach twists like a leaden-grey, cold, thin snake in its high, steep, stony bed.

The night is clear and kind. We walk along side by side. The moon shines and the snow is white and radiant. It sparkles and crackles under our feet. We walk on silently, as happy as children. And again the man with me is an entirely different and new man. The drawing-room atmosphere has faded just as the romance of the Flying Dutchman had. Someone who is still, simple, kind, has stepped into their place, enjoys the fresh air, the white light, the breeze — perhaps the nearness of a warm heart. Now he stops abruptly, drops my arm heedlessly and bends forward excitedly, pointing at a little black heap which the half-frozen Spree carries along on its white surface to the bridge —

'Do you see . . . Down there . . . Do you see those birds? . . . Northland ducks! . . . Compatriots! I know their secrets from home. Every spring when the ice breaks they assemble on our coasts in large flocks.' A deep tenderness is in his voice. I hear a banished, homesick child who all of a sudden with aching heart perceives his beloved little feathered friends. Sweden has taken possession of him at that moment, his own Sweden.

The little flock flutters and disperses and then once more collects high up in the sky. Hastily he seizes my hand.

'They are singing . . . Do you hear them sing? People say, they do not sing . . . but they do.'

I listen. A low, almost inaudible humming travels through the air as though tiny throats were stretching silvery strings.

'They sing!' he repeats, and a pious faith lights up in his eyes.

And I, also, have heard their song in that white night.

BERLIN

February, 1893

THE FIRST VISIT

HERR AUGUST STRINDBERG has accepted an invitation to dinner in my flat: 'For February 6th, at seven.'

My guest arrives, punctual to the minute, wearing his great flapping cloak and smiling with the melancholy but eternally adventurous smile of the Flying Dutchman. Then, quietly and with dignity he takes off the cloak and the melancholy like the well-bred guest of a well-bred young lady, appreciatively surveys the room which is graced by a big basket of lovely roses, takes note of the azaleas, the leopard, the Rembrandt, and, above all, the desk with its wide flanks.

He likes the food, he likes the wine, he seems to like my harmless prattle. He is care-free, indulgent, communicative, and so full of light and brightness that it is not long before we are sitting together in a magic castle high up on a sunny mountain, right under the sky. We chat about everything in this wild mining-camp of ours, Berlin, to which chance has wafted us, neither of us knowing how or why, and which we both like very much, just this very moment.

We agree on this. And we agree on quite a lot of other things as well. We are related — of course, distantly, as the house kitten to the royal tiger. But we both love life and experience more than anything else. Neither of us will chain himself to the day which is past or pledge himself to that which is to come. We believe in personality as in the Creator. And both of us are born propagandists.

'Art, what is art? A confession and a battle. All true art derives from an experience and from the urge to propaganda. In order to create artistically, you must have previously lived the thing in some way or other.'

Human suffering has turned Strindberg into an accuser — an accuser with blood on his hand. So he declares, and playfully, yet with a hidden seriousness, he shows me the palm of his right hand. On the mound of the thumb and on the second joint of the fingers there are scars, scarcely closed, rough thick callouses apt to break open again at any time.

I had grown quite pale.

'It is only an innocent eczema, but I have had it since I was a child and there is no chance of my getting rid of it again. An inheritance of my maternal impoverished ancestors, most likely. When anything bad happens to me the wound opens and bleeds. The physicians don't understand anything about it. They don't understand about me, either.'

'Maybe you are too healthy for them and for our whole generation?'

A gratified look in Strindberg's face rewards me. His chest expands with the joy and force of life. The eyes of a boy shine, full of youth, joy and curiosity, as though the world were a fairy tale, which he would love to hear. But then his glance sweeps past the roses and clouds over with resentment. No doubt he mistakes them for an admirer's gift.

A heavy, sweet scent rises from the roses and mixes with my own perfume of ambergris. Silence, alone, speaks for a while.

'Aren't they beautiful?' I ask. 'A friend sent them to me. And you shall have the finest.'

I am on my knees and am looking for the scissors on the lowest shelf of the bookcase. Oh, the poor roses — sign of our times — they are on wire, it is impossible to undo them by hand. At last one is loosened. Still on my knees I hold it out to him and remember a verse:

Unenvious in the hall where gods rejoice
And heroes on the golden benches wait
I look — the pygmy-born have but one choice,
Freely to give themselves unto the great.

'Roses and rhyme?' he exclaims, 'that reminds me of one of my own ballads.'

The wine sparkles red in the glass, I lift mine. Now he, too, empties his glass to the last drop.

An hour passes. Twice he makes a move as if to take leave. Each time I keep him back. Who can tell when it will be so wonderful again? But he frowns and shakes his head. 'You are a young lady and have to be careful about your reputation.'

'I want to be an author and you — are August Strindberg.'

'That is exactly what you will not be forgiven. But I have never yet caused gossip about any nice girl.'

He insists that we must part. I finally accompany him to the door and in my preoccupation I forget the existence of my discreetly hidden washstand.

'Oh!' I cannot suppress a low cry of pain; the creature has sharp iron edges. My apology sounds rather confused. That makes things worse than ever. Strindberg's imagination has awakened, his mistrust is now let loose. Both are gigantic. His glances, grey and sharp, pierce through the curtain of the Mystery of the Harem. This Mystery has already attracted his attention more than once in the course of the evening most unpleasantly, whenever the voices of the boarders or a ray of light came through.

He hesitates, takes his leave with a last questioning glance — then is gone.

I step to the table absent-mindedly emptying my glass. There lies, forgotten, my poor flower.

Two days later —

August Strindberg, Berlin, to Freda Uhl

'Dear Fräulein Uhl: Let me know if you are still here, I beg of you! I must ask your forgiveness for so many stupidities which were the fault of temporary indisposition. I must thank you for an unforgettable evening; I must tell you that I did not forget the rose, but left it behind on purpose, in order to have an excuse for calling to get it next day, although I lacked the courage to do so when the time came.

'In short, there are so many things that I must say to you — at the peril of losing your respect which means less to me than your goodwill.

'Hoping for an amicable word from you, I remain, believe me — Your most obedient, August Strindberg.'

PICTURES

Fifteen minutes late! 11.45 already, and I was to have met August Strindberg at 11.30, at the National Picture Gallery.

A radiant sun. I rush across the Schloss Platz. Fifteen minutes late! And Strindberg is waiting.

Or is he not waiting any longer? Quick, across the bridge — the National Gallery at last appears.

Yes, he is waiting and here he is.

'So you have really come. I had really begun to fear that you would take revenge.'

I stare at him without understanding. 'Take revenge — I — on you?'

'You are a woman. I have offended them.'

Oh, how wonderfully it makes me feel to be taken for a proud avenger of my sex. By such a man! Kind heavens, if he knew that I am only a silly schoolgirl who has come too late because the post had brought her another letter from her father in telegram style, ordering once more her immediate departure. If he knew! Well, he shan't. I glide at his side

with the smile of the sphinx — and feel ashamed that I have
not the courage to say :'I am not an interesting fiend, only
a young thing flung between two generations and two
philosophies, who is still eating her father's bread and has,
therefore, no rights of her own.'

I take a look at him on the sly. He has undergone another
change within the last few days. The patriarch has vanished
as the storm-cloak had before. A yellowish-brown English
redingote beats about him, a gay necktie is knotted over a soft
collar; in his buttonhole a white gardenia. On his lion's
mane a stiff hat balances itself bravely and adroitly.

We talk and walk up and down. Walk up and down and
talk.

On both sides of the way the naked branches of the hedge
turn to the sun, and call for warmth. I feel quite touched.
My hand gently caresses them. 'Just see, they are growing
green!'

A tiny sprout has ventured out on one of the lilacs.

'Indeed, it is growing green, already — spring has come
once more.'

He speaks in a low voice, speaks hesitatingly, as though
talking of a miracle, and glances, doubting whether it
could be true — from the little green twigs to me.

In the National Gallery are both antique and modern
paintings. Facing the entrance shines a large Rubens. My
friend passes by with polite reserve.

'Too much flesh and too much carnality,' — he nods
approvingly to a delicate Watteau. But we have come to
see 'The Isle of the Dead', his favourite. Under a deep
blue sky bathed in sun there rises a wall of dark cypresses
silently and solemnly from a white rock in the Grecian sea.
No one knows what hides behind the black wall and within
the silent white castle of stone. Phantoms alone may enter
it, and dreams.

He has a dream and tells it me. Death is naught but a door to a new form of life. On the Island of the Dead, humans find peace and liberation from earth's torturing discord and darkness. Beyond the cypresses on the white rocks live the blessed delivered from animalism, flesh and carnality.

'The antithesis — to Rubens!'

'Yes, the very antithesis. That is the redemption from the past. After thirty years they fall asleep without suffering, without knowing it, to proceed towards perfection on some other plane. The Isle of the Dead, however, continues to glide gently and noiselessly along on waves which may be air or water or light; it glides along and never rests.

'Then your dream would be a new life but without a trace which the old one has etched . . . Well, why couldn't that become reality?'

'Could it? If that were possible, everything would be possible!' His eyes are shining, and his varying hair is yellow like gold.

Thus, then, August Strindberg could look when happy.

HIS MELODY

Grey fog in the street across which the wind drives a thin rain like hard cold needles. My room is warm and cosy. I have lit the standing lamp in honour of the concert.

Punctually at five the bell rings. I fling open the door, August Strindberg enters. Aquarius in person. Rubbers on his feet, a storm-reddened face, glittering drops in his moustache and hair. The Dutchman cloak swells mightily around a hidden thing which Strindberg carries in his arm as lovingly as a baby — his guitar! It immediately becomes the centre. It is no longer young. I can see that, as a faithful companion, it has shared many a vicissitude, nights of revelry, the misery of the garret, endless hours in trains, and it was never made of that noble wood which time and suffering render more noble still. But it is light, with broad hips, strong. He smiles, well pleased, and considers it a matter of course that I offer to his friend the seat of honour on the sofa, make it really comfortable there, and then sit down facing it.

'Do play . . . Please!' I at last beg in a low voice. He nods. 'But first you must turn on the lights, all the lights.'

His fair hair now seems to breathe and raise itself. His eyes shine. He holds the guitar on his knees, his hands turn the pegs, delicately, but deftly and with determination. He is experimenting with it, seeking to get it in tune, but not as we generally understand the term.

'The very first thing to know about the guitar is that it never must be tuned exactly, always must it be kept just a little bit suspended. The imperfection is its charm. And faultlessly regular instruments run the risk of becoming boresome just like too regular beauty.'

It uplifts me considerably to hear this, for I am anything but a regular beauty. 'Faultless people are utterly unbearable!' I energetically agree and feel my stature increase.

'In life, also, nothing is ever absolutely in tune, all things are suspended.'

Silence. Then the guitar sounds. It voices a question and imperiously demands an answer. But the answer is in its turn again a question.

'. . . g . . . c sharp . . . g sharp . . . b flat . . . e . . .'

He plays the melody, and ever the same melody, until it burns like suffering in my heart. Melody without a beginning, melody without an end. Melody resembling Life, which he has dubbed an eternal fragment. Then the strings are silent.

'Now you also know my guitar and my melody. To have a melody of his own, a song phrase which is himself, is man's highest possession. I built *Samoun*, my one-act African play of vengeance, on it; I wrote down the notes without regard to usage and rules. When first the actors read the score, they screamed: 'Impossible to play or sing that!' But I sprang on the stage and played it for them on the piano — and then they sang it without more ado.

'But it has grown late, seven o'clock! I must be going. In Berlin the "prosperous citizen" is just gathering his family around the festal board.'

My cheeks burn red with shame; that was like an encouragement to an invitation . . . and I can issue no invitation . . . the iron code has brought it about that my landlady refuses to do any cooking for my friends. What matter? Restaurants exist for the benefit of the homeless. Does it matter whether he is my guest here or there?

'If you like,' I propose, 'we might have a little more time together. I am a regular *habituée* of a nice little place in the Tiergarten. Come along.'

The evening is cold and wet. We flee hastily along the streets. Only a few passers-by cross our path. No wonder, the air is raw with fog, one sees one's own breath.

I am glad when we are under cover. The little restaurant is cosily warm. It has not been going long. It caters for a well-to-do Bohemian public from the western suburbs; tries to imitate Munich in its decorations and its beer. Ludwig, a genuine good old Bavarian waiter, hurries to meet me, takes my leopard skin coat and is obsequiously attentive to my companion. Ludwig has always served in artistic restaurants. He has a nose for personality. He scents the man of note in Strindberg.

I did not wait to change, I merely threw a wrap about me. When I slid out of its folds I notice Strindberg's appraising gaze. All honour to the tight green dress. It fits me like a snake-skin and wriggles along behind me in a little pointed train.

'SS-ssss' hisses the silk lining every time I move. ' . . . Green leaves . . . yellow sun . . . love . . . joy-of-life . . . Spring-before-the-door . . . ss-sss.'

His face is rather flushed. His eyes laugh. He suddenly has a strangely humble, pleading air. Needs it so little to bridge over the unfathomable gulf between the Eternal and the Maiden? Only a green dress, a pointed train and a little 'ss-sss!'

'What we would like, Ludwig? *Hors d'œuvres* . . . the very best. This is a Swedish gentleman . . . lobster . . . chicken . . . you know!'

'And a bottle of Chianti!' orders my guest.

It is red wine and heavy. Dark, hot blood of Southern grapes.

'Skaal!' Our glasses clink together. How jolly we both feel, all of a sudden, how free of care.

'The wine is good. Beware of yourself and your secrets!' he says with a smile.

It is true, everything is for the best in the best of all possible worlds!

But in this best of all possible worlds the most incredibly painful moments have a way of occurring. Especially for a conceited young woman in a well-cut green dress lined with silk.

'How could such a thing happen to me — how was it possible?' I ask myself. I had invited him and therefore he was my guest. I also ordered the food, everything that was good and expensive. It was for me an understood thing that I should pay the bill and not he. Was he to undergo priva-tions just for the doubtful pleasure of my company? He surely could not think . . .

But he evidently did think and most emphatically. He asked for the bill as a matter of course. I had discreetly discharged it long before.

Ludwig behaved perfectly: 'It is all right, sir, the young lady has seen to it. The young lady is a regular customer.'

It did not help him, the deep and brilliant blue eyes began to flash lightnings. You could positively hear a whole electric battery beginning to crackle about him, the moustache and the curls stood on end. He shot at the waiter: 'The bill!' Without deigning me a glance. His admiration for my youthfulness — away with it! The power of the train — away with it! All humility has left him. He looks like an angry judge. What have I done? Does it make any difference whether I entertain my friend here or at home? What do I care for custom? Has the cursed thing called money any importance for people like us? Why should freedom and equality come to a sudden stop just at one point, where the question of money steps in? I give him a pert look, but the words are frozen on my lips.

'The bill!' sounds the ultimatum once again, cold and cutting.

Ludwig is already busy with a long manuscript. My guest does not wait for him to finish, but throws down a banknote, worth three times the amount with an impatient and final gesture.

'Our coats!'

'SS . . . sss' hisses the snake pathetically as I creep along behind Strindberg like a schoolgirl in disgrace. 'O snake, my dearest snake, he has bruised thy head. But it serves you perfectly right, you boarding-school miss without any tact!'

Now we are in the street again. A paralysing feeling of helplessness overcomes me. The wind is icy cold. Tiny white spears prick my cheeks and my veil is wet . . . I believe it is not the rain, nor my breath; no, it is true enough, I am crying quietly as I go. . . .

'Don't be angry,' I beg softly, and my hand strokes the rough, dark surface of the Flying Dutchman.

'No, I am not angry,' he says, suddenly tender. 'But don't do that again.' We wander dumbly back to town.

'Are you going "down there" this evening?' I ask, hesitatingly, as he bids me good night at the door of my house. 'And does our appointment hold good with the critic Brahm at the Deutsches Theater to-morrow, Saturday? He is so useful.'

'A "Ferkel" Brother is leaving to-day. I will do penance to-morrow, Saturday, for a Friday full of sin and will suffer the theatre and theatrical business, but to-day I must go to my friends. Good night.'

That was good-bye. But when I am long since up in my room, he still stands down below, waiting in the night.

I call out to him . . . tear the guitar from its corner, race down to the street with it and carefully lay his good friend in his arms.

Oh, to find the right note! Shyly I make my plea: 'Do you know, I have been thinking over what you said this afternoon . . . about the guitar . . . and the charm of imperfection . . . I don't know if you have noticed it . . . I have a great deal of this charm, even if it is my only one . . . I have endless faults and failings . . . I am Imperfection . . . you must be patient with me . . . please!'

How bright his eyes are now! It was the right note!

*

August Strindberg, Berlin, to Freda Uhl

'Dear Fräulein Uhl: I am plunged in despair, indeed I am! Your card did not reach me till 6.15 and at 6.30 I was at your house. Well, to-morrow we shall meet, shan't we! Do not forget that the Linden Hotel has a telephone.

'I cannot tell you how much I regret this lost evening! 'Your respectful and obedient, August Strindberg.'

'Dear Friend,—In order not to miss any more of your company, which has come to be my most priceless hours, I hasten to inform you that my portrait keeps me busy every day from 10 to 12, and that I have to go and see Director Grube at the Schauspielhaus next Monday afternoon at 4 o'clock.

'All that I ask of life is fulfilling itself and yet I am unhappy. If you are really my friend and are not playing with me, you will not go to Munich without delivering me from the Hell in which I live. In eight days' time I shall have finished, shall be ready to travel and I may count upon you, mayn't I?

'You are so good to me that you will even forgive the annoying after-effects of the black humours that persecute me.

'If you have not left, then here's to our meeting soon! — Your August Strindberg.'

We have met in the Tiergarten by that still stretch of water which surrounds the Rousseau Island. At other times Joy used to be on the spot before us, to-day I miss it yearningly. Black shreds of clouds on the trees. The wind cuts barkingly. Deep furrows have marred Strindberg's face since I have seen him last. His light-heartedness has vanished, his glance is shy. And yet he would not miss his pains. His torturer this time is the Unknown in him, his genius. Strindberg is at work.

The Unknown! He is part of the universe's creative forces, part of its magnetic powers; the memory of the ages and the eye that sees the future, the flame which flashes from subconsciousness to consciousness.

He is for Strindberg a constant revelation, an ever new surprise; he contemplates him piously and deferentially and bears himself with proud still dignity like a king. It is the crown of the Unknown which shines over August Strindberg's head.

Who is this August Strindberg, walking at my side, the man with the tall figure, the shining eyes, the gentle mouth? This kind, charming, marvellous man? There are times when he can be as simple and gay as a child, unexacting, where he laughs as laughs a babe. I dare say he could kiss too, and hold a woman in his arms.

I have asked myself sometimes how it would be, to be kissed by him?

But the Unknown is also a devourer.

'When I write,' Strindberg tells me now, 'I put aside my conscious being. I plunge for conquest into the primeval, origin and eternity. The effort is too great though, my undeveloped brains cannot cope with it. Often they leave the messages at the threshold of my consciousness, without arranging them according to time and place. The popular vocabulary for the Unknown, the Spontaneous, is Genius, its word for what lies beyond the reach of consciousness is madness. — Do you think I am mad?'

He has brusquely stopped and looks upon me as though it depended upon my answer whether we should go on our way further together or not.

'No.'

'Then you are probably the only one. All the more honour to you.'

He stretches himself to his full height, as if throwing off a burden. The wind has ceased, the clouds are gone. The sun hangs in the sky like a lustrous yellow ball.

Joy has come late, but it has come.

LOVE BURGEONS

August Strindberg, Berlin, to Freda Uhl

'Dear Fräulein and friend: I cannot tell you how much our walk in the park did, to chain the evil spirits that persecute me. I can only thank you and congratulate myself.

'You called yourself my old friend. Good! You will never be as old as I am and never such a child!

'But I must see you every day, even if it should compromise you, and if I do compromise you — let me tell you — you will find me prepared to give you the honest satisfaction that is demanded from a man of honour. Is that enough? Your old friend, August Strindberg.'

*

Marriage as the price of the escape from solitude and for the company of a good woman? It may be the habitual thing. But for us two, my admirable friend, this would not be matrimony, but just a social sacrifice, which neither God nor Caesar must demand for an honest friendship. You are overrating me, my friend, unless you underrate me. I am not worthy to become your wife. Frankly speaking, I do not know the mortal who would be worthy. But to marry merely for the purpose of pleasing conservative minds — I am too good for that. Let us try to find a less desperate expedient, then. How about a watch-dog? I know a charming young maiden. . . .

May T. sits opposite me, while I read Strindberg's letter. She is a sculptor and is now sketching me as a graceful Dryad, my green crêpe de chine gown had inspired her.

May T. is a regular visitor. She is a pretty and bright girl who resembles me in a way, but is my opposite. She is a far more precious edition than I, however; taller, slimmer, myself blonde, with an accentuated distinction, infallibly ladylike. Her father was in the Prussian army, stationed at Potsdam, too. This parts us, while our young womanhood, a craving for independence and our artistic aspirations bring us together. We feel a little like two young warriors, personally congenial, but not marching under the same flag.

I like her, but at times her faultlessness, her immaculate good manners, irritate, annoy me!

66

I throw a glance at her. Why should she walk through
life for ever without knowing it?

'It won't hurt you a bit to be useful for once, my girl,' I
conclude in my mind. And I throw out my lasso.

'Listen, darling. Strindberg really ought to interest you
from the point of art. He has a head, a head, I tell you!
That head is bound to make a sculptor famous!'

'I quite admit it. I have nothing to say against him as a
bust. He would even tempt me.'

I laugh silently and say aloud: 'You ought to see him close
by. I tell you what, I am going to invite you two. Come and
have dinner with him and me to-night.'

'That is impossible. I cannot show myself alone with you
and him in a decent restaurant. It's a pity. I should have
liked to have a look at him close by,' the perfect lady states
after due consideration.

'All that can be arranged, my dear. No Caesar shall
think any less of you. We are going to have dinner here in
my room.' She consents to that. Now you can come, my
friend. The little watch-dog will safeguard respectability.

August Strindberg, Berlin, to Freda Uhl

'Dear Friend: To-day you were very good to me and I
thank you for letting me be with you.

'I did not say very much to you, but your mere presence
was enough; it made me feel happy, composed and
forgiving.

'I take pleasure in thinking of to-morrow evening, I beg
of you not to call it off. If you think it absolutely necessary
to have a moral guard, then don't let it be a man, for I
shall murder him. On the contrary, and if it must be, invite
our pleasant lady Cerberus of to-day, if she should like to
come. I like the little sage more than I dare confess to her
friend.

'I would propose Schulte's Weinstube, Unter den Linden, between the Friedrichstrasse and the Passage Panoptikum. This is a thoroughly refined place imbued with atmosphere, never crowded, where one is served adroitly and respectfully. I press your hand — until to-morrow! — August Strindberg.'

Oh, Mr. Flying Dutchman, is it really true as you say, that some unseen power grudges you woman? It almost seems so. I cannot see you to-night either. My beloved father in Vienna lays a heavy hand upon my shoulder.

When father writes as a father, his style is that of the German Emperor when he uses the telephone in the castle. Every communication to his officers, whatever communication it be, William II introduces with the words: 'I order . . .!' Similarly father orders (even where he does not use the word, his Wilhelmian tone suggests it), 'in four days, at the very latest, you depart for Munich!'

And during these four days I must write four articles and dispatch them to him. That means that I can scarcely leave my room, having to read the books first before I write on them.

What will you do, Herr August Strindberg, while I, by hard labour, am enriching the *Belles Lettres*? The sun shines, the sun laughs, spring goes on blooming. And you . . .?

What will you do?

August Strindberg to Freda Uhl

'My dear lady: Is it really possible that you are going away on Wednesday? And without a leave-taking? What will become of me? Or shall I make preparations to follow you next Saturday?

'I am sad to-day and lament the loss of yesterday evening. Would you permit me to meet you to-morrow, in the museum, under the arcades or in the park? I burn with longing for a good talk together, just we two. It seems to me that I owe you so many replies left in the air, so many explanations cut off mid-way, an infinite number of excuses! I should like to stroll at your side for ever without end under the trees, on the sea-shore, over hill and dale. Is this madness? Have I wearied you? Are you afraid to dissolve your soul with mine? Do you think I shall swallow you up like a cannibal? Are you so self-conscious that you can no longer give yourself up to the sweetest illusion life offers, the divine lie which makes us happier than the most sublime truth? Does it all matter to me? Perhaps.

'Send me a word, I beg of you, and believe me to be your already far too devoted — August Strindberg.'

You, August Strindberg, and I . . .?

It would scarcely be wise to resist the temptation. Father was wrong. Fathers always are. A romance with you is worth more than all the books of the world which he may send me, and worth more than what I might write about them.

I do believe that we shall arrange another meeting after all . . . I do believe it to be imperative that I see you again . . . Soon, soon.

What would you do without me?

*

Well, we have met again. That very same night. It was none too soon.

He is about to conquer Rome. Zacconi, the great Italian actor, will produce *Father* early next season — and August Strindberg would have to spend his first Italian payment on wine and spaghetti without me.

Ah, always this same wild joy, the same secret jubilation, when we see each other again after a day's parting, the same effort to hide our feelings; but only animals may show their gladness when their master returns without whom their life is empty. There are lights flickering in our eyes, there is a smile around our lips that tells, but that is all. Not a word. We fear words. How would it sound, if all of a sudden my thoughts became loud, 'There is not one moment of Joy for me when you are not there, you Great one', and if he replied audibly, 'I love you, little girl, genius does not protect one from Love'.

We silently raise our glasses. Chianti, red as blood. The old Romans already drank this wine, from golden cups or women's lips they drank it. It is redolent of the sun, it uplifts.

Is it true that he likes wine? He laughs. 'Yes. I do like wine. With good cause. It liberates the soul from physical bondage, it helps her to gain heights where all weights drop. To have visions no one ever saw before and find expressions which no one else has phrased.

'The Romans knew it: they drank, to Victory and love.'

Ermete Zacconi . . . August Strindberg . . . the Eternal City. . . .

It awes me and I look at him shyly, dreamily.

He nods. 'Yes, this is power. Art may refuse to her servant a piece of bread, but bestows on him the rule over spirits and hearts all over the world. Art tears down barriers and borders, speaks that language which all men feel to be their own. Take us two, here we sit, quietly and humbly, you and I, and at this very moment, perhaps, in some far country my Word may carry strength and comfort. Unable though I often am to help myself, yet thousands owe to me their liberation and that mysterious vital unison with the great Source of Life. It is in them that I live, more than in my own body. I am their Conscience and their Law.'

Railway maps and posters are looking down on us from the crude tavern walls, exaggerated colours, a glaringly blue sea, blackest pines, an Italian landscape, Sicily ... We are sitting in a little Osteria which he has discovered during our separation.

The posters are cheap but alluring. They invite you to study the time-table. They make one wish to travel — with each other — to travel into the Sun — together.

It must be the wine. Hastily I draw back my glass.

'And the Porker?' I ask. 'What does the Porker say to your infidelity?'

'The Porker is very busy just now. It does not even miss me. It intends to admit ladies to its Round Table,' he reports, 'in a gold-miner's camp that is risky. Women mean colour and life but conflict and evil as well. It's only natural that every man should want to have a woman of his own in his tent. That has been man's prerogative since Paradise. But not one of us has. Animosity is already stirring; the coming of woman proclaims itself by the sharp tension between the men, just as the whale's coming may be perceived when the still surface of the water suddenly shivers and hurls up a sudden spout.'

'Are they ... ladies?'

'Indeed, yes. So far only one has sent her portrait as an opening. That was wise of her. Suspense is always good. It rouses curiosity, imagination begins to play. She comes from a highly respected family in Lund and has graduated from the Academy in pianoforte playing. She is the friend of the Norwegian painter, Munch. But he hides her like a miser and simply will not bring her to the Ferkel where the crowd is already licking its lips red and shouting itself hoarse.'

'I can understand Herr Munch.'

'But he will not be able to keep his monopoly much longer. That young boy, Bengt Lidfors, has found out that he knew her well in Sweden.'

'Poor Munch.'

'Munch is not afraid of Lidfors — but he is afraid of me.'

'Of — you?' It may be rude, but I am speechlessly staring at him. I can see him as the chased animal, but not as the huntsman.

'My enemies make it easy for me. They do not guess how many beauties are being lured by my reputation as a "woman-hater",' he remarks, blushing a profound red and smiling apologetically.

THE HARBOUR

August Strindberg, Berlin, to Freda Uhl

'Dear, good friend: After sitting to Krogh for two hours, I started to see Schlenther; but on the Schlossplatz I began to feel ill; I rode home and went to bed. So nothing was done to-day. Don't take it amiss. It is not my fault. I am poorly, full of spring sickness, hypochondriacal — God knows what!

'And yet yesterday was such a beautiful day. You, yourself, were full of troubles and anxieties and all the same you bore with my worries.

'I went home on foot in order to tire myself out, and landed in the Ferkel purposely, to triumph over temptation. If I feel anything like myself this evening, I shall go to the Neumann-Hofers' at eight o'clock in the certain hope of finding you there. Afraid, though, that I have a return of my old ague.

'To-day, I write you in German, because it sounds less tender than French and does not beguile the poor scribbler into lyrics which never get answered anyhow. — With very best regards to my wise old friend, her foolish young friend, August Strindberg.'

*

Miracles will happen. The Neumann-Hofers, as a rule the most frequently invited couple in Berlin, are at home and are alone. Annie is in *déshabillé*, Otto in a velvet jacket. The room with its pretty yellow paper and the mellow lights suggests a ripened idyll.

'Strindberg is very likely to surprise you to-night,' I venture to say, 'he having hinted as much to me yesterday.'

'He will not surprise us a bit,' Annie corrects me amiably and at that moment Strindberg enters.

The evening passes most pleasantly. The two men talk of business and of the stage. Annie and I prattle softly. We have supper. After that their child is brought in, it is a well-fed, six-months-old little girl. You should see Strindberg's radiant face! He takes it with gentle, experienced hands and makes it laugh. He is an authority, no sooner has the mother betrayed her fear in regard to the babe's teething than he prescribes how rise of temperature can be avoided in such a case. He is quite familiar with infantile complaints. When one of his own children was ill, he nursed it himself. He saved his little daughter's life by praying and by the sheer force of his will power, when she stood on the threshold of death.

'Marriage can be very beautiful,' I venture to say thoughtfully, whilst Annie is absorbed in her embroidery.

'Marriage is Heaven — whenever it is not Hell,' she instructs me with a most disenchanting emphasis on her last word.

'On what does that depend?'

'For a woman it depends on the husband. He must be of the right kind. All men marry sooner or latter, yet there are but few born husbands. That means that in married life the solo is not of so much importance as is the talent for the duet.'

'I'd rather listen to a fine solo.'

'Quite so, for two hours, in the evening and at a concert. But when the concert is over, you want to get back home. Such a home, my dear, is Otto. I give thanks to God that I married him and not that other man with whom I was in love when I first came to Berlin. It was a far more passionate affair, but it would not have been a happy marriage. He is a great soloist and a very spoilt monsieur. I am spoilt, too; and there is not room enough for two *prima donnas* in one house, as my friend Huneker in the States used to say.'

'And can't one lose oneself entirely in the other one if he is worth it?'

She looks suspiciously from Strindberg to me. 'In that case the woman, too, must be a genius as far as love is concerned, or else — a silly goose.'

She blows azure cloudlets of smoke towards the ceiling. She, certainly, is not a goose.

The two men at the desk are brightly illuminated by the lamp and are in lively discussion. They are certainly very different. Otto, round, short and animated, pivots on his revolving chair. The other man moves very little and, when he does, with impressive dignity. Light gleams from his eyes and from his brow. He sends me a smile. Immediately I again feel certain of my case.

'I am sorry to contradict you,' I exclaim, 'but I do believe that genius in a man is most convenient for a woman. She need have no brains, he has enough for two.'

'He has, and he provides you with them so thoroughly that in the end there is not a thought of your own left to you, no feeling of your own. You have no life of your own and only the wish to be allowed to be once more yourself.'

The two men rise. Strindberg's eyes take in the happy domesticity.

A home! Would not a home be redemption for the Flying Dutchman?

Once more he and I are walking up the Spree embankment. He asks:

'When do we leave? I am ready.'

'I have to wait for a letter from sister. It must come soon, but I do not know when.'

'That's bad. I ought to be off, else I'll dissipate my fortune.'

'How big is your fortune?'

He takes four one-hundred mark notes out of his pocket — the remainder of the one thousand marks, which a recent book (*Plea of One Insane*) — the story of his marriage — has obtained for him in advance. Five hundred marks he has sent to his wife and the family of this marriage.

'Can you still be surprised that I am done with *les belles lettres*? This literature disgusts me! Think of the horrors of that profession! To skin one's nearest and dearest and then offer the skin for sale. It is like the huntsman who cuts off his dog's tail, gnaws off the meat and throws to the dog the bone, his own bone! To spy out people's secrets, to find the moles on a woman's body, to vivisect humans like rabbits, to kill, to violate, to burn down — ugh!'

He has ceased speaking, shivering with excitement. The silence becomes unendurable. In order to dispel it my words gush out:

'No pain can be too high a price for any experience which is so vital that it becomes through you the property of the world. Is it not your supreme law to express yourself and to create?'

Now he is again all joy and vigour: 'Quite so. That's exactly what I said to myself, when I looked at this novel of mine the other day. What matters is the experience and not the price. — By the way, would you take charge of my fortune and keep it for me?

He pleadingly stretches out the notes to me. I am about to take them when a sudden pain, like a burn, thrills along my fingers. I shiver and for one moment close my eyes. But the wind dancing by sweeps the last autumn leaves out of our way and flutters the banknotes in my hand. How light an artist's marriage weighs!

75

MARRIAGE WITH GENIUS

From August Strindberg's Diary

Last night at the Café Bellevue with the Neumann-Hofers. Waited in vain for Freda Uhl until three in the morning.

BATTLING WITH THE ELEMENTS

August Strindberg, Berlin, to Freda Uhl

'Dear, dearest friend: Where are you? I forgot my soul with you and you have run away with my soul, so that I wander like a ghost. In earnest. On my life!

'If you have been playing with me, I want to die. Without a reproach! You have taken revenge and quite rightly. I die and bless you, sweet lady! I have never demanded of you that you should love me, but only that you should permit me to love you. Is that too much to ask?

'Let me see you to-day, before nightfall, or I shall go mad. Best of all at your house or in our own little Ferkel at the world's end.

'I am at home and waiting, waiting, waiting! Your August Strindberg.

'P.S. The money has come, the bills are paid, everything is ready.'

*

We are sitting face to face, neither of us with a proud air. But we are happy now that we have met once more. We have not seen each other for three days. In a fit of independence, we have tried life without each other, but found it taste lukewarm and stale.

There is a grey cloud on his forehead.

'Well, that was a terrible experience!'

'What was?' I ask, smiling involuntarily at his funereal air.

'Last evening in the Ferkel. You had abandoned me. I cannot bear solitude. So I went there. The friends are on the verge of becoming enemies. Two of them were missing, out of a wild jealous chase of the lady, I have told you of her, who was dining with a third one somewhere in town. There was a peevish constraint and finally an ugly quarrel.'

'Foe in the bay! — What is the fair maiden like?' I inquire, amused.

'I could not tell you,' Strindberg answers. 'I have not seen her. But I can tell you how Munch sees her. It does not concern him how others see her. All that man demands of woman is, that she should be able to awaken an illusion in him and not destroy it again immediately. Woman is and ever will be the clay which man moulds into his ideal according to his needs.'

'And how does Munch see and paint her?'

'A most modern type, refined and delicate, a temptress of the mind rather than of the flesh, a highly differentiated creature. No Phryne but an Aspasia, indeed. Her face is unusual, aristocratic, sympathetically alive. There is something searching in it; a trembling of her nostrils. Her lids are lowered, but the eyes underneath them pertly prey on things. Her throat is thin but her shoulders are round and womanly.'

'It certainly means something if an artist like Munch sees her that way. — But how did it end?' I force myself to smile.

'Well, that is more than I could say. The whole thing had become so utterly disgusting that I simply could not stand it any longer. I absented myself, therefore.'

'You went away?'

'No, I did not go. Why should I have cleared the field? The others finally withdrew. But I have at times the power to make my mind change the scene. Then I no longer hear what happens around me and I no longer see what is present. I am somewhere else, far away. My soul escapes the prison of the body.'

'Is that so simple?'

'Quite simple, but it is very fatiguing. Whenever I become conscious again I feel like waking from a sleep which has weakened me instead of giving me strength. In that way I absented myself.'

'And where did you journey to?'

He smiles.

'I let myself be guided by dramatic contrast, I felt stifled by the city atmosphere. The big city resembles a lion's cave; all footsteps lead into it, and not one of them can ever be traced back. An old peasant full of experience said to me one day: "The city is a malignant ulcer, it sucks all the vital juices of the body and turns them into putrefaction!" — Take the precious herb of the absinthe, for example. On our low plane it confuses and stupefies men; and yet it has grown up high on the mountain in the most invigorating air and the breath of the pines caressed it at its birth. It ends its life on the dusty floor of a public house. There you have your city career! Therefore I fled back to nature.'

'To your Swedish islands?'

'There is a little white silver moor. I'm going to write about that now. The story came to me last night all of a sudden and took hold of me. I remember its every detail.'

'Then you really ought to thank the Ferkel.'

'So you do not condemn me after all?'

But my absolution is not what he wants. The grey clouds linger on his brow.

Just for the length of one hour he shakes off his depression, in that hour, sparkling with vitality, he tells me about his scientific experiments. This time he has declared war on the elements themselves. He denies their indivisibility and insists that they possess the faculty of transmutation. Sulphur as well as — gold!

Heresy! They mock at him, they will stone him and put him into a lunatic asylum some day — but nothing and no one will make August Strindberg untrue to his Truth.

He reads my boundless admiration in my eyes and turns

away, sombre and disheartened. It is not my admiration that he wants.

'Are we going to see each other to-morrow?' I am asking timidly.

'No.' But when he takes leave silently and aloof and threatens to go, my helplessness bursts out despairingly.

'I am certain the weather will be fine to-morrow . . .' I say and implore him with my eyes.

It must have sounded overwhelmingly brilliant! He laughs amused and reconciled.

'I shall write to you before and your reply to that letter then shall decide. — Good-night, you child!'

The last hope . . .! And I am afraid of it. . . . It will be a proposal.

*

This day has beaten down my joy of life like hail. It started with unpleasantness from Vienna. Father thinks that Berlin and Munich are still too close to each other; he seriously considers banishing me to Mother and the Phaecians on the Danube. That for me would be the seventh Hell.

For me the Phaecians are an obsession. I shudder when I think of my grandparents' house. I experience an unexplicable stifling fear. Fear — I do not know of what, I fear the wide river, in spite of its beauty, the mysticism of the land. The exuberant wealth of that big house is like a tomb of the spirit. I dread it much as Life dreads Death.

This morning the hours were reluctant to pass, it seemed like days before it grew dark. In spite of the fact that I do not want to marry, I am waiting, I am waiting for Strindberg's proposal — firmly determined to decline it. Logic and consistency are not among my talents.

I am lighting the candles on my dressing-table and contemplate myself. The white lace droops from my shoulders and my arms. I don't look bad, yet there is nothing striking about me.

My face is expressive, that is the best about it. Besides — ? Hazel hair, greyish-blue eyes with big pupils, the mouth looks small when it is closed but when I laugh it opens wide over small teeth, and then its corners curl high up. My skin is white. The nose does not know what it wants, it strives up, it strives down. That does not matter — I am young.

Then Strindberg's letter comes.

By the light of the candle I read it again and again. It is a proposal and it is the most beautiful letter, the most beautiful poetry August Strindberg ever wrote. — Oh, the lovely fairy tale of the king's son who loves me! And I am expected to reply to that, I? To reply before I meet him to-night?

My image looks at me from out of the mirror — a girl just like thousands of others. That is reality.

My friend, I am not a princess. You are inventing my beauty, most likely you are also inventing your own love. You write: 'Let us go to your parents in the mountains, to-morrow, dear girl of mine!' . . . My friend, my parents are not living in the mountains in winter time. Father has reached the climax of his ambition; he lives in the dark Hofburg of the Habsburgs, he holds a high charge, but he lives like a prisoner all the same. Mother lives in the valley of the Phaecians. To them your bride elect is just a schoolgirl whom one sends to bed when she is cheeky enough to wink at Life.

The flame in front of the mirror shoots up, I have played with the letter in my hand and the paper has caught fire. Good that my washstand is within reach, the soapy, perfumed water quickly kills the flame.

'It's good' — I repeat, 'that was a symbol.' Then I make a resolution.

I owe him the truth about myself.

BERLIN

Freda Uhl to August Strindberg

'My dear friend: I have only two minutes to answer your letter if I am not to be late at our rendezvous, nor have I much to say. You asked me once what made me look so mature though I was still so young. It really is nothing particular, in fact it never was anything at all. And that was the worst thing about it. Well, to-morrow will be the anniversary, we may spend it together, you and I. One does not die because a few illusions die. I am in perfect health, but I have grown old and cold. I am sincerely devoted to you as a friend and there is nothing I would not do to help you or give you pleasure. But I am unfit for any feeling of passion. I believe this to be good for you. As you assure me that you love me, I do not doubt it. You are too generous to trifle with a young girl who cannot interest you as a study and who has not done you any evil. But I am convinced that this Love is only an illusion. You love Love, you love the dream in your own heart, you want to see your dream come true — so you deceive yourself.

'But there will come, so I hope, for you the day on which you will find a woman who is your mate and loves you, and then you will be happy. Up to that day let me remain your friend, the most sincere, the most devoted, the most affectionate. That is the only choice, believe me, and the best.

'Reach out your hand if you agree with me. Freda.'

*

Was ever woman in this humour woo'd?
Was ever woman in this humour won?
Richard III, Act 1, Sc. 2.

I see him already from the cab. He walks up and down expectantly. He carries his head high like a king, joyously, youthfully. The young trees along the pavement stand abreast and present arms.

Every other thought is wiped out. I enjoy the present moment unrestrained. We shake hands. We smile. The air is mild. There is just enough darkness to indicate the glittering of the stars behind it. How beautiful the night is, and how beautiful is life.

He asks me: 'Did you get my letter?'

'I got your letter and I've written you a letter. But I've not had time to post it, so there it is. — But, please, don't read it now . . . do what you like, but don't read it now . . . Don't read it before we are in Munich.' — It suddenly dawns on me that I have committed a fateful blunder, I don't know what I am stammering.

Does my decision not matter to him? Is the poet in him stronger than the man and does he enjoy the dramatic situation, forgetful of reality? He smiles, as though utterly unconcerned, pockets my verdict as a teacher would a pupil's test paper or a king a petition. Then he walks ahead. He carries his head no less high, no less joyously, no less youthful. The young trees continue to salute.

I trot behind him, awkward, bewildered, angered — but I do feel relieved.

We sit down at our table in the restaurant. Everything is charming, the place has atmosphere. He carefully selects the wine and the dishes. He raises his glass in which the Asti sparkles. 'To our trip — Skaal!'

I do not hesitate one second. 'To our trip!'

The glasses clink and stand opposite each other, both empty to the last drop. Now his eyes plunge into mine and anchor there. Then he composedly draws with a benign smile a heavy, old-fashioned pistol out of his coat pocket and places it carefully on the white tablecloth.

'Is that meant for the trip — ?' I ask, trying to laugh.

'No,' he replies in deadly earnest. 'No, I have only put it into my pocket because I did not know which way you would decide. — Skaal!'

'Skaal!' I force out and in my terror I again try to smile. 'Do, do put it back again,' I urge.

Underneath the table I drive my nails into my palm. Now courage! courage! If he leaves me with this abomination in his pocket and if, at home, he opens and reads my 'No', it means the end of all things. I must prevent that at any price.

Our conversation is most animated, it flies from one topic to the other. He has never been more brilliant.

'What news have you of your children?' I ask after a short pause. Immediately a tender emotion settles on his face.

'They do not write. They are not allowed to, I dare say. But I trust all is well with them, now they have the money.'

'The advance on your novel?'

'Yes, the *Plea of One Insane.*'

'Then this publication was necessary?'

'Yes, indispensable. The children had nothing to eat.'

The children — August Strindberg's children — had nothing to eat? Is — that — possible?

'I would like to see a photo of your children,' I plead. 'Have you got one?'

'Of course I have!' He puts his hand to his heart, where, like a compass through stormy seas, he always carries an old leather letter-case; it used to be black, but now it is rubbed and grey; he takes three pictures out of it. An evil spell seems to have lifted. The dreamy smile has gone — here is his reality. Around this radiates his warmth and his affection. With gentle, tender hands he touches the little images like priceless treasures. 'Here they are.'

He gives me his children! But why should that stir me as it does? Had he not wanted to give them to me before, when he had asked me to become his wife? I was to have become the mother of his children whom he loves, without whom his life will be an eternal torture and whom no woman in the world will ever replace to him. And there in front of us lies this pistol, an old stage property pistol belonging to a prehistoric period of sentiment — which, however, will outlive us all. There it lies beside the three angels' heads. How they resemble him! — as August Strindberg looked when faith was in his eyes, before life tore it to pieces.

'That's Karin,' he explains and points to the eldest. She has a sweet little face with big round eyes. 'She wants to become a teacher. And this is Greta.' Greta looks gayer, more playful. 'She wants to marry and become a mother. Now Hans — Hans will probably become a student of chemistry. He wants to do research work, the life I missed.'

Hans, not six yet, is delightful beyond words. I'd love to kiss Hans right here on the spot.

Hans has settled the matter for me. 'Quite so,' I say. 'When a man has children like those . . . please, do put that iron horror back in your pocket! . . . children like those, he commands the future. The whole world belongs to the man who has such children.'

'That was my idea. But life is strange, it always shoots surprises at you.'

'Do you remember what you said the other day about life being a fragment, the beginning of which no one recollects and the end of which no one knows? That sounds plausible. It's the only explanation for what we fail to understand . . . Do, please give me back that letter!' I abruptly plead.

If only he would give back that letter!

But he stores it together with the photos of the children in his leather letter-case and shakes his head without a word. Fear and helplessness are beating against my temples. What shall I do, what shall I do . . . ? If I cannot recover that letter, I must neutralize it somehow. This abominable letter touching the little angels, harming them — that must not be.

When we are back in the street a cold wind rises from the Spree, the trees bend under its lashing. Ice crackles under our feet. He has silently offered me his arm. More and more fiercely the wind sweeps along. It catches in the Dutchman cloak as we walk. It blows up and the rough, hard wing of the cape beats into my face at every step. The night after we had first met comes back to me. 'I have dreamt all this already,' I say softly.

'That we walked arm in arm like this?'

'No, but that black, heavy pinions were savagely whipping my face and that these pinions belonged to your "Flying Dutchman".'

'The Dutchman does not whip, he is being whipped.'

'Like every one of us à son tour.'

We have become silent once more. I feel like caressing the 'Dutchman', he beats but does not hurt. We have arrived now at my door. Once it has closed he will start on his way home with my Letter on his heart — the letter with my 'No'. Then, in his hotel room, he will read the letter and he will know that he must remain without a home and will not see his children so soon — And then?

No, everything, but not that.

I've thrown my arms around his neck, I have lowered my veil until it covers my eyes and my mouth and through the veil I now offer him my lips.

Enraptured, surprised, he wants to fold me in his embrace. But I am already inside the house and have slammed the door.

I can hear him walking up and down in front of the house quite a long while. Then his light steps die away.

THE DAY AFTER

My young sculptress friend, who is back from Dresden, sits correctly in her tailor-made suit at my bedside when I wake up.

'Good morning, baby. You certainly slept well. I suppose you were on the spree last night?'

'No, I was in bed at eleven.'

'I dare say you were debating with Strindberg about free love?'

I hate her most sincerely at that moment.

'Quite the contrary.'

'What do you mean?'

'We had a most fruitful talk about Holy Matrimony.'

'Are you mad?'

'Yes ... no ... yes ... perhaps ... but, what does it matter if I am, as long as he's mad, also?'

She takes it for a joke. She would refuse to believe that any grown-up young lady should deal as frivolously as that with a matter of lifelong security.

'It's never possible to talk sensibly with you,' she scolds, staging a dramatic exit.

But when she turns back at the door, she finds me sobbing convulsively.

'What have I done ... what have I done?'

I have allowed an old rusty pistol to be too much for me. Have I not known marriage and have I not feared it, since I was a child and saw the shipwreck of my parents' union, and all the shipwrecks around us. I have always seen it running apart from love and in a different direction, and yet ...?

I have thrown myself on Strindberg's neck, most generously so, but I certainly am the most unfit wife for him in all the universe.

'What have I done ...! I am going to lose Strindberg now. You do not know what he has been to me, a Guide, a God, a Friend, a Lover — all that I am going to lose ...'

She tries to comfort me: 'Must that be final?'

No. Why should it? Madness indeed, to let the most spontaneous thing, a kiss, decide a destiny! Yesterday I refused

86

to become Strindberg's mate because I had kissed another man a year ago, and to-day—? How can one fugitive minute determine a whole long life?

That cannot, must not be! Yesterday was — yesterday.

'Write to him, as though nothing had happened,' she advises. 'He may thank you for it some day.'

I look at her, half indignant, half amused, but — I write.

*

'Dear friend: I should much appreciate it, if you would call for me to-night at seven, but I am unavoidably in the company of Herr A. Moszkowski, brother of the composer, and I must say in his favour that he has none of the attributes of a rival.

'I am enclosing 50 marks for the purchase of a spring coat, which reduces your deposit accordingly. Yours, Freda Uhl.'

*

'Dear friend: I gratefully acknowledge the receipt of 50 (fifty) marks, I am prepared to fetch you punctually at 7 o'clock and I shall be unutterably delighted to make the acquaintance of Herr Moszkowski. In haste, your August Strindberg.'

*

Maurice Moszkowski's brother has none of the attributes which would madden any ordinary jealous lover, but Strindberg is like Othello — his imagination supplies what the other man lacks. We spent the evening in most distinguished fashion in the distinguished Kaiserhof and I have never seen two men wishing each other to Hell so politely. We parted early and lamely. I had hoped to say one good word to Strindberg alone, but the two would not separate. They clung to each other up to my door. It would have been no use to look out of the window. Either both had gone, or they were still promenading — both. I laugh, but I feel ashamed. And something's aching.

On my night table I find a letter of his, dated yesterday evening. It has been there most likely while I was with him and further away from him than ever.

To whom is that letter addressed, to the girl who offered herself to him in a kiss? Or to the pusillanimous little *bourgeoise* who 'refused' him?

*

August Strindberg, Berlin, to Freda Uhl

'Dear, dear girl: What has happened and what do you mean? Was it pity or was it love? And after the letter of last evening? I read over what I intended to say to you to-day: Does it worry you that I love you? Is it burdensome to you that I am so fond of you?

'This was my dream — now I will tell it you.

'We were sitting together at your hospitable table, you took my left hand and kissed it and said: "I never said that (that I did not love you!)" and then we kissed one another like doves or angels.

'And when you uttered those same words last evening, I thought the dream must be something beautiful, something that was gone and would never come back.

'And then . . .!

'What is to happen now? And what is your will? Do not despise me, because I have treated you with reverence. I love you, but he who cannot become a child again, cannot love.

'You were sixteen years young (not old) yesterday. It seemed to me as if you had been dressed up as an old woman and now revealed yourself in all the majesty of your youthful beauty, in order to make me still more unhappy! And yet . . . Now I am so happy that I weep.

'Do we leave Berlin together as an engaged couple? In three days' time I shall have borrowed 2,000 marks and we will go to Vienna and see your parents; and then — to Italy! . . . Is that all right?

'Begging for an answer, — your August Strindberg.'

*

Nearly midnight! — Quick, my hat and coat! Quick, quick, to the next telephone!

'Is that the Linden Hotel? . . . You're the night porter? . . . Has Herr Strindberg come home already? . . . No? . . . Then please take down a message and put it into his room. . . . Are you ready, got your pencil? . . . Well, then go ahead!

'Fräulein Uhl — quite right, U-h-l, asks him to call for her to-morrow at one o'clock without fail! — No, he knows the address. But don't forget "without fail!"''

BETROTHAL

Telegram to Freda Uhl
'Habel's Weinstube, 2 p.m. Shall not come — Want answer first — Strindberg.'

Linden Hotel speaking
At 10.30 a.m.: Herr Strindberg is not up yet.
At 12 o'clock: Herr Strindberg has gone out.
At 1 o'clock: Sorry, the message was delivered to him all right.

Telegram to Freda Uhl
'Demand your immediate departure Munich — Uhl.'

Freda Uhl's Monologue
2.30 p.m. — Munich! All right. But not without him.
3.00. — My trunk is packed, everything ready. Ready?
4.00. — Good Heavens, he is not coming.
6.00. — It is getting dark . . . dark . . .
8.00. — I do not want to lose him!

89

'Kleine Kirchgasse, Unter den Linden — drive as fast as you can,' I order the cab when I cannot bear to wait any longer.

The Kirchgasse is a short blind alley, like a narrow paved throat. Before it ends, it widens toward the left, the houses step back and, in a sort of front court, stand some miserably naked lime trees. To the right is his hotel, the Linden Hotel. Not one of the poor trees has a green sprout and only a dim little light burns above the entrance. My letter is in a tiny envelope and I press it into the driver's hand.

'Don't let the clerk have it, you give it personally to the gentleman.'

'I understand. I shan't part with it.'

I sat in the cab and waited.

What will happen if the cabman comes back and tells me that the gentleman is sorry, but he is engaged . . . or actually if he's not at home . . . shall I wait then until he comes back or go in search of him? . . . I can bear anything, but I cannot wait, cannot sit still and wait.

Thank heavens, there's the man! And he is not alone. In the opening of the door behind him rises the dark form of the Flying Dutchman. August Strindberg gets into my cab.

'Where to, sir?' the driver asks. Strindberg waits for my decision.

'Lützow Ufer . . . through the Tiergarten,' I beg. There is no reason why there more than anywhere else.

The cab tumbles along in the shadows. I dare not look up.

'Don't speak,' I implore him and burst out crying.

He soothingly puts his arm around me and slowly kisses my lips. At that moment a magic strength, such as I have never experienced before, miraculously pulses through me.

'Did you not know that I am an accumulator?' he laughs when I tell him. 'When I am being attacked, I deal blows like an electric eel and kill my enemies. But I, also, can make the weak strong, and I have already healed the sick. Whether two people belong together reveals itself only in the kiss, which is a blending of the body as well as of the soul.'

We got out at the Lützow Ufer. He dismissed the cab. The man had winked at me significantly and I in my delight winked back at him. Whereupon August Strindberg ran after him and the cab and presented him with an extra tip.

Then we walked along the river bank arm in arm. The water is black, the ice has melted long ago. The brown soil is redolent of sprouting green things.

'So I have been granted a second Spring after all . . . But what will happen now?'

'I do not know what will happen . . . But what did happen I know . . . Yonder, underneath the bridge amidst the snow your little Swedish ducks rested, my friend, when we heard them sing in that white night . . . They have surely found home since then . . . Have we, too, found home now?'

'That is in your hands. Will you take me as your husband? There's no harm in the question. If you answer "No", the distinction will remain with you that August Strindberg wanted to marry you and you will be able to say some day, "Strindberg loved me, but I refused him?" That secures you a place in literary history.'

'Thank you very much for this place — as an idiot.'

'But if you say "Yes", I shall be a good husband to you, who loves you and is true to you.'

'If the decision rests with me, then I say neither "Yes" nor "No". — Then I say: "Let us go to Munich, this very night, together — but let us not go into matrimony as hurriedly. In Munich we are free. There is a wind on the hills. In matrimony we two will be stifled.'

'We two will never be stifled, because there exists no standstill for us. We shall set out discovering life anew each day. That is and remains ever interesting. Marriage is a much used and a much misused institution; but still it remains the best existing shelter for man, woman and child. We only must take care that our marriage be a modern and real one.'

I am in despair and happy beyond words.

'Do you realize that — apart from my unlucky experience, which was no experience at all though it killed something in me in the bud — you are marrying the most unfit girl? My mother ruined my father's career (as far as that was possible — with all his activity and talent) by her appalling slovenliness; as long as they lived in one house together, his hands and feet were chained. Six days of the week wild chaos reigned; on the seventh day she made a great effort and started cleaning with a horde of servants; so thoroughly did she go about it that she never finished in due time. A prince and a prime minister narrowly escaped drowning in a pail, which was treacherously in ambush in the darkness of an unlit entrance hall in spite of an invitation and of supper-time.'

'I am not taking you as a wife so that you should clean the house. There are maids for that.'

'I have no talent for diapers.'

'That's because you have not had a child so far. We shall engage a nurse.'

'I cannot cook.'

'We shall engage a cook, there are many. But you are the only woman for me as a wife.'

'That makes three servants already! They cost money. I have no money at all, I only have debts.'

'I, too!'

A mad spell of laughter overcomes us.

'Exactly what do you see in me? I am not really beautiful.'

'For me you are the bride of whom I have been dreaming since my youth. You are the one and only; for what has been before exists no longer, like the hour that just passed by. You are and will remain my soul's mate, you are the embodiment of kindness.'

'You love me so much? . . . And in spite of it you do not want to come with me to Munich?'

'Not in spite but because of it.'

'But yesterday you did want to go?'

'Yesterday gossip would have been unjustified. To-day! Everything has changed now, you do not understand that, dear. I love to fight and I never was afraid for my own self. But I do not want to expose the woman whom I love to the mockery or the disdain of the crowd.'

His arm is around me as we walk home. The rough over-coat wraps me up, keeps me warm.

'How wonderful, to be harboured in a heart. Is that true marriage?'

'Yes — that is true marriage.'

*

'Now we belong to each other, and yet must part.'

I looked at him surprised. 'Part? Are you not following me soon? To separate for a few days — is that to part?'

'You calculate like youth. When one grows older, like me, every day counts. Now I shall live again as I lived before you came. Lonely days and noisy nights. No purpose. Hypochondria.'

'When you go to the Ferkel — for you must go, of course, if it attracts you — there is only one thing I beg of you, never take me there.'

'What do you mean, child? . . . Surely I have never wanted to take you there, nor would I take my wife.'

'I do not mean that . . . I mean, do not mention me . . . Do not tell anyone of our betrothal — please!'

'I'll promise that. But why . . .'

'I am afraid. I don't know, myself, what I fear. It is to me as though all that is finest in what unites us two would wither if any third person touches it. You said a very beautiful

93

thing the other day, do you remember, when you talked about the wedding of the Bees? Little as they are, they mate like the eagle high up near the sky where no human eye can detect them. "Animals have a right to their secrets", you said. I do want not to part with my right to my secret. Nor do I want to share it with another human soul, at least not all at once. Do you promise?'

Silently he kisses me on the forehead.

'And now . . . Farewell!'

*

Otto was adamant; he took me, himself, to the train. I believe he feels relieved in his inmost heart but does not dare to believe in my departure before he has witnessed me rolling away. Does he suspect anything? Guilefully I lead the conversation to Strindberg.

'A genius!' he cries enthusiastically. 'The greatest genius in all Europe. But a most unhappy man and a born victim of women. By the by, they want to introduce to him Munch's "Aspasia". Our friends are already very much excited as to how this acquaintance will develop.'

'So — o?' I laugh, I have no fear. The lady in question in my opinion arrives too late. If a man has conquered the girl he loves, he is indifferent to all other women, surely! It seems to me highly improbable that a man should want to shoot himself one day because Fräulein Uhl does not want to marry him, and that he should fling himself at 'Aspasia's' feet the day after. That would be beyond my comprehension. But I would like to see her. I beg Otto to describe her to me.

'I just had a passing glance at her, and that was all. I cannot say that she impressed me one way or the other. I suppose her chief charm consists in her being the only unmarried piece of femininity in the camp and that she is apt to turn it to her advantage. I am told that she is a good

model for every ideal which may be wanted; that, too, is a
gift which must not be underrated, especially not in that
crowd. But otherwise she seems to me to be rather limited,
in a purely sensual sense as well, no roundness. She is more of
the Serpent than Eve. Nevertheless, she might cause a Fall.'

He jumps from the running board just in time. The train
is moving.

These are the last words I hear; now they keep echoing in
my ears! 'Nevertheless, she might cause a Fall.'

Greyish vapours rise up abruptly. Like a compact wall
that parts me from the city and from men, the cloud vanishes
only after we have left. By the time it lifts, houses have become sparse, building grounds border on open fields. Then
the pine trees of the Mark of Brandenburg commence,
scattered at first, then closer to each other, until lance after
lance grows black out of the soil and stretches a dark roof of
needles over it, as a sombre reflection of the sad and desert
land. The night sky lowers grey as lead.

Then a pert puff of wind tears the lifeless stillness and un-
veils the stars. They glitter high up in the deep azure infinity
and wind themselves into letters.

> Just such joy as in winter
> Burneth my fear into sparks,
> They sprinkle a name in the darkness,
> Gigantic . . .
> STRINDBERG![1]

---

[1] 'An Immortal.' R. Dehmel.

III

BERLIN AND MUNICH

March 1893

THE SECRET

THE sun burns down on the Marienplatz like a gigantic yellow flame, lit by crazy Spring. It warms everything into new life. The Blessed Virgin on her pedestal, whose well-behaved little attendant cherubs so boldly tread the monsters under their feet, the solemn towers of the city hall, and the surging masses of humanity, intoxicated with light — all of them, old and young, stone and flesh and blood, glow in the yellow flame. The food market, usually prosaic with carrots and cabbages, has become a sea of flowers overnight, nothing but great waves of purple anemones, violets, yellow daffodils and mimosa, forget-me-nots, tulips, lilacs, rosy dielytra, called by the pretty name of 'ladies' hearts', and Easter lilies. The waves run so high, they swallow up the saleswomen.

Past the old city hall and the city gates, the old Burgstrasse runs on into the dusk, to the old Residency. Tall houses stand in rank, grey with age and chary of the light; secretly, behind the row to the right, an arm of the river Isar embraces them, clasping them fast; restless, quivering, green as a water fay's hair. There live Heinrich and Minna, with whom I stay, they were Richard Wagner's champions in days when this still cost blood. Dear good Heinrich, it did not suit you at all one year ago that I should fare to Berlin in search of life. Munich was just big enough for me, you thought. But if I must — 'Do what you like,' you said, 'but don't marry a monkey, marry a man.' A man for you is one who is willing to live and die for his faith.

Freda Uhl, Munich, to August Strindberg, Berlin

'My dear friend: Just one line in haste to tell you that I have arrived at Munich with the ardent wish soon to see you here. I spent a horrid night perched between two women, who alternately flung their cushions at me, now from the right, now from the left, so ruthlessly the train was swaying. It was so cold and so dark and a fear overcame me — a maddening fear that the past was nothing but a dream and that the future would be only a cruel awakening. At last the night has gone and to-day in the bright sunshine I am happy once more as I run through the streets to seek a little room for myself and a fine big apartment for you. Because you are coming, are you not, coming soon? Freda.'

August Strindberg, Berlin, to Freda Uhl, Munich

'Dear, cherished child: At last a good letter. And you are longing for me? What more do I need to know? But now people are beginning to talk about our engagement. The rumour may reach your parents and then the fat will be in the fire. So listen to the advice of your good friend, Neumann-Hofer, for I told him everything yesterday, everything, my child.

'Be as wise as you are beautiful and be sure that we are only thinking what is best for you. If I leave Berlin, all is lost, my future and yours! Neumann-Hofer simply forbade me to, since he is responsible for you. As long as people chatter about an engagement, all is well and highly respectable, but about a liaison — ugh!

'We went home at one o'clock a.m. yesterday and I only drank two glasses of wine with aerated water. Strange, isn't it, that I don't care for drink any longer. You have set me afire so that I need no firing with wine!

'It is spring here, but if you were here, it would be summer. Farewell and think of me as I think of you day and night. Thy — August Strindberg.

'PS. — Neumann-Hofer did not know that I was legally divorced. Of course I am. Could you imagine anything else?'

Why can't I feel happy about this letter? It's a beautiful, kind, honourable letter. Alas, I wanted no letter, I wanted him.

Why did he tell to our friends and give away our secret?

A young bee lies on the pavement in front of me. Just a few moments past both the bee and I were soaring and were jubilant high up in the clouds. Now it is lame and creeps. So soon.

BRIDAL LETTERS

'Dearest Little one: I have my ague and am sad.

'Neumann-Hofer told me yesterday that your father hated me and that our engagement may cause him and you a great deal of trouble You are not strong and I am so weary, weary, weary . . . Il se pourrait que je m'en aille.

'It is too much for me, all this, and I am afraid of happiness. You loved me one night in Spring and that has given me courage to die happy.

'I kiss you, bless you, and say: Farewell, child! My love has given you strength and confidence in yourself. That comforts me.

'Was it not splendid to be loved? Thine — August Strindberg.'

*

'Dear, good, beautiful, bad little thing: What are you doing in Munich? Come back here, we will put an end to the gossip, exchange rings, pay visits and be engaged. If you are afraid of marriage, we will wait and test ourselves. An engagement is not a bond. You are longing for me, aren't you, and you are afraid that it was all a dream! It is no dream, only the simple truth that I love, love you, love you!

'It is not useless to return to Berlin! There you will get a husband who loves you and whom you will not have to look down upon. A husband who will be true to you, whether he wants to or not, because you are so young and so fair and so clever and so crazy. Yes indeed, I love all the mad things you do; when you tell lies, as only a poet can, a poet like me, then I love you, because your lips are so lovely and your little teeth so marvellously white; when you are cross, I love you, because your deep eyes spit fire; I love you when you are so abominably clever and niggardly, because you write your horrid business letters for my sake.

'Well then; come back here and live in the west-end and I will live there too and then I will work and love you so much that you will be quite beside yourself, you will! Now you know everything!

'Good night, my child! Thine — August.'

*

'Dear Girl: What are you doing? Come here and protect me, so that I can work, or everything will go wrong. An evil conscience, bad news and reviews from Stockholm, restlessness, drive me to the Ferkel. If we are agreed, then in the end everything else depends upon the uncanny economic question. And from the moment you become engaged to me, you are also my wife, in that I look after you, except for the fact that you will help me with my business correspondence. If you agree and think this all right, then send me a wire and I and Frau Neumann-Hofer will look for a nice room for you here in the west-end or a boarding-house!

'Don't stay away any longer! I won't eat you up. You must become a writer and remain independent! — is that not so? You have a grain of manhood in you and I a drop of womanhood? That ought to make a fine mad pair! Don't you think so? Thine — August.'

*

'Dear wise dame-spouse: Well and so you are mine and I am thine. But! I am afraid of myself. I have so many things on my conscience these last few days, since you have been away, that I want to die. And the money flows, rolls, meanders away. Oh! But to-day I will gird up my loins . . . invent a financial project, borrow 3000 marks, pay your debts and mine, pull you back from Munich to Berlin and start work with you. That is the only way to save us.

'How can you imagine that I can stay at home alone, the whole hypochondriacal spring evening, when you are no longer at my side, watching over me with your good and lovely eyes?

'Do you hear, my love, it simply will not do. Wretch that I am, but how can I help it?

'My court physician and friend, Schleich, talks to me now like this: Cannot one get engaged, although one has debts? — and like this: As an engaged man you can pay your debts; not being engaged, very likely not, on account of lack of energy.

'Isn't that right? Just ponder the matter. Don't you think the flame of love also needs feeding?

'For me your personal presence is indispensable. I am so weak when you are not here . . . Thy husband — August.'

*

'Beloved little wife: I have just read your letter, in which you say so much that is wise and flattering. Ah! You suggest a spiritual marriage for six months, which would have the result of putting your all-too-earthly husband into a madhouse.

'If you won't reconsider it, I bow beneath your mighty hand, but on condition that during this cruel time, you leave me my independence. You confess, beloved angel, that you are incapable of love. I believe you word for word and am only waiting to see white wings beginning to grow out of your charming shoulders. Heaven forbid that you should fly up above the clouds and that I should lose you out of my sight. I am a poor son of earth and could not follow you. Well, what is to be done? Wait. But danger is threatening and I expect a misfortune to happen . . .'

*

'Beloved child: Now the moment has come when I must tell you everything, in spite of the danger of falling into disfavour with you.

'An honourable courtship, leading to marriage, has its economic side, that I acknowledge without contradiction, but marriage must not be a business arrangement. You have played the part of my good old aunt and the game amused me, because everything you do is becoming to you. But you have grown too set in your part, you have abused the power I gave you and I have become your absurd slave.

'From pity to contempt is but a step, and you already despise me; that you are ready to dispense me from remaining true to you, — wounded me, for it proves that you do not love me.

'From now on I forbid you to concern yourself in any way with my business, in any way! We shall see if our love can live on its own fire, without this horrible nourishment. This does not mean that I intend to neglect my business, on the contrary. I have been occupied with it since yesterday and am determined to get everything in order by May, in accordance with the conditions you set up for me . . .

'I love love, because you are my love. You, however, love my disordered affairs, because they give you the upper hand in the battle of the sexes for the preservation of personality.

'You have cast your silken net over my head and I am already struggling in the meshes and foresee the moment when your Hercules will seize a spindle. Oh! Omphale, if things go on as they have up to now.

'You are convinced that your motive is your motherly love for me. Just look at that! What does a little creature like you know of what is going on in a human soul under the mask of feeling? The powers of darkness go on with their hateful play, and only the seer's vision is clear.

'I am a seer and I will not be the plaything of my own creative power in a young woman, enchanting enough to tempt a God.

'However great your power may be, Vivian, you will not bind me with chains, for it was I myself who taught you my magic arts.

'Away from here! Once he has air beneath his wings, the eagle, plucked and ruffled by the smaller fowl, will yet rise into the upper airs beyond the blue firmament, whither the little angels cannot follow him — August.'

*

'Dear Freda: Think of that! You love me! And you are a good and sensible girl to confess your faults. But this is not your fault, this comedy played by nature, by hidden passion. It is much more my fault. The first evening, that delightful, unforgettable evening with you which was your gift to me, you worshipped me as a divinity and offered me roses and wine. From the very moment I was head over heels in love, but your youthfulness inspired me with a deep reverence and the more you set me up as a great man, the more I squeezed myself into a smaller part, to give you a possibility of winning me.

'I played the role of someone small and weak, without being aware of it, so that you might be able to love me, no matter why and how. Thus did I steal my way into your heart. And you, born to be a mother, developed the motherly aspect of your need of love.

'I do not know if this was what actually happened, but at the moment it seems to me to be so.

'Do you see, beloved maid, this is love's law of adaptation, to which we are all made subject.

'Oh, now it is my turn to write to you *en bourgeois*. Don't be anxious, I have got everything in order all by myself, without a notary and without Herr Paul . . . Enough!

'Next Sunday I am going to Vienna, partly to control that manager, Herr Lautenburg, partly in order to be present at the performance of *Creditors* — a gala performance, the Emperor will be there! I shall stay until the first of April, if you are there, all is said and done.

'First love, then business! Listen, little one! Business can be done better under the almighty influence of love than in the loneliness of the celibate life. Off to Vienna and *vogue la galère*.

'Incredible! The Scandinavian newspapers announce Strindberg's engagement but without mentioning the name of the bride! No going back now! Is there? And our battle-cry is: To Vienna!

'I embrace you from here as best I can! Thine — August.'

*

THE WIRES PLAY

Freda Uhl to Annie Neumann-Hofer

'If Strindberg now goes Vienna, break with papa unavoidable. What shall I do?'

Freda Uhl to her mother, Maria Uhl

'August Strindberg wants to become your son. Implore you, meet me to-morrow noon at Amstetten railway station. Must come with me Vienna, soothe papa, otherwise all is lost. Wire.'

Maria Uhl to Freda Uhl

'Becoming queen mother after all? Delighted. Punctually at the train. Shall bring Father Strindberg's *People of Hemsö*.'

Freda Uhl to Annie Neumann-Hofer

'Please immediately inform Strindberg that I await him with consenting mother to-morrow night, eleven, in front of Karl Theater, Vienna. Wire, whether can rely on his coming!'

Annie Neumann-Hofer to August Strindberg

'Dear Herr Strindberg: I received these two telegrams to-day. Will you not come to see us before you leave to-morrow? Neumann-Hofer.'

Annie Neumann-Hofer to Freda Uhl

'Mother too early. Strindberg remains here; made a mistake in the date.'

*

Freda Uhl, Munich, to August Strindberg, Berlin

'My dear, dear friend: So there is no need for me to shake the world? What emotions a wrong date may cause.

'But you made a most important discovery I do love you with all my heart and all my soul and all that is in me. — For that very reason, my first feeling when hearing of your trip to Vienna, was one of dismay. I pictured what effects the sudden news would have on my unsuspecting father.

'I myself, do not fear, I even cherish, the thought that we may have hard times at first, it tempts me to fight on your side, to share your worries. My father might look at things differently, however. I am in love with you and he is not. We must, therefore, devise beforehand, how one can make our marriage look attractive to him. My idea was to take mother with me to Vienna. She is in our confidence now and she admires you so highly as a poet that our betrothal simply delights her. We can rely on her. All the same, I have not mentioned our financial difficulties to her either. Perhaps the thought will not even occur to her.

'I should be most grateful to you if you could postpone Vienna until the 10th April and if you write in the meantime to my sister, Frau Maria Weyr, Rochusgasse 12, Wien III, that we intend to marry and that I have asked you to appeal to her for such good advice as she is used to giving me whenever I am in need.

'You and she will get along splendidly, she is as clever as she is kind. I even fear she will outshine me, she is perfection and I am a monster. But I am not jealous of this loved rival.

'Talking of rivals, I hope that you will be having a dangerous one soon. As soon as we are married, I want to take a young man into the house. He is the most beautiful being in the world, with an adorable soul shining in his eyes. I shall love him as much as I love you and shall kiss him all day long.

'At least I am frank, telling you all this? I am going to tell you his name, too — he is your son. I loved him at sight, knowing how much you love him. Tell me, do you really believe that his mother will give him to you? You would be such a wonderful teacher and I promise I would be a good, devoted mother. I would, of course, be terribly happy to take the little girls, also. That is for you to decide. As far as I am concerned, the more of your children you bring to me, the happier you will make me. My only fear is that it might be cruel to rob the poor mother of them. Well, you know her, you know whether it would pain her to part with them. If she would willingly consent, then I shall take them and I shall do everything to give them a home. Won't that be too wonderful for words? Don't you think it will be wonderful?

'I only wish we already were so far. I fear marriage no longer. After all, it is not any more dangerous than a betrothal, upon my holiest oath, I promise it shall never become a prison for you. If one of us — I shall not be the one — should ever want a dissolution of the tie, you shall be free. I shall never chain you down.

'Reply immediately, please, dearest. For ever yours — Freda.'

*

August Strindberg, Berlin, to Freda Uhl, Munich

'Dear Freda: I shall not go to Vienna, because I cannot and because I think it would be useless, for many reasons. . . .

'Let us be quiet and wait. I own that the money question decides everything; this is why I think of nothing now but money.

'Dear Freda, it is my part as a man to write you love-letters and your part to read my mewlings. What you say about my children touches me very much, but my little fair-haired rival is bound to stay with his mother for the present.

'Frau von Essen wrote me a very friendly letter recently, but I am not sure whether she had read the notice of our engagement. The announcement of my re-marriage, however, has sent my creditors in Sweden all crazy, so that things are more complicated than ever, unfortunately; and there are moments when I find the burden worse than oppressive.

'With you — everything; away from you — nothing! Come what may — patience and hope!

'I fear only one thing; not that I am too old to play the part of a young husband, but to act with propriety as the son of your father and mother. On the other hand, to be the

brother-in-law of your sister suits me admirably. I am convinced that she is just as charming as you are.

'And so, here's to the end of May! My beautiful wife!
August.'

MERRY BREAKFAST

'All will be well . . . Sleep well!' Despite the late hour I
had wired him that pious wish at night, in affectionate
reply to his letter. Then I had gone to bed well satisfied
and had got up again well satisfied. There could not have
been a finer Spring morn; the sky was a dream of pink and
azure. The sun smiled. My little room with its old-fashioned
bay-window high above the Isar and near the clouds was
adorable. The coffee tasted well, and it tasted well to be a
free bachelor woman in a soft morning gown with satin
slippers on naked feet revelling in the thought of that love in
Berlin, which showered its wealth on me and yet was not a tie.
Life, youth and love were all divine.

In a leisurely mood I began to read the paper. It was a
delightful breakfast. I shall never forget it.

I shall never forget how, all of a sudden, whilst I read on,
something black and threatening grew up before my eyes,
a wall grew up, which encircled me, an iron hand stretched
forth, snatched me, became my fate. A thing, totally strange,
which came neither from me nor from him, nor from parents
nor friends, but which suddenly was there with power to
decide, was making a toy of me.

I was the daughter of a newspaper man and, ever since a
child, I had looked down on printer's ink with the superiority
of the person who knows how it comes about. But it was all-
powerful and it crushed me when — looking for news — in
the *Deutsche Zeitung* — I read, Vienna, 22 March:—

'As we hear from Berlin, August Strindberg is expected in
Vienna soon. He will attend the first night of his *Creditors*.

The Viennese will be interested to hear that August Strindberg has become engaged to Fräulein Freda Uhl, daughter of Court Councillor Friedrich Uhl of this city.'

My thoughts are pivoting mechanically around an axle.

'The Viennese will be interested' . . . Yes, they will! And so am I . . . And I know someone else, whom it will interest to read about a daughter of Court Councillor Friedrich Uhl in Vienna . . . That is the Court Councillor Friedrich Uhl himself . . . He is thoroughly familiar with newspapers. No question, he is used to seeing his name in print. Print is one half of his life. He knows the humbug to its very bottom, he is fond of it but does not overestimate it. This abrupt little announcement however will be too much for his composure. I can see how he will stare at it, clench his teeth, dash the paper down.

And I? I shall have to allow it to be true.

Marry, Freda Uhl, marry! That means — marry, if you can and may.

TIES

Maria Weyr, Vienna, to Freda Uhl, Munich

'Dear Sister: This morning I was called to papa. It was just ten when I got there but I found him already at his sixth cigarette. He silently handed me the *Deutsche Zeitung*. I am enclosing the notice which excited him so much.

'At the same time, however, papa wishes me to tell you that he is happy that he need not permit this union since you had not asked for his permission. He begs you, however, not to expose him to new shame. He puts it up to you whether you prefer to spend the time until your wedding with your mother in Dornach, or with your fiancé in Berlin, who will then be responsible for you. I would advise you to hurry to Berlin and to get Strindberg to beg our father for your hand. Father has really not deserved to be treated so lightly.

'Fortunately I have succeeded in persuading him that you were not aware of this publication and that it was probably only a rumour. But I have long dreaded something like it. It was the unavoidable result of your relationship to modern literature. These people are very interesting in books, but they are utterly impossible in life. You will find that out, yourself — unfortunately.

'But now you cannot step back. Papa would resent the gossip more than an actual marriage with your king of poets, whom he fortunately greatly admires. He had to admit his admiration, but he added that he would have preferred giving to the author of *Father* a laurel wreath rather than his daughter. I, myself, felt terribly concerned, not only for father's sake, but also for your sake, my little sister. You have been like a child to me. It has not been my fault if I could not protect you any better. You have never had a home. May the man whom you have chosen give it you.

'I am praying for it to God. Ever yours — Mitzi.'

'P.S. I enclose 50 gulden for your trip; you will have use for them. I have just sold an article of which my husband does not know. If you need more, I will send it to you to Berlin.'

August Strindberg, Berlin, to Fru Siri von Essen[1], *Finland*

'Siri: Perhaps you have seen in the papers, that I am engaged.

'This is true and all the same it is not true, and in order that you may not be anxious about the children, I will tell you as much: a new marriage, which would diminish the share of my heirs, will not come to pass until my economic position is fully secured. I am still battling with myself as to whether I should be unfaithful to my children and do not know whether it will happen. In any case, I shall take care that Karin, Greta and Hans, who are next my heart, shall retain all

[1] His divorced wife.

advantages, as far as it is possible under the laws of the land.

'The engagement is not yet public and will not perhaps be made public before autumn. So that at present it is only a rumour.

'There are times when I am tired of the whole game of life, weary of honour and dishonour, and moreover I am living in a country where, according to custom, every man must always be prepared for his end. I have considered mine most carefully.

'Remember well everything I write you in this letter and perhaps in some others — above all, names and addresses.

'You need not answer this note if it is disagreeable to you. I will send the money as soon as possible — it will not be long in coming — and then direct to you. In friendship — August Strindberg.'

HEARTS IN PAIN

Freda Uhl, Munich, to August Strindberg, Berlin

'Dear friend: Just a few lines in haste, I do want this to leave in time. Please find here enclosed the newspaper cutting which sister Mitzi sent me yesterday. She has told my father the whole truth. He admires you and gladly consents.

'I love you. Think it over well. If you really believe that I can make you happy, I promise you my whole self for a life time. In that case sit down at once and write to father quite simply that you love me and all the rest. That's enough. Then we can marry in autumn or whenever we choose. I have now only one fear left and that is that you do not love me any longer and want to have your children back. If that is so, tell it to me honestly, I beseech you. I love you so much that I want you to be happy even at the price of my own happiness. You have only to write one word to me and I shall send to the papers a denial of the news. Then everything between us will be as though nothing had ever happened. But for the sake of mercy, let me have an answer soon, I die of fear.

'I am also nervous about your health. Lautenburg has told my father that you are ill. I am in fear lest my letters have offended you. I meant well, but I am so stupid. Do, answer at once, please do! — F.'

*

Telegram: August Strindberg, Berlin, to Freda Uhl, Munich

'Since my position unaltered in spite of Viennese success, propose return status quo. That is: interim secret engagement. Newspaper notice does not decide our destiny. You know that I cannot fulfil your conditions within the year. Therefore: engagement without forced contract. Letter following. Strindberg.'

Freda Uhl, Munich, to August Strindberg, Berlin

'My dear friend: Here I am sending you a few little flowers born of the sun which for the last few days is burning over Munich. All things seem as if fulfilled. I, alone, am restless because I have no news from you. Whatever it be that you may want to tell me, write it quietly as long as it is for your best. I am reading your letters now, slowly, and am reading them over again full of sadness. Except the fact contained in each word, that I have become to you a stranger, I seem to feel a big, general depression in them. I beseech you, do not lose courage. Think of all you have already conquered in your life. You have supported and have vanquished quite other difficulties than the present ones. You have grown strong fighting with fate, and fate will smile at you in the future more than ever. Courage!

'The whole of Europe bows down before your genius. Your affairs will soon be settled, and then you will enjoy the rest which you need. Have courage and have confidence.

August Strindberg, Berlin, to Freda Uhl, Munich

'Dear Beloved: Who was afraid first? I was. Now I am afraid of becoming a knave. Then let us both be punished. No, not you. It seems to me as if I could not write you any more without shame! Poor girl, who loves me so much.

'Riddle that you are. You are trying to marry me to Frau von Essen again . . .

'You want to adopt my children, you are not discouraged by my hopeless prospects: you give me your heart, your soul, your youth, your beauty! And what do I give you? My shame, my pangs of conscience.

'But once more, patience and may fate be good to us! — August.'

August Strindberg, Berlin, to Freda Uhl, Munich

'Dear Freda: I love you! How often must I tell you so? Once a day for two months, that makes sixty times! If you were here, I would convince you with one embrace, stronger than sixty letters, leaving the telegrams out of account.

'And yet you doubt it . . .

'With regard to the letter which duty compels me to write to your father, I am postponing it until the day when I shall be able to give him an answer to the question he is entitled to put: Are you in a position to keep a wife! Please tell him to wait, as I am waiting and as you must wait, if you love me.

'I am not well, but I am not ill! Lautenburg was lying, as usual. I called off the journey to Vienna. And that's that. . . .

'I cannot get away from Berlin. I am chained here. And you to Munich. What a weird engagement. Loving one another by post! Merciful heavens! And in spite of everything we do love one another, at any rate

'I love you. Believe it — August.'

112

IV

BERLIN

April, 1893

REPORTED ILL

At last, Berlin. Is it really not more than twenty days since I left? Have I been away at all?

I have wired him that I would be coming. Why do I not see him—? A black throng on the platform — but I am looking out for a face of which no double exists . . . for the storm-cloak of the Flying Dutchman . . . In vain I seek him . . . here . . . there . . . fifty times I think I see him, but neck after neck puts on an ordinary unknown head. Finally Otto and Annie disengage themselves from the crowd and walk up to me. They have brought me flowers, but they are alone.

'Where's Strindberg?'

'That's what I've been asking myself for quite a while,' Annie answers ambiguously.

Otto disapprovingly cuts her short. 'We have ordered a room in the Leipziger Hof for you, Fräulein Freda. Take your luggage there and then come on with us.' Thus saying he precedes us.

'You mean . . . ?' I ask Madame as soon as Monsieur has turned his back.

'He has not shown up in our quarters. But he is supposed to be in the Ferkel every night and always in the company of the same lady, a Norwegian pianist, whom Munch took there first.'

'Aspasia!'

'I don't know her name. But if she is playing Aspasia, Strindberg for the time being is her Pericles.'

'So that's it. And exactly this one thing had never occurred to me!'

'It was unwise of you to get engaged and still more unwise to go away. You have made a thorough mess of things, my dear.'

'I know. Man needs woman. But why involve our soul if he can dispense with it so well?'

Annie laughs, a pitying little laugh.

'Have you dined on the train? No? Then you will enjoy the supper I have ready. I would enjoy it in your place. And as to your friend, I would write him a short letter to find out what he intends to do. It's no good running after a man.'

Freda Uhl, Berlin, to August Strindberg, Berlin

'. . . I have come to Berlin to spend Easter with you and to decide about our future, whatever that shall be. If I receive no reply from you before to-morrow, four o'clock, I shall consider that an answer, too. I shall return your letters then, and request you to return mine — Freda Uhl.'

There. The letter is in the envelope. The writing is quite blurred.

'He can see at the first glance, how excited you were. One should keep up appearances,' Annie scolds. 'What will he think of you?'

'I refuse to bribe him.'

A messenger boy is entrusted with this delivery. 'Hand it, personally, to the gentleman himself, you understand, and to no one else. If he is not at home, bring back the letter.'

'Shall I wait for an answer?'

'No, that's not necessary!' Annie interjects and sends the

boy away. 'One should never show a man that one cares
for him,' she teaches me.

Maybe she is right. She ought to have told me that sooner,
it is rather late now. I have lacked caution. But it would not
have helped much, I cannot be educated.

The boy has hurried, the clerk must have hurried and
August Strindberg seems in a hurry, too. Surprisingly soon
the telephone rings.

'Dr. Carl Ludwig Schleich speaking . . . for Herr Strindberg, who is in bed, not well. Is Fräulein Uhl still there?'

'Fräulein Uhl is standing beside me,' Otto answers it.
'What is wrong with Herr Strindberg?'

A short silence on the other side. Is it anxiety or embarrassment that causes it?

'We do not quite agree so far, my colleague, Dr. Asch and
I. Dr. Asch fears pneumonia. But I would not go so far.'

Otto looks from the telephone to me. He repeats the
message, but composedly; at the last words he even laughs.
'Have you a trained nurse or do you believe that Fräulein
Uhl would do? . . . Not necessary . . . He wants her to come
and see him to-morrow morning? Just one moment, Doctor.'

I have gripped the receiver: 'Freda Uhl speaking. I would
like very much to see Herr Strindberg to-night if he is ill . . .
I mean, seriously ill. Can you stay with him until I come,
Doctor? I will come immediately.'

A kind resonant voice says, 'That's good. It's nothing
serious and you will cure him. I can hear that by your words.
I shall be here.'

*

'Herr Strindberg? Third floor,' the clerk says reluctantly.
Obviously he judges me too much of a lady to visit a bachelor.
Then a sudden inspiration sets him beaming. 'Dr. Schleich
is still upstairs, please go right up, madame.'

He takes me for Frau Schleich and I am legitimate. Very well, I shall remain so for the present.

On the third floor a young Siegfried rushes up to me and introduces himself — 'Carl Ludwig Schleich.'

'Is there any danger?'

He smiles benignly. 'Not at present. — Come with me.'

A small low square room. To the front a wide bay-window just like a giant bird-cage. To the right, between the bay-window and the wall, an austere bed, with high, white pillows. Sitting up in it August Strindberg. With a poor pallid face but radiant smile he holds out his hand to me. He looks like a man who has been severely tried and has not yet completely recovered, but has found peace.

I bend over him. I look into his eyes. I look into their very depth. And I feel ashamed of my lack of faith. I have my answer now. How could I ever have doubted?

Dr. Schleich has stepped into the window cage of glass and examines the naked lime trees across the street as though they need a prescription. Then he turns around, looks at us, tries to laugh but has to blow his nose in his emotion; it sounds like a trumpet; it embarrasses him tremendously. And all of a sudden we all three laugh.

'Then it isn't so bad? What is really the matter?'

They exchange embarrassed glances.

'My colleague, Dr. Asch thinks . . .'

'What do you, yourself, think?'

'I think and I say that he'd better stay in bed a few days, that means to-morrow, and that you should stay with him, now and ever.'

EASTER

I have bought up the whole Spring on sale in the street — pussy-willow and narcissus, mimosa, primroses, Easter lilies. Under the vaulted roof of the Panopticum Passage I had found big glazed nuts named 'Kaiser-Kisses'. I am bringing a whole bag of them to August Strindberg.

The clerk is fully informed to-day. He respectfully receives the fiancée — the 'Fräulein Braut'.

This time his room is bright. The sun pours into the giant cage, only now I see how small the garret is, how low the ceiling and how marvellously clean and in perfect order it is kept. To the left stands a big couch, in front of it a square table, a mahogany rocking-chair and a footstool. Next to the window the writing-desk; on it a tower of expensive Lessebo parchment is stacked and an eagle's quill. He uses the parchment for his manuscripts. Its pages are covered with a beautiful, rounded, even writing, with almost no corrections.

Under the table rests a low brown trunk and on it a bag of dark green glazed linen about one yard in length with gentle billowing summits and valleys. A black button fastens it.

So that is the 'Green Bag' with its hundreds of little notes, rapid sketches and thoughts, caught and pinned down and stored away on his way through life. It contains Strindberg's new theory that the plants have nerves. It contains the evidence that an element can split. In this bag Newton is refuted, famous astronomers are being led on *ad absurdum*. Many sciences of the future repose in this simple green bag. It harbours countless analyses of spirit and of matter providing knowledge with a new life. Moreover it holds a magic power — it embodies the spell on which August Strindberg's life depends.

In front of the window stands an easel with a newly-begun painting. A bright blue sea and a white sand-hill; in the sand a lonely yellow flower lies dying, crushed by a careless foot. Something has passed over it, which was stronger and for which it had no value.

August Strindberg I do not see at once. He lies in bed as he did yesterday, but five men are grouped around him, two at the head and three at the end of the bed. It looks as if he were giving an audience.

He lies there like a big, fine, sick lion; still a trifle fatigued, he has found again nevertheless the beaming smile of the child in wonderland, with anxious lips and eyes expectantly awaiting what big adventures life may hold in store for him. He reaches out his hand to me as a troth in the presence of all and I lay my hand in his. With this I am acknowledged among his disciples.

Now all the men are being introduced to me. So early in the day. Most likely they have come straight from the Ferkel. But they greet me soberly, solemnly and devotedly. Just think of it, August Strindberg's betrothed!

Two are still quite young. The smaller of them is Strindberg's familiar spirit, Adolf Paul. The taller is Bengt Lidfors from Lund, a student of biology and plant physiology. He is slim and graceful like a big boy. He has soft, smooth, fair hair and intelligent Mongolian eyes as brown as a nut. Strindberg has a father's tenderness for him.

The two others are between thirty and forty. The fat man is a wood merchant, who, under Schleich's patronage, has been permitted to join the syndicate which, during the winter, has been providing Strindberg with an income of 150 marks a month, thus holding wolves at bay. And Ashe, the tall man, resembling a king of Persia, at his side, is a physician and misogynist — the colleague. He likes to act the part of Mephistopheles. His bow to me is just a trifle too deep. He defiantly calls Spring a dangerous season. He hints at pneumonia being on its way. A comparatively mild pneumonia, maybe, but all the same necessitating a permanent ice-bag on the patient's head and another on his chest. I feel icy all through. But then I see August Strindberg's face grow a deep red. I laugh right out. Asch looks at me with disapproval, then turns away and walks to the bay-window.

'Don't you want to take off your things?' Paul interposes tactfully.

Of course I want to and in one second my hat and coat hang on his arms and my parcels and flowers have been carefully placed on the table. For the sake of politeness one talks of this and that and then the visitors take their leave. Schleich is the last one to depart. He stops at the door and impresses on me:

'My friend Asch was only talking symbolically when he mentioned the ice-bag. It reads — our friend needs warmth, I mean a gentle hand.'

'Trust me to give it.'

It is bright and still. We have found each other.

Before his joyous eyes I proudly unpack my treasures, the lively tulips, the chaste mimosa, the primroses, the anemones, the violets which first saw the light in the south and had to journey far to keep Easter with us. A beautiful twig with silver pussy-willows I significantly plant at the end of the bed, as a token of penitence but on the table the 'Kaiser-Küsse' symbolize forgiveness and forgetting.

'And now one after the other. First of all I am your nurse. What shall we do for your illness?'

'You have heard that Asch advises an ice-bag and Schleich plenty of warmth. That's very simple.'

'Let us try Schleich first. Do congratulate me, warmly, please, on our engagement.'

'It's for you to congratulate me.'

'First, confess!'

'What?'

'The story of the Ferkel, and of the serpent with the Greek name. I do not wish to be more explicit.'

'You know about that, too?'

'I arrived in Berlin yesterday, at 6.30, knew about it at

6.45. In two days I shall be twenty-one, at that age one knows everything. There is only one thing I cannot understand, and that you must explain to me: why did you do it? Why? You do not love her and you do love me.'

'Can one ever explain why? There is never a reason and there are so many.'

And now he narrates, occasionally slowing down, but pertinently and without embellishment. He has nothing to confess, the thing just happened.

'Do you really think that I could stay at home alone on these evenings and nights of Spring when you are there no longer and are not watching me with your beautiful, kind eyes?' Had he not written these words to me, and had he not added, 'fear and restlessness drive me to the Schwarze Ferkel? Come and guard me'.

So he had been driven to the Ferkel. It had become once more the shrine upon which the disciples extolled him when he flung his treasures to them with full hands. A human nearness was what they paid back to him, but not human warmth. He knew it and he felt it. They did not really belong to him; they would become his enemies at any moment. But they helped him chase away solitude for a few hours, at least.

Then a woman had chanced to cross his path.

How absurd it was that he should ever be called a woman-hater! He could not live without a woman; he was so much of a man that even his thoughts matured better when, becoming Word, they fell on feminine conceptive soil, while talking with a woman.

Munch had brought his Norwegian girl friend — Aspasia — to the Round Table after all. She knew every string of a man's soul, and she not only knew how to play, she also knew how to listen. Strindberg had been much of a temptation to her. When they met at last she had eyes for him alone, dropped Munch mercilessly, forgot the others or pretended to forget them. She provided him with the illusion that she owed to him her soul and life.

'The happiness of talking of you lures me,' he had written to me. Aspasia had given him this happiness.

It had started by his talking to her about me. She, too, was a woman and he had talked to her about me for hours and hours.

'I feel deeply touched. But how did it end?'

'Just like every experience of false friendship with a woman of that sort. In bed.'

After a week (that now was three days ago) it had, in truth, ended there. After a night of carousing together. He had been brilliant for hours, delighting her with fireworks of eloquence, until she grew warm under his sparks and, in her turn, began to glow. They had been drinking, beer, wine, toddy, Swedish punch, absinthe. He had not been drunk, he declared, he never was drunk; but he had not been sober either. In a semi-fog he had taken her home — 'Strindberg knows what's proper!'

She had invited him in and he had gone with her to her room. That, of course, was not exactly proper. But then outlines had become blurred, and blurred too, was his recollection — up to the moment of his exit from the semi-fog. When his senses had grown cold, he had become conscious. He had suddenly found himself in bed in an unknown, untidy room. He caught sight of hairpins on the carpet and of ugly powder spots on a drab red plush sofa. Disgust rose up in him. Then he perceived the woman lying by his side. He was unable to reason, he obeyed an urge which ordered him to break away from the vulgar situation. He had jumped up. He had dragged Aspasia out of bed, had pushed her out of the room and bolted the door. He had lived in so many hotels during the last few years that it had not occurred to him that he had not achieved all this in his

own room, but in Aspasia's. Physically and morally relieved, he had again gone to bed, and slept until late in the
day.

'And that poor girl . . .?' I stammer, overwhelmed. 'What
happened to her in that costume, in the cold, in a cheap
Berlin hotel!'

'I don't know what lies she invented. But it did her no
harm and she was not angry with me. She had no chance of
showing anger; that would have meant to confess a defeat
and her vanity forbade that. She found her experience, on
the contrary, quite novel and original . . .'

'It was that, no doubt, dear friend.'

'And in the morning she gave me another rendezvous for
the next night.'

But now comes the psychologically interesting point. In
his scorn he had thought nothing of turning her cold-
bloodedly out of her own room. He had ruthlessly let her
sit in the dark in her nightgown until the house woke up.
But he could not force himself to intensify that humiliation
still more forcibly in broad daylight. He accepted the rendezvous. Had he formed a new tie? Had he betrayed me,
whom he loved? It was a dramatic situation and complicated. Slowly, his humour rose to the surface. The entire
story had been a farce and not a tragedy; therefore it should
have its happy end. He went to the rendezvous on the
minute. But he did not go alone. Schleich went with him.
There was a piano in the *chambre séparée* where they met
Aspasia. Schleich had one weakness, his tenor voice. Aspasia
was a great accompanist. The two made music like angels.
There was an interminable amount to say about it, and they
started saying it to each other.

Strindberg had slipped away. He had regained his liberty
and had not made her shed one tear, still less a drop of
blood.

He alone paid. No sooner had he come home than complete exhaustion overtook him, for he had acted a part which was foreign to his true nature and which created a void in him. He had thrown himself on his bed fatigued and disgusted. And after that he had felt paralysed. He had frequently been in that trance-like condition. At such moments, in his spirit he lived over again some experience which he had gone through in real life, and he lived it again so intensely that it fixed itself in his mind with every detail. All the time this went on he was lying like a dead man. His bodily life seemed extinguished through the strain of the effort which turned the past into a lasting thing. Now this, too, had been fulfilled and was accomplished. But when my telegram arrived he had not strength enough to face me, much as he longed for me. Not if our lives had been at stake, could he have met me. That was the story of August Strindberg acting the part of Pericles.

'And now you know that I have deserved the whip. Will you forgive me?'

'Willingly! — But are you certain that the poor girl is not grieving?'

'No fear of that. She has left me and not I her. Her self-respect is satisfied. She and Schleich made music again yesterday and they are making music again to-night. That will continue for quite a while yet, until the fear of his wife possesses him. But by that time she will have found another singer.'

'So the thorn is out of the paw and the sick lion will soon get up again and be quite well?'

'The sick lion enjoys his sickness far too much.'

*

Next day he is up and dressed in his jacket. He never wears a dressing-gown, always a loose grey jacket of flannel, much like a forester's coat, and with it a yellowish-white flannel shirt with a soft low collar. But his blond hair is still lying flat and has not yet regained its luminosity. He is pale but he looks joyous.

'And father in Vienna?' he asks.

'Merciful heavens! I quite forgot to tell you the main thing. Father gives his consent — which nobody asked for. Poor, dear man.'

'Then we must be especially polite now and send him our very best thanks.'

And on his beautiful parchment paper he writes with his slim eagle's quill to the angry Court Councillor Friedrich Uhl in Vienna. He encloses — as a wooer should — a survey of his affairs, the same list of hopes which he at one time sent to me to Munich. There is a long row of dramas, which in the capitals of the whole world either have a first night in store or a sensational storm behind them; a long row of novels, masterpieces of their kind; volume after volume of scientific treatises which in each field of knowledge smash accepted dogmas into ruins. There is enough to fill every man of intellect with deep respect and there is enough to make every business man shrug his shoulders in despair.

*

Parallel with his street runs the Neustädtische Kirchstrasse, with its sumptuous Hotel Continental. There are less sumptuous rooms to let in number One. Frau Redmann, the tenant, is a lean elderly widow, clean and quiet. So are her rooms, a sitting-room and bedroom. Each has two windows. And from each of these windows you can see the church at the corner of the Dorotheenstrasse. It has a garden in front of it, Gothic gates, a tower, and on the tower a clock with massive black hands. Strindberg must pass by that church wherever he wants to go. Be it the tavern or the post office, he must pass the church: on the corner I now stand.

The rooms are not cheap. 70 marks. It is worth while though to have one's fiancé within reach.

And then — my fiancé makes gold.

'There is no mistake, is there, you can make gold?' I serenely inquire. We have just had a cup of coffee in his room and I take my leisure in a corner of his sofa, nibbling a piece of Turkish delight. My question reveals most admirably both the unlimited confidence which I have in his power and the remarkable composure which we maintain towards the fact itself. Scientifically, my question happens to be perfectly justified; he has just reassured me that, as a believer in transmutation, he believed in a primary matter, out of which all the rest has developed by splitting, condensation, diluting, copulating, crossing, etc.

He replies with an assurance as great as my own.

'I have expected this question and I could easily evade a distinct answer, saying for instance, "That I can trace the descent of a cat, does not signify that I can produce a cat". But I need no evasion. I hold ready my reply to your question.'

He takes out of his desk a few long strips of parchment. On them strange formations are glittering, some with pale yellowish shine like gold, others with greenish metallic reflections.

'A more or less finished gold,' he explains in a matter-of-fact way.

I hold my breath, stare at the nobly coloured scales.

'Is — this — gold?' I stammer, confused. Observed with the naked eye, these tinsels really have the appearance of gold.

'I suppose they must be considered as an intermediary stage, as a more or less perfect gold which, when melted with other substances, might result in refined gold.'

'Then, so far, it is not gold yet after all . . .' I have recovered my composure. 'Never mind, one might perhaps

be able to use these products all the same, to increase our
cash funds?'

But there are subjects in which August Strindberg understands no joke. To sell science? What a sin against the
Holy Ghost!

DUET

August and Freda, Berlin, to Maria Weyr, Vienna

'Beloved little sister: A radiantly happy girl writes her
first letter as bride-to-be to-day to you, together with a
husband *in spe* whom she loves in proportion to how little
she deserves him — Freda.'

'It is much nearer the truth when this husband declares
himself to be the least worthy of all masculine creatures in
the German Empire to possess such a treasure as Freda for a
wife and Mitzi for a sister-in-law — August.'

'Listen, my treasure, you will agree that both of us, my
husband and I, have behaved ourselves with remarkable
humility and ample mutual admiration in the above lines!
I hope you will duly appreciate our preliminary exercises
in married deportment! And if you could see our faces,
radiant with happiness, you would take us to your heart,
as we have long since taken you to ours. We have been
together now for three days. I left Munich in a great hurry,
to clear up all the clouds of misunderstanding which my
letters had raised — Freda.'

'I hope, my dear sister-in-law, that you will not believe
in the "clouds of misunderstanding" of which my divine
little wife talks, so long as everything remains as it is at
present. And I can assure you that your sister is just as mad
as I am supposed to be — madly in love! With it all, she is

goody-goody, just like me. Freda and August Strindberg.'

'*Enclosed:* Two photographs. 1. *Strindberg avant*, 2. *Strindberg après le permis de mariage.*'

FACE TO FACE WITH ASPASIA

We are holding siesta in his room at the Linden Hotel. He has made tea and is now cutting delightful little Swedish sandwiches. We are sitting opposite each other. The sun is smiling at us. He has his back turned to the door, which stands slightly ajar; spring is already shedding warmth, and the corridor is empty.

All of a sudden steps come near, lightly, trippingly. An unseen hand firmly pushes open the door. Two ladies. One passes by so quickly that her scarlet dress seems like a hasty flame, the second one, however, takes her time, she stops and looks with easy composure into the room, neglecting to put her foot upon the threshold or to give a greeting. How strange. I feel as though I had already met her somewhere. She is tall and slim, dressed in a refined way. Blonde hair curls above her brows; a small nose jumps out pertly. Her lips are thin and twist in an alluringly red line over white teeth. Her most marked distinctions are her aristocratic hands, her well groomed, narrow foot and her lack of weight. She is not *une belle femme* in the exact sense of the word, nor is she the traditional *femme fatale*. But her face is significantly expressive. It reminds me of Strindberg's description: 'a most modern type, highly differentiated, spiritual and refined, rather an intellectual siren than a temptress of the flesh. A vampire longing for higher things. No Phryne — an Aspasia'.

She inspects our room most thoroughly as a matter of course and at her ease, as though she were inspecting her own room to make sure that every well-known object is in its place. Only on me her clear eyes linger as on a piece of furniture that had been newly added. She looks approving, benevolent, but insultingly surprised as a woman at the woman. Not a bit unfriendly or malicious, but undisguisedly curious and strictly professional. Hers is the expert's eye examining the article and quite contrary to expectancy finding it of merit.

Now she has infected me, too, with her curiosity, and I, in my turn, infect my fiancé, who, until now, has sat with his back to the door and has not noticed her. He turns round with a smile — that very moment, the sandwich, which he was just about to furnish with a salmon layer, dashes down with its buttered face on to the plate. He forgets his surroundings and proffers a savage Swedish oath: '*Tybsanierla! Satanskvinnan!*' (Hell, devil of a woman!) His baritone is at its deepest and the door slams at its loudest as it closes itself before the pert little nose.

After a while he steps slowly back to the table, still flushed and heaving a deep sigh. A second curse rolls through the room, this time *sotto voce*, just a matter of ridding his throat of it. Then a silence and then a question,

'Do you know who that is?'

'I believe I do by now — But what did Aspasia want?'

'She wanted to see what Strindberg's fiancée was like. Now she has seen you and will take revenge!'

'She looked entirely unconcerned,' I am trying to soothe him.

'She never is concerned. That's exactly it. The snake, too, remains cold; that does not prevent her bite from being deadly.'

I take the half-finished sandwich from the plate.

'Give me a bite of salmon and never mind the snake!' I plead.

I get my salmon. I get even far too much salmon. His mind is no longer on the sandwiches. I believe it is no longer in the room at all, but is hustling along, terrified and shaken, behind some unknown, gruesome danger. The visitor has shed a dark shadow, it hovers over us like a nightmare. I have not the power to banish it.

WEDDING IN VIEW

The wedding draws nearer. It is close on me. My heart, my head and both my hands are full of it. And *tout Berlin* participates. Since that first news about our engagement, the newspapers have become alive. They are interested in us, we are headliners. In fine variety, the news items flash now: about a Strindberg play, about a Strindberg book, about Strindberg himself. Most of all about his new marriage.

August Strindberg blooms and thrives in the crude light. The shy, timid man who resents it if people look at him, who avoids the slightest crowd, is an entirely different being where print is concerned. He loves the turmoil of the letters, he loves the boisterousness of the journals. He loves the intensity of life which they diffuse. '*Rien n'est pire que d'être pendu obscurément*', he seems to say with Mirabeau.

To-day in the Tiergarten we passed Herr X, the painter. He seemed to be in a hurry, ran with his head low and did not notice us. I was about to call him cheerfully, when a look at my fiancé's face forbade me. His eyes were fixedly riveted on the ground, his cheeks were a deep purple.

What a catastrophe! So Strindberg believes me to be the Odalisque with the immodest back, whom X won't exhibit, because his model was not a professional, but a young Viennese poetess, J.D.

A young Viennese Poetess? That is enough for Strindberg. He will not listen to her name, he will not look at her back. He has never hinted it to me, but it torments him cruelly, he bears it and forgives like a martyr,

I feel inclined to laugh, I would like to cry.

Does he know me so little? In the convent, where I was brought up, no odalisques are bred. There they see in nakedness a mortal sin. Why, at 'Aux Oiseaux' in Paris we wore a long, chaste linen chemise even in our bath, that fastened at the back and fell down to the ankles. To raise one corner of that chemise was considered a sin.

Alas, if I should sin — it would never be with X.

Silent and spiteful, I walk at Strindberg's side — if he suspects me wrongly, let him suffer.

To-morrow my sister arrives, the dearest and nearest person to me in life, for mother is of a different kind. All the sun of my youth, my lake and my mountains are coming with her. Only with Mitzi acting as 'Bride's Mother' will it be a complete and real wedding, at which with all due etiquette the little round-faced angels could partake, who are fiddling and blowing the trombone so valiantly on the altars of my home church in Mondsee. I would have sorely minded it if the friends of my youth had not been present at the ceremony. Sister brings the dowry as well. And furthermore, she brings father's written consent which permits my marrying; without it I must remain a maiden for I am not yet of age. She brings my birth certificate. Now the ceremony can be performed.

'Have you got your papers ready too?' I inquire of the happy bridegroom when he and I are embellishing the room with flowers for the 'Bride Mother's' reception.

'Do you doubt it?' he asks, quite hurt. 'They all lie ready in my trunk with the exception of one and that is in even better care — I mean my divorce decree. The Swedish authorities still have that, and my brother Oscar has been trusted to fetch it there and send it on to me.'

Oscar is his eldest brother; he is a shipping agent as the

father was and he acts as trustee for August Strindberg's children. Oscar, in the eyes of the whole family, represents the genius for order, precision and punctuality in the Strindberg family. Whatever Oscar touches is as good as achieved.

'Oscar will send the document on the very day on which he receives my request.'

August Strindberg has bought a huge bouquet of lilac for the joyfully expected sister-in-law. Frau Redman, my landlady, has given Mitzi and me a double bedroom, adjoining the sitting-room. The Persian lilac has heavy umbels and the entire room is redolent with their sensuous, sweet perfume. On the desk in the sitting-room are Easter lilies. Strindberg loves them, 'they have drunk in the sun with their deep yellow chalices', he says. On the table are early hothouse roses. The table-linen is smooth and white. Before the Bride's Mother arrives and before we become a married couple, we want to be joyful and young once more.

'How beautiful this time of betrothal was! I am sorry it is over. It will never again be so beautiful.'

He does not answer but looks musingly at me. He has brought *asti spumante* and fills my glass and his own glass in glad expectancy of Mitzi's coming and fills the glasses once more. Then he starts to dream, dream of his Scharen Islands in the cool, blue Baltic Sea, of the white birches and the dark pines and the light Nordic summer which knows no night. That is my new home which is awaiting me. I have nestled in his arm. I, too, am dreaming.

Who said there should be a wedding? For what purpose is the lilac giving such sweet and languorous perfume? The story about the wedding is no longer true.

The Bride's Mother will be here in a few hours now. She could have spared herself the trip. Nothing awaits her except a couple whom love, which should have made them one, has parted.

What happened — ? A flash of lightning down a blue sky. Too much electric tension in the air, presumably.

The topic had shifted to modern woman's clothes, to the folds and pleats and frills which have become an erotic enticement rather than a chaste prohibition. And then to Love and to the Sacred Nudity which had preceded the Fall of Man in Paradise.

'Supposing the story of the Fall of Man were true after all, it would explain many an incomprehensible thing,' he muses. — And then, in an abrupt assault, he wants me to confess that I had indeed sat as a semi-nude model to Herr X.

Merciful heavens! I denied it hotly, but in words which he misunderstood.

He snatches them up greedily: 'You know about it then, that means you admit it! You say: "Another woman!" What a clever lie. Unfortunately for you I have been married thirteen years, I know this lie as I knew the others!'

I had revolted. And he had departed. Strange, strange and sad.

When he had walked out I shook with despair, I tore open the window and called him back. He heard me but he never turned.

The morning is grey and cold. In me is a wild longing for the sun and a green soil — for Paradise!

*

Freda Uhl, Berlin, to August Strindberg, Berlin

'Sir: You have reminded me — exactly at the moment which I had hoped would wipe out your memories — of the fact that you have already been married and for no less a period than thirteen years. I have not been married so far, and if this blow was meant to grant me an insight into matrimony, I no longer wish to marry. It does not matter to me whether this will expose me to public disdain and to the gossip of the world. What good can the respect of the world do me, if I no longer can respect myself? You are free, therefore, quite free. You need not fear that our sudden rupture might cause you any inconvenience. I am taking the entire blame and shall tell my sister so. And everyone else.

'Please allow me a little time, and I shall remit all your affairs to you in perfect condition. You shall not notice that there ever has been and has left you — Freda Uhl.'

August Strindberg, Berlin, to Freda Uhl, Berlin

'Dear Freda: You do not believe that it hurts me to leave you thus? I was so fond of you and had so become a part of your life that I begin to feel as if I were broken in two. And you do not believe that your sufferings cause me to suffer? What is to happen now? And how can I help you? I feel responsible for you, for you are a young girl and yet you are so strong and cruel. It comforts me that you have the strength to go your way alone. . . .

'Can everything be at an end? Can we part after all that has been? It does not seem so to me! But what shall we do?

'I am so tired, and I suffer to think that you suffer.

'I cannot hurt others. If I only could! What shall we do? Tell me! Tell me! — your faithful Badger.[1]

'BRIDE'S MOTHER'

'I came here to attend your wedding and not your divorce. But if you are in earnest about it and if you can still avoid this fatal marriage, my own dear pet, I am ready to take all blame and all unpleasantness . . . and you start a new life!'

'Tell me, sister, what shall I do?'

[1] 'Badger' was a pet name he had been in the habit of using.

'Well, let me see how matters really stand. Which of you two has given *congé* to the other?'

'I did.'

'Whose fault was it?'

'Mine.'

'Kindly leave off riding a Rosinante. It's bad enough if a man plays Don Quixote, but a woman is sure to tumble down and break her neck. Test your own self and then say honestly; if father, on my instance, would let you go abroad until grass has grown over the affair . . . will you remain there or are you going to rush back at his first tender note?'

'Honestly? Does the human being exist, who is honestly certain to do such and such a thing at that and that moment?'

'That'll do. In that case, don't waste your time, please; steer clear of gossip, marry as quickly as you can and continue to quarrel afterwards. In marriage fights are legitimate and usual.'

The 'Bride's Mother' arrived in Berlin early in the morning. It is evening now. She has spent the entire forenoon and afternoon drying my tears and sweetly evading the invitations which shower upon us. A wire from my brother-in-law, wishing us bliss and begging for more news has finally extorted this explanation from me. She swings the telegram through the air like a sharply whetted scythe, walking up and down.

Our room looks dreary and bare. Frau Redmann has maliciously taken away all our many beautiful flowers. She blames them for my headache and also for the noise I made when I tore open the window at night. It had awakened her.

It is striking eight o'clock from the near-by church.

'I have never lived in furnished rooms,' my sister remarks disapprovingly, and condemns the sparse furniture with a haughty glance. 'It might be better after all if this marriage did not take place.'

But I no longer hear what she says, I only hear my thoughts: 'Eight o'clock . . . He will be wanting company. Where will he seek it? . . . Never mind, whether he chooses the church, the tavern, or the post office, he must pass by that corner, it's the cross-way . . .' I stand at the window and watch through the dusk. Frau Redmann has lit the lamp.

'There he goes . . . Do you see him? . . . Yes, that tall man there . . . That is August Strindberg.'

He's coming this way! — No, he has stopped at the corner of the street, he seems to be waiting . . . He's writing on the pavement with his stick . . . What can he be writing? . . . He does not look up. He looks fixedly down on the wet asphalt at his feet and absent-mindedly, wearily, draws with his stick. Is he waiting for me?

No, now he walks off.

He has decided for the Ferkel.

'He's most striking! My sculptor husband would go mad about him for a bust . . . But to marry him — oh, my poor darling!'

He unexpectedly wheels around. Is he coming back? Only a few steps. At the portal of the church stands a disabled soldier, his 'client' as he calls him. He puts the daily gift into his hand. He had forgotten him, it had grown late for the poor man. I suppose he had been waiting all day for Strindberg — like myself.

Then the Dutchman once more sets sail. No joyous wind is swelling his pinions to-day. Limply they droop around a weary man.

Mitzi heaves a sigh and shakes her head.

After a while she sits down at the desk. She starts absent-mindedly to write a long letter to her husband, then tears it up again. She drums on the desk with her slim fingers. A second letter satisfies her:

'I am telling Rudolf that Strindberg is ill and that I have not yet been able to see him. That gives us time!' The slim fingers exercise again, this time they are playing the piano, *legato*. Then she breaks off, eats up the last 'Kaiser-küsse' which has remained from our feast. She takes the pen which August Strindberg himself gave me and scribbles down a few lines to the illustrious poet who up to last midnight was her brother-in-law to be. It does not take her two minutes.

With a unique feminine charm and naivety she has expressed to him her desire to meet him. Then she sprinkles the letter with *chypre*. 'You'll wear out any man with too much tragedy,' she preaches, '*la main douce*, little sister, *la main douce!* Otherwise, what's the good of being a woman? . . . Is there anything more to do?' she adds, and yawns exhausted. 'I really would like to get to bed after my journey.'

'What about the invitations?' I stammer confused. 'Dozens of hospitable mansions are anxious to arrange teas and dinners in our honour . . . But, of course, not for a broken engagement. How shall we enlighten them? What on earth are we to do?'

'Let us do as the Spaniards did with their dead Cid. After it was all over with him they placed his dead body upon a horse; more was not necessary. We have the great advantage that our Cid is going to come to life again. A gentleman who stops at the street corner and confides unto the pavement stones, that gentleman comes back . . . even out of the Ferkel. Therefore we shall make it known for the moment that Strindberg is ill and march to battle without him.'

August Strindberg, Berlin, to Maria Weyr

'Dear Madam: Do I owe you an explanation for my absence? I do not think so since your sister herself brought it about. This is the second time that, in a fit of young girl's waywardness, she has given me back the engagement ring, and I am not disposed to beg for love that I once captured.

'Should a reconciliation be brought about, I should still need to be left in peace for some time after the storms that I have gone through during the last few days.

'I most deeply regret the troubles that I have not caused you and beg you to have faith in my sincerity — August Strindberg.'

The letter is cold and formal, he treats me like a little girl who has been naughty, he speaks to my sister like one grown-up person to another. And yet . . .! I, in my turn, am waiting in the dusk to-night at the corner of the street in front of the church, where he was waiting yesterday. What a dreary long while I have been waiting. Waiting in vain — just as he did yesterday. With the sole difference that I have not written on the pavement. That has proved futile. Strange tracks have long ago upset his message and the street cleaner has swept it away with the rubbish. And yet . . .!

Am I merely imagining it or are there really two figures standing behind the lighted panes of the door?

It is Strindberg close to my sister.

He came the other way around through the Linden, to welcome his sister-in-law as soon as he had got her note and he has conquered her in a rush. Mitzi beams and radiates all over her face. The extent of her delight reveals to me for the first time the anxiety which she had felt and had hidden from me. The two have become great friends at first sight. He calls her 'mother-in-law'. And she, in order to prove that even a 'mother-in-law' is human, impulsively expresses an unquenchable longing to see the Berlin opera; she wants to hear at least the last act of *Traviata*, she dresses

like a flash and leaves us alone with a thousand most superfluous apologies.

'Can you explain it to me?' I ask, 'how it is that but a few
hours ago I believed that we should never set eyes on each
other again, that my whole soul was bleeding . . . yet I was
determined to give you back your liberty. I thought you
wanted it back as I am only a silly girl. Have I deceived
myself, have I lied to myself, was I not in real earnest?
And you? . . . tell me!'

'It had to be, I suppose,' Strindberg answers. 'We had
to part in order to realize that we cannot live without each
other. We hated each other because we love each other
and fear the big melting-pot of love in which personality
dissolves. But this is supposition only . . . and not knowledge. No human mind knows the maze of the human
heart. It proceeds from devotion and tenderness to hatred,
from hatred to contempt . . . returns to its starting point,
with a side leap in the end, and has gained two steps. The
Good and the Evil, the Sublime and the Grotesque, Faith-
lessness and Love Eternal, Kisses and Outrages, Adoration
and Blasphemy . . . who can arrange them in their order?
There exists only one rule of life, that is never to look back
and ever to walk ahead. The whole of life, believe me, is
only a poem. Let's throw the ballast of brooding over-
board. It is better to glide over mire, even though it be
mire, than to seek with one's feet on firm ground which does
not exist and to suffocate in the morass.'

THE 'BRIDE'S MOTHER'S' FIRST REPORT

Maria Weyr, Berlin, to Rudolf Weyr, Vienna

'Dear Rudolf: Strindberg is at the bottom of his heart
a most noble nature, gentle to the point of weakness. But he

has a sad life behind him, which misleads him often and, once he had formed a conception, he sticks to it. His health is perfect, he has no bad habits. He is living here like a monk and is supposed to have lived that way since his divorce and previous to it. He has not read what the papers write about him for the past ten years. In order to keep his personality intact he reads only works of science; as far as novels go, only Balzac and the French psychologists. He is unfit to deal with managers and publishers, his nerves cannot stand it. As a result, he earns almost nothing. He has piles of manuscripts, stories, plays; he is the hardest worker in the world, but he is no business man. Freda is now calling on publishers and managers. They flirt with her, but do not buy. Whenever he does not write he paints . . . just as well as he writes. He has tried sculpturing, too, and plays the guitar; there is nothing he cannot do. He's the man to turn a desert island into a Paradise, but he also is the man to perish in the midst of culture out of sheer helplessness, shyness, fear of mockery. He understands no fun, rarely jokes, continually believes himself to be persecuted and disdained. He cannot walk on the shady side of the street. He speaks eight languages, including Chinese. He does not speak them well, but he has them at his command in writing . . . with the one exception of German, which he finds most difficult; nevertheless, he has got it into his head to reform the German language and he drives his translators to despair.

'He lives here in a small hotel, owns nothing besides a trunk, has left all his furniture to his first wife, cannot make himself familiar with the idea of any permanency, never knows whether he has any money or how much he has. He goes to bed at nine o'clock, gets up at five, lives on almost nothing: vegetables, fish, claret.

'He blushes like a young girl, at anything, and that endows his face with a bewitching beauty. His mouth and his eyes, anyhow, are wonderful, the latter are as blue as a bright sea. There is much grey already in his hair and there are cruel furrows in his face — he is a man of fatal destiny. He goes on his knees before a flower, he can starve but will buy a flower-pot. When he imagines a thing he can become savage with men, but he dares not even contradict a girl. When he and Freda disagree, he says: "I can't stand it" and rushes away without his hat. Then, when he comes back, he asks: "Have you offended me or have I offended you?" He will not know to-morrow what he has done to-day; nor does he remember what he has written. He works as in a trance; no sooner is something on paper than it vanishes from his mind. As a contrast the future is always present with him, he is brim-full of ideas and plans of what he is going to write — Mitzi.'

WORLDLY AND UNWORLDLY CARES

Sister has brought the dowry, just imagine 4000 marks! It is worth while marrying for that alone. Strindberg has ordered a beige home-spun suit, a white straw hat to go with it, and a soft wide silk tie, black with dark green stripes.

For my special benefit, apparently, a huge, unbelievably cheap department store by the name of Wertheim has been opened recently in the Leipziger Strasse. Berlin has never seen the like of it. It is a real *Au bonheur des Dames*, a most brilliant imitation of Paris. Originally mother had wanted to provide the linen. On my grandparents' estate the maidens weave a kind of linen which is strong enough to outlive three generations. If you permit a chemise of such linen to slip to the floor, it stands erect by its own strength. Mother still possesses shelves and shelves full of night jackets and of pantalettes reaching down to the ankles, they are of thick white dimity, scalloped and embroidered; they originate from her own trousseau and she wanted to bestow them on me to save me the expense. They were a bit wide for me, really a bit too wide, but mother remarked quite justly that matrimony quickly enough doubles a woman's size. All the same, darling mother, I don't like these self-assured chemises, swelled with their own importance; I refuse any relationship with this unerring conceited dimity. I want a thin cool batiste and I sketch what I want in a few strokes. Strindberg also loves lace and perfume.

But in a higher sense, too, he has provided for our most urgent, immediate future. 'Bride's Mother' and I have been invited to his exhibition. On his desk and on his table, on every shelf and on the floor there is a wealth of pot-bellied flasks, cups and lamps, mortars and test tubes, scales and instruments — a brighter medley of colours than his canvases on the easel and on the wall which my sister is contemplating dubiously. A painter who has never studied painting and yet knows how to paint, is something new to her.

This scientific arsenal which he intends to take with him on his journeys and into matrimony looks most alluring, pretty and innocent. But no sooner does he start to explain the kind of experiments for which these diverse, pious little lamps and little white mortars are to serve than my sister's apprehensions are diverted from the pictures to the crucibles. Sulphur, which falsely pretends to be an element, is to be unmasked, and must be compelled for the first time to reveal its complexities. Evidence is to prove that carbon and especially nitrogen are likewise of a complicated nature. And all the time his research is to continue and his efforts to make gold, whether it be from mercury or from lead, or perhaps from silver or even synthetically . . .

'Is that all?' my sister inquires with dangerous calm. This mad heresy offends her. But Strindberg is again engrossed in his own thoughts and does not even notice the mockery. He is now telling her of his latest studies, during those days of solitude in wintry Brevik, where he had tried to master the electricity of the air and put it at man's service and where — embittered against woman — he had tried his hand at the problem of Homunculus, while the lamp lit dimly his miserable cottage and the storm at night was wailing through the high dark pines.

'Well,' he heaves a belated sigh of grief over his failure. 'I am thoroughly independent, save in one point. I cannot make children alone. I need a woman for that!'

'What a pity' — I repeat his sigh. 'It is really a shame!'

Again he does not even notice the mischievous teasing. I feel humbled in my own eyes, my mockery was out of place.

'Well, after all, perhaps you are really marrying a man who solves the problem of Man's putting the children into the world himself!' is Mitzi's biting remark after we had gone to bed that night.

'We shall not fail to send you the prescription!' I retort.

August Strindberg sets the impress of his personality on all the inanimate matter which surrounds him. By this I do not mean the real close companions, such as his guitar, his books, his instruments, his pictures, or his great green sack! I mean just everyday things, a grey house-coat, a Faust cap, a brown wooden pipe, a green and white foot-bath which accompanies him like cleanliness itself from one hotel and house to another. All these things are part of him, every single one of them.

But he has never been able to merge his closest companions in himself. I always had the feeling about many of these 'friends' that they have been artificially joined on, the nails and screws are quite loose and may break off any moment — in my heart I wish they would, the sooner the better!

His best-beloved disciple is the Pole, Stanislaus Przybyszewski, whose pet name is 'Stachus' or 'Poland'. A little while ago he was supposed to call on me.

'Poland begs to be allowed to kiss the hem of the robe of

August Strindberg's bride' — So Strindberg reported to me
in high spirits and with obvious satisfaction. I found this
very creditable in the gallant Pole and, indeed, most modest.
I feared and had almost expected that he would demand
more, for Stachus' own hospitality extends much further.
At carousals it is said to be his custom to press the key to his
marital chamber into the hand of his momentary bosom
friend. He lives with his lady-love, who has presented him
with two children. Although he does not marry this good
and beautiful girl, out of masculine pride and contempt of
woman, he loves her after his fashion. Last New Year's
night he said to Strindberg, his master and father: 'Here is
my key, go home and sleep with my Maschka! My Maschka
thinks a lot of you, she is my most precious possession! Here
is the key, Master, go and sleep with her!' The key, to be
sure, wandered back into his pocket, unused, quickly,
gently, unperceived.

Even if he had not been moved by this touching patriarchal
spirit, Strindberg was not the man to take advantage of his
disciple's bacchic extravagances. But I felt a little shy of
Stachus Przybyszewski after hearing this story. It was quite
possible, after imbibing several tumblers full of cognac, that
he might be struck by the idea of demanding a little key
to fit the Master's marital chamber. It was kind of him to be
satisfied with the hem of my gown.

When he did come, he did not even take advantage of
this slight favour. He only made a deep obeisance and
pressed his lips to my hand in a flattering manner. He looked
very handsome in so doing, this young Pole. Fair-haired,
slender as a sapling, with thin, delicate nostrils, a fine,
sensitive mouth, eternally and painfully yearning after red
wine or sweet blood to drink. That is how he looks.

'I am afraid I am too old to play the part of son to your
parents, but to be your sister's brother-in-law will suit me

admirably!' Strindberg playfully asserted the other day. Yet his reading of the part is not altogether satisfactory. He treats sister as a parent and calls her 'Mother-in-law', while she with her twenty-nine years does not feel an ancestor yet. This 'son' of forty-three with whom I have provided her without consent is becoming embarrassing, especially in society.

A few more things, too, are becoming embarrassing. The banns cannot be proclaimed yet. Although an infinite number of Strindberg's documents arrive they never include that supreme one which his brother is to send, the divorce decree which must be produced before the authorities will grant a new legal tie. He had not been concerned about this at that time. The decree had been delayed and that had not affected him because he had not thought of marrying again. But now we are awaiting it as Israel awaits its Redeemer. The temperature rises dangerously high at times — but the divorce decree does not arrive.

Luckily Strindberg discovers a superb way of hastening the procedure. He has been informed that English church right is still recognized and is still in function on the Isle of Heligoland, which England conceded to Germany in 1890 in exchange for Zanzibar. The minister of Heligoland needs no banns, he marries bridal couples on the spot.

'Off to Heligoland!' August Strindberg advises. 'Then we, at least, are there and on the spot. The divorce decree will come!' he assures us.

THE 'BRIDE'S MOTHER'S' SECOND REPORT

Maria Weyr, Berlin, to Professor Rudolf Weyr, Vienna

'... It is impossible for you to imagine, and no more could I ever have imagined, what a most astounding human species the people are among whom Freda now lives. They are most unnatural, unwholesome, eccentric, queer and odd, nothing but talent and not a spark of common sense, it is unbelievable. Strindberg towers high above them but he would be apt to drive an ordinary being like myself insane. I have never in my life met such a man before, there isn't the like of him . . . thank God! I shall not be able to stand it much longer. He weighs on my nerves like lead. At first he seems far better-looking and more attractive than in his pictures and there are moments when he looks much younger; but then his face will change brusquely to that of an old man when he often starts to brood all of a sudden and entirely forgets in the middle of a sentence that anyone is listening. He manages to remain absorbed in his thoughts for a quarter of an hour at a time, not saying a word and not hearing what is said to him. I never can shake off the fear of seeing him unexpectedly become insane. At the same time he more and more impresses me as a great genius. It sounds like gruesome fairy-tales when he talks of his last winter in Sweden, when during the long nights he gave himself up to scientific experiments. It is terribly strenuous to hear him talk. You almost see how his thoughts work and rush ahead and he cannot follow with his speech and suffers martyrdom. Half of what he says you must really guess. He also paints; there, too, he is a law unto himself, naturalistic symbolism, he calls it. He finishes a picture in two or three days, he paints surprisingly well considering that he never learnt to paint. He is so full of talent that he doesn't seem to know what to do with it. But his is not a joyful way of creating. It is more like the savage impulse driving a murderer to his crime. To me he is uncanny. I cannot understand Freda nor how she risks entrusting her future to the hands of such a man. But these two can no longer be separated; I must, on the contrary do all within my power to marry them as quickly as possible. I am afraid his love for her is mere passion, as a mentality she is not his equal, nor will any

K   145

woman ever be. He does not seem to demand that either, his opinion of woman being the lowest possible. He is a kind of hermit and relies much on his own company. I am determined not to leave Freda again alone with him before they are married. I would not assume that responsibility. He, himself, urges a prompt marriage; he wants us to go to Heligoland, where the English minister dispenses with the banns. It could all be over within eight or ten days then, while it will take three or four more weeks here in Berlin. He is most polite and charmingly amiable with me, yet I am perfectly sure that in his heart he wishes me at the end of the world. As a result I do not leave Freda's side, not even when they are working together. They are now translating a book of his. Freda is in the seventh heaven to have me with her. Her love for Strindberg, as a contrast to his, seems utterly of the mind, she admires, nay, she idolizes his genius. I believe she would never dare to embrace him unless he permitted or demanded it first. God alone knows how this will end in the long run. My confidence in this marriage under these circumstances is very limited and I fear results. Freda, in her divine idiocy, expects from him heaven on earth. All I can do is to give her a bit of sensible advice for her trousseau and to support her and his wish for a speedy wedding. Then I shall take the very next train home.

'Strindberg is still forced through his recent illness to stay at home a good deal, and I am grateful for that. His company is more painful than pleasant, and the part of a "mother-in-law" (as he calls me) is not to my taste. I feel most ridiculous.'

I AM DISCOVERED AS A GENIUS

His boundless generosity makes him share everything with the woman he loves, his sensations, his experiences, and his thoughts. One thing is certain, if he ever captures and owns the mystery of the universe, I shall become keeper of its keys.

Not that I am dependent any longer on matrimony for a career! I, myself, have been discovered as a genius.

Sister, as a professor's wife, had been invited to tea by one of the university's High Priests, a professor of literature.

The entire afternoon passed by but sister did not come home; there are no limitations to the theme of 'Goethe'.

August Strindberg sat in his rocking chair, at the Linden, I at his feet. His eyes were shining, while, with a happy pride, he poured out to me the story of his latest scientific achievements. He had been quite preoccupied of late, analysing air. The dogmas which Science upholds to-day he holds to be false. He, for some time, had thought he knew better, now he felt certain and was ready to challenge the 'learned faculty'. Clear as a crystal his fundamental idea had seemed as he had expounded it to me. There was a blissful transparency about us, when suddenly, before playing out his last card, he unexpectedly, almost solemnly, put me the question:

'Do you know of which elements air is composed?'

He expected to hear the reply which was being taught at school, he then would refute it. This was our custom, he would deliver a monologue, I personifying the dead school learning, at which he aimed his blows.

Alas, no doubt I had swallowed chunks of this school wisdom for years and had babbled it in my parrot-like way, but at this moment my nervousness was so great that it made me forget every word. Not at the price of my life and his could I have remembered what I had known by heart so well. I dared not confess it. My own scientific incompetence had never before stood between us. He always had done all the talking, he had done it superbly and I had listened, with ears and eyes spellbound. Was I now to be unmasked as a shameful ignoramus? Indeed, that must not be. I still trusted that my tongue might stammer mechanically the well known terms which had only vanished from my mind because of too great a veneration for the Master's presence. I pushed my hair back from my forehead, pulled myself together, sat erect, met his eyes with a warlike spirit and began:

'Air is composed . . . the elements composing air . . . the elements composing . . . are hydrogen and oxygen . . . hydrogen and oxygen . . .!'

Of course, there was still another highly respected element involved, but the fatal nitrogen simply would not occur to me. I could think of nothing but hydrogen and oxygen . . .!

I finished off with a long pause and imploringly looked up into the Master's face. To my surprise he looked positively cowed. There was a respect almost amounting to admiration, in his air. For quite a while he found no words.

'You are a genius, my darling.' He heaved a sigh. It was not easy for him, so I felt, to recognize this fact unselfishly. He really could not help the very natural regret of the explorer seeing himself robbed of his laurels in the very moment of his triumph by some unknown person.

'Yes, you are a genius!' Again he sighed. But his glance this time sneaked furtively, full of suspicion, from me to his 'Green Bag'. Had I taken my knowledge treacherously from this source?

We did not talk any more on serious subjects that night. Still he was absent-minded.

What had happened?

The adept had taken the words out of the Master's mouth. Strindberg's latest research work tended to establish that nitrogen was not an element at all despite the entire learned faculty! And had I not also insisted on passing over nitrogen in silence when counting up the elements?

August Strindberg and I, we two, are the only minds in the scientific world to-day who are of that opinion. We stand alone. Indeed, I must be a genius.

In order that posterity shall not dispute my merits, I herewith state: This happened under the Sign of the Ram, in April, 1893. Please, scientists of the world, remember that early date!

Nor did August Strindberg dethrone me when I confessed to him at last that I had not unmasked nitrogen as he had done but had merely allowed it to be wiped out of my mind as an element.

'So you can wipe out of your mind what you have learned in school? You unusual woman! Whoever can do that, my child, is saved.'

There was a new warmth in his kiss.

'BRIDE'S MOTHER'S' THIRD REPORT

Maria Weyr, Berlin, to Hofrat Friedrich Uhl, Vienna

'. . . So I hope to leave here on Thursday next for Cux-haven; early on Friday we cross to Heligoland, subject to the condition that Strindberg has by then recovered posses-sion of the wretched decree— The better I grow to know Strindberg, the more I feel that he is a good man at heart, in the real true sense of the world. His heart is in the right place but his intellect and his tendency to brood and to analyse, which at times borders on insanity, often lead him astray. . . . I have by no means finished studying him yet; that would take years. He speaks little and with a certain difficulty; it makes him so nervous to go to a theatre or into a shop or an office, that he is capable of turning round and running away. He said to me one day, "All I want is quiet and peace enough to work, enough money so as not to starve, and a wife who will let me love her and will not hate me in return. As a rule woman hates man because he is her superior."

'I do not dream of cultivating such discussions with him, they are Freda's affairs. If she is a good, unselfish wife to him, then I am convinced he will be good to her. But she must renounce any personality of her own and she must be able to understand him, otherwise she may drive him into a lunatic asylum. The man is melancholic by nature, a pessimist and he has suffered so cruelly that any big emotion or grief will throw him off his balance. The long and short of my observations is that he is profoundly sincere and decent. But, unfortunately, most unfortunately, he is embittered, eccentric and full of *idées fixes*. . . .'

THE GREEN LIGHT

Now the trunks are packed. My bridal underlinen and his chemical instruments are waiting to be moved. The wedding announcements have been printed; we have written out the five hundred addresses: they are ready to be dispatched, if only . . .!

'Perhaps the document has been sent to Heligoland by mistake and it is waiting for us there,' 'Bride's mother' exclaims.

'Why certainly, most certainly!' August Strindberg reassures her nervously. 'I am legally divorced, there is no doubt about that whatever. Or do you not believe me?'

'I do believe you!' Mitzi cries, and she means it. 'But you have bad luck!'

The evening before our wedding! We pilgrimage to the Lehrter Bahnhof, all three of us, to ask when the trains go and to buy the tickets. The sun is low when we pass by our magic castle. A silent, affectionate nod we send up to him and then we walk along underneath sprouting trees until we see the new station building surrounded by its still feeble new park — one second later the cold, dank stone giant has swallowed us.

Fortunately our business is soon settled. I shudder in the semi-obscurity of the long corridor with the light of day shut out. I am longing to get back to the sun. This is like a grave. On all sides, grey walls. Only one large, fallow green light, some signal or other, grins maliciously at a turning, as phosphorous gleams in a tomb of putrefaction. Instinctively I reach for August Strindberg's arm but I touch empty space. When I turn round in search, Strindberg has vanished.

'There he chases along,' Mitzi calls out startled and points at the green light, 'he has suddenly seen two men pass by whom he seems to know. One of them looked rather portly and wore a light suit. Compatriots of his, I dare say.'

I am just in time to see Strindberg disappear in the wide throat of a black corridor behind a green lamp. After that, darkness stares at me.

A short quarter of an hour passes by. We are still standing on the same spot and are still waiting.

'I intend to go home now, you must know whether you wish to stay here any longer. But I have done with waiting, also with waiting for the divorce decree. Such situations are simply impossible. Do we belong to society . . . or not?'

The moment is rather ill-chosen for that question, and it is not easy to reply. A fellow has just passed by with an insolent smile. It was not the kind of smile for a lady. — Fortunately my fiancé is now emerging from behind the green light. But it chills me when he comes closer. He looks like a dead man rising from a grave. And his face still looks livid after we have been away from the green light for quite a while and are back under the sky. He has taken off his hat, passing his hand over his forehead, chasing a dream. His hair clings in a lump of grey to his temples. Even Mitzi notices his distraction.

He does not wait for her to speak. 'I met the husband of my first wife. The man in the light suit was Baron Wrangel of Stockholm. He has married again and he is going with his young wife on a trip the same as I. I had a strange feeling just now when he shook my hand and congratulated me on my new marriage. He displayed as much sentiment as he had displayed on the day on which he congratulated me on my first marriage, despite the fact that it had robbed him of his wife. In those days I used to admire his composure and his wisdom which enabled him to comprehend that there is always more than only one cause for everything and that one cannot speak of guilt. But to-day I felt startled to see him turning up at this very moment, offering me his best wishes. Perhaps it was not at all a wish he repeated, but a curse. Everything comes back, I dare say, remembrance and destiny.'

Mitzi has called a cab. We get in. None of us speak. August Strindberg sits opposite us. I can see his brows grow more and more overshadowed.

'I do hope you will forgive me, sister, but I feel like walking.'

And before I can follow him, he has disappeared behind the trees of the Tiergarten. It has started to rain.

JOURNEY INTO THE SUN

A new and early morning. A radiant sun.

Even before Frau Redmann can come up, August Strindberg in person appears at our door in his travelling coat, ready to fetch us jubilant.

Was the sombre evening a dream or was it reality? To-day Strindberg's eyes are shining. Everything is prepared. His luggage towers on a cab. His brown trunk and green bag have been joined by a large travelling basket into which the chemical instruments have moved. His enamelled tub is of the party. After my earthly possessions have also been added one would say that some little family was changing quarters or that well-to-do gipsies had adapted themselves to a city atmosphere. Thus we rumble down the Linden. The magic castle glares. And, behold, a wonder! — the tall chestnut tree which did not want to commence blooming at all has lit up white candles over night, wedding candles.

My 'Empire' coat bulges like a globe at each breath of the wind. Thus I go sailing past the green light at Strindberg's side. On the platform at the train we meet our friends. They are nice boys after all. What a beautiful fragrant bunch of roses they have brought me! My heart aches when I think how much it must have cost them. The same thought must be paining Strindberg; he hurriedly turns away and gnaws at his moustache when I thank them emotionally.

Why, and there is the Finnish actress, Madame Tavastierna, sweeping along the platform in wild haste as though she had missed her cue . . . what does she want?

Strindberg is displeased with her because she has caused a play of his to be taken off the bill. . . . I am displeased because, prior to this, he had adored her — a year ago, for a whole week.

Before she can explain, however, the train starts moving. I can see young Bengt Lidfors waving. Paul waves too, Strindberg responds with his hat. After that the two vanish and everything has vanished. Only the sweet-scented bunch of roses on my lap remains with me. Now I voice my fears from a most grateful heart. 'If only the dear boys have not sacrificed their meals for this!'

'They would have done that willingly, but it's the end of the month. Don't worry, Lidfors found the right way out. He borrowed the money from me the very first thing this morning. You have the flowers and he is none the poorer for it.'

Sister and I are sitting side by side, Strindberg sits opposite us. The train rushes past town and country. The sun races ahead of it. It sends in kisses through the open window. In the net above us Strindberg's green bag rocks close to my leopard-skin. The day before, it had been an effort to close the bag, the hundreds of large sheets and again hundreds of small slips of paper with his notes on them find they no longer have enough room in it. Especially the little scraps are always threatening to glide out. 'Why do you write on these little slips and not rather on a full-sized page?' I had asked. He had explained it simply enough.

'The beautiful parchment paper is very expensive!' A scientist as well as a poet must be economical. And he absolutely insisted that the green bag must stay with us in the carriage and not go into the luggage-van. To begin with, it would be in danger there, it might be stolen or get lost. And secondly, there again, finances came into question. It weighed too much.

So I happen to have a fiancé who has so many thoughts that he can scarcely afford the paper on which to write them — so many thoughts that freightage for them would be too dear.

Sister, in deference to good breeding, has first ventured into conversation, then she has sunk down behind the newspaper. But when, after a time, she sees my foot stealing towards his and notices his blissful smile, she contemptuously closes her eyes and falls asleep.

'*Mon Dieu*, how childish!' says her yawn, 'how childish! Is it really worth while being a genius?'

'Yes, little sister, it is worth while! In moments like this, to be a genius and to be a fool, pays so royally, that no pains and no suffering exist, for which it would not pay.'

And thus we two journey into the sun.

V

HELIGOLAND

May 1893

THE WOMAN-HATER'S WEDDING

In summer-time ships cross every day between Heligoland
and the Continent laden with tourists. But during winter-
time and until the season starts, the Heligolander rarely
goes abroad (and then only for business purposes) and his
few visitors are bridal couples, who for highly regrettable
reasons cannot afford the regular German six weeks' banns.
A single ship copes with the traffic. It crawls twice a week
from Cuxhaven to Heligoland, carrying letters and sinners.
This cutter is an old fogey to whom even this bit of exercise
is rather painful.

August Strindberg, the seafarer, has detected this state of
senility at the first critical glance which he bored into the
machinery. Despite my protest he beds me carefully on a
bench on deck and protectingly wraps me up in the Dutchman. Sister has quite a fame in Viennese drawing-rooms as
a good sailor; yet he forced her gently but irresistibly into
a deck chair. He, himself, has become a different man. He
is at home here. His pace is elastic as never on shore; his
skin has gained colour in a flash; he victoriously and joyfully surveys the horizon. He is a proud and happy man
since he has the sea-breeze in his nostrils and the wind at his
back. But the old cutter speedily justifies Strindberg's worst
suspicions. She reels from the very beginning, reels before
we have even left the harbour. My sister grows pale. The
last thing I see is how she leans back, pressing her veil to her

face — then I close my eyes. Now the old ship jumps high, like a drunkard at a fair, hurls herself into the air, seems to leap clean out of the water. The sea has gone mad, too, and joins in the dance. Everything is dancing. The waves roll over the deck and my sister's waterproof sticks to her like a fish skin. Blessed be the Dutchman, it keeps me warm.

August Strindberg is sitting beside me with my head on his lap. My body and soul no longer hold together. I feel like an infant and am whining for a still more remote state; by and by it is as though I were sucking my whole strength from Strindberg. The mysterious electric currents emanating from him fortify me; I am done for if he removes his hand. I think. But he does not remove his hand, not for fully four hours. I am ashamed of myself, but it cannot be helped. For fully four hours he never moves but holds his hand on my forehead and I lie still, half asleep. It comes to my mind that he told me one day that he had called back to life his little daughter, Greta, that way. And I remember a queer saying of Schleich's: 'Your fiancé has most mysterious cosmic coherences.'

When land is at last in sight, I am quite well but too much exhausted even to open my eyes, still less am I able to stand on my feet. The tenders come and load the human cargo — it is too shallow for the cutter to land. Strindberg carries me down the ladder. I am fast asleep. He does not wake me up but carries me ashore; he carries me right up to the hotel and puts me on a couch. I have not yet quite wakened up.

Two hours later the blue sea laughs at me across the open window. The sun is shining. The door gently opens, Strindberg enters, a bright, young, victorious, rejoicing hero, by the magic of the sun and the sea. He swings his cap:

'Finished sleeping? — Do you know, ladies, what I have been doing in the meantime? I have posted the wedding announcements. The old girl who brought us here is going to take them with her when she goes back, postmarked Heligoland. So that's that!

'All the five hundred?' Mitzi asks, startled.

'All the five hundred! I have finished writing the last addresses. Also to brother Rudolf and father-in-law.'

Mitzi moans, almost inaudible, but she moans.

'Don't be afraid, little sister. *Qui vivra verra!* The divorce decree is certain to arrive, never fear. On top of that I have just wired our address to my brother, Oscar, and have begged him to wire back in case he has already dispatched it, otherwise as soon as he shall dispatch it. There will soon be a telegram for me!'

The minister, the Rev. Mr. Schroeder, is a man of the world and a good Shepherd who has long since learned to be mild to the little sheep gone astray. He does not believe us and never will believe that we have no other cause than our impatience to shorten our engagement. He is convinced that there are more vital reasons. He has pity upon my supposed weakness; he undisguisedly disapproves of Strindberg's supposed guilty haste and would gladly wish our union to take the form of a penance for him.

Before he has the divorce decree in his hands, he cannot celebrate our wedlock though. He must have proof that the first marriage has been dissolved.

'I am bound to such precaution, even for your sake,' he says; and, addressing Strindberg, 'You would not like to be a bigamist?' he asks in icy mordant tones.

'Years and years of Hard Labour!' his tone implies.

Strindberg has grown pallid. His experiences on the occasion of his divorce have sufficed to rouse in him a sickly fear of any renewal of acquaintanceship with the authorities.

'I certainly do not intend to become a bigamist!' he exclaims. 'But how could I become a bigamist since it is a fact that my first marriage has been legally dissolved?'

'That's exactly what I want to see with my own eyes. All due honour to your statement, my dear sir, but the Law and the Church only admit what is in writing.'

His face does not brighten again until we are back at the hotel and set eyes on Mitzi who stands triumphantly at the window waving a telegram.

'From Oscar!' He heaves a sigh of relief. 'He has sent off the document. That's lucky now, at least, your sister and the clergyman will believe that I am not an impostor.'

Mitzi almost cries for joy. 'Thanks be to God!' That is all her emotion allows her to utter as she holds out the telegram. He tears it open with one rip and turns white. It contains the hearty congratulations of a big newspaper. — 'Our warmest congratulations to the newly-wed!'

'The first echo to the five hundred wedding announcements!' Mitzi moans. 'The whole world by now is being told that you were married — and perhaps you never will be!'

He has humour and he needs it. The telegrams are now hailing a downpour of congratulations.

'Does it not prove your popularity?' I try to comfort him each time a wire arrives, which does not state that our marriage is at last becoming possible but proves the rejoicing of the world in that marriage which seems far off and wickedly bewitched.

'The woman-hater's wedding!' he parodies with a sour gaiety. Then a resourceful idea brightens him. There's comedy in it. I shall write this comedy. Our position is certainly novel and amusing: Congratulation upon congratulation on a wedding you want to conclude and cannot. All at once life seems to consist of nothing but good wishes.'

If the comedy would only not last so endlessly long! The fun is becoming too much, even for me; it repeats itself the whole day long about a hundred times. And on the following day as well. Again and again the feverish tearing open of telegrams and always this discouraging fatal 'a thousand good wishes to the newly-wed' from all the countries of the world.

About three hundred telegrams the letter carrier has already delivered faultlessly, but on the third day he holds one which he obviously dares not part with. He stands irresolutely on the threshold, turns it around in his hands, learns it by heart and then suspiciously allows me a glimpse at it.

'Does that, perhaps, also happen to be for the gentleman? We could not make out the full name. The first word is Strindberg all right, but the second . . . Who's that "Författare" . . . Strindberg Författare . . . ?'

'*Författare* — that's I. All that it means is "author-writer". It is quite a hard thing at times to be a *Författare*, but that the mere word should prevent a man from marrying, that, anyhow, is new. That can presumably only happen to me.'

It does not take long now to agree with the clergyman about the ceremony. We decide it shall take place to-morrow. By then the cutter will have landed once more and this time she will remit to us the legal certificate that August Strindberg is free and may marry me.

To the left of the church across the street a straight line of little white houses runs along between gardens to the cliffs. Fisherfolk have built villas and let the rooms they can dispense with during the summer. Each of them looks like the other and it will be difficult for us to pick one out. But the last one in the line, close to the edge, has a white veranda and over it leans a tree. This house we select.

Trees and sky, wherever you look, and farther off, the sea. Three rooms; one for the gentleman, one for the lady, and one for both together.

'We shall arrange for catering,' Strindberg proposes. 'That

rids us of household cares. Each of us dresses in his own room; that saves us from whatever is painful in certain moments when any human being, to put it mildly, is human . . .'

We are to have, each one, our own cupboard, our own desk, and a door which can be locked. The key to this door is the key to Perfect Marriage. It is indispensable that one may close the door now and then behind one's own thoughts, one's own feelings. One's happiness otherwise flies away. Strindberg hates the unavoidable, the raping (as he calls it) of the marital bed as much as I dread it. And he tenderly pictures to me chivalrous visits, an affectionate 'good night' and a happy 'good morning' which take the place of 'here I am and here I stay!' You also need time to think of the other person. A wife must always remain a man's beloved, that is what the French understand so well.

Birds are nesting on our little house. In front of our windows spring is blossoming and the sun rises — May Bride!

The divorce decree has arrived. Triumphantly Strindberg swings it in his hand, waves to my sister with it, salutes the exacting clergyman, greets me, greets the Sea, the Sun and the new life which opens before him.

Hurrah! The divorce decree has come.

He is free! Free!

The memory of one great day has remained alive in me since my childhood.

A spring morn rose over my Mondsee. The lake and the mountains were gleaming like an opal in their tender pink, blue and green, through a veil of dew. The hills and dales resounded far off with the echo of gay rifle shots. Horns were blaring, trumpets pealing; under a canopy of leaves a long bright procession came moving up the wide avenue of lime trees; men with little nosegays of flowers and chamois-beards in their hats, women with silken shawls around their shoulders and bonnets heavy with gold. The doors of the church had been flung open wide, the crowd was thronging and jubilating. Two people were marching through the portal and were stepping before God. Through clouds of incense candles were shining across the altar. And once more the lake and the mountains reverberated to the gay crackling of rifle shots.

That had been a peasant wedding.

Things are not so solemn, still less are they so gorgeous with us. No church for us, the minister's office only, sober and bare. Its entire furniture consists of a large desk in front of which the minister stands. Two pilots humbly wait in the background. They are in the habit of standing that way twice a week waiting for the moment when they will have to sign and testify that Mr. So-and-so and Miss So-and-so have, after all, obtained the church's sanction to their union. Each of them receives a Taler (three marks); in expectation of this they wear their Sunday suits in which they do not look half as nice as in their sailor jackets and they shift uneasily in land-lubber's shoes. I detect them spying surreptitiously past us at the sea, and stretching longingly with gaze fixed on the open sky. Furthermore there are present the 'bride's mother', representing the bride's family, the bride herself, and the bridegroom.

The bridegroom wears his light home-spun; one of the boys' rosebuds still lives in his buttonhole. The bride and 'bride's-mother', and for good reasons, look like sisters; each of them wears one of the nice inexpensive dresses from the Berlin *Au bonheur des Dames*.

This is a Poet's Wedding.

As a rule the marriage ceremony is short and takes no more time than the taler of the witnesses is worth. On the Continent the usual six weeks' banns are meant to show up

L   161

all possible impeachments; here these impeachments have been summarized in a very clear and precise way in twenty-three questions. England rightfully assumes that every person knows more about himself than his intimate friends or even his enemies. For this good reason one does not ask the friends or enemies, but the pretendants to marriage, themselves, about their lives. They must swear an oath. If they commit perjury they are forfeited to Justice, which is supposed to be blind but can be most inconveniently lynx-eyed all the same. The parson is reciting each of the twenty-three questions, pausing after each one. Then it is the bride and bridegroom's turn — first he, then she must place one hand on the Bible and with the other take the oath, then repeat the wording of the question and answer with a veracious 'no', that no impeachment exists, and they are worthy to enter the Paradise of Marriage.

Marriage remains marriage, take it as you will. August Strindberg and I are both moved and nervous. I feel shy, he feels elated. Anyone looking at him and at the parson at this moment would take him for the High Priest and the other man for the husband.

Unfortunately, however, this very elation has deeply regrettable consequences, not at all in keeping with the solemn atmosphere. The slightest emotion, be it of a painful or joyful nature, forces August Strindberg into a sudden fierce feud with the German language. He can no longer find words or he finds the wrong words. His Swedish accent springs up and slaughters the German. With an utter disdain for its death he becomes more vehement at every question he answers and his answers become dangerously incorrect and sound most out of place.

And if I were hanging high up on the gallows and something tickled my sense of humour, I would have to laugh! Thus I laugh now. May heaven protect me! I laugh like a mad woman although tradition and custom demand that at one's wedding one should weep in advance and beware of rejoicing too early. I laugh ... Could I help laughing?

The last question of the parson was so frightfully indiscreet!

'Will you swear that you do not carry another man's child under your heart?'

The inquiry was designed for the bride alone. Out of absent-mindedness, however, he had also put it to August Strindberg. And in his nervousness August Strindberg had ...

It serves him right! Is he really not going to concede to me as a woman the tiniest prerogative?

Although it was exclusively my affair, August Strindberg had placed one hand upon the Bible and raised the other hand for the oath and had sworn most solemnly and in Truth, with utter defiance to German grammar and with indescribable dignity:

'I state upon my oath that I carry no child from no other man under my heart!'

The pious words ... and the still more pious mien. . . .

Utterly forgetful of where I am, I surrender to the explosion of a most hilarious laughter. The parson and August Strindberg turn to stone and stare at me. My sister is sweating blood; she has grasped the situation; she, too, is tempted to laugh, but the poor girl would rather die. She does not know how to save our faces; she imperiously holds out her little lace handkerchief, trying to make the audience believe that I am shedding tears. She presses it into my hands, she presses it to my eyes, and perfidiously pinches me in the arm when no one is looking.

'Pull yourself together!' the poor, sweet voice urges. But the only result is a still wilder gush of laughter. At last exhaustion puts a stop to it. I render thanks to God that he allows my strength to be exhausted ere the minister's patience give out. The parson sternly objects to brides who laugh. He softens only as he now sees genuine tears roll down my cheeks. It does not matter why they roll, they roll and bathe my face.

The rest of the ceremony is speedily accomplished without further obstacles.

'Much like a school examination,' I cannot help thinking.

And my hilarity? It was the laughter of a schoolgirl — before she ventures into the world.

Then we sign our names in the church register.

The two pilots also sign. August Strindberg presents each of them with a ten mark piece. Their expressions of surprised joy tell me that for such a sum they wouldn't have minded my laughing longer.

The Reverend Schroeder and Frau Schroeder accept our invitation to dinner.

And now August Strindberg and I are husband and wife — for better, for worse, till death us do part.

HELIGOLAND

May 1893

BRIDE IN MAY

HE stands on the outermost edge of the cliff as though he were borne on the air and stretches himself up towards the sun. The heavens are as wide and blue as if they stood open to everyone who had the courage to soar up to them. It must be possible to fly right in. The sun is so warm, everything smells sweet. Sheer under his feet the ocean foams and dashes up in wild white breakers. But it falls back impotent from the red rocks of the Isle of Heligoland, where we have just been married — Strindberg and I.

He is himself once more. He has cast off the city with its dust and soot, the past has dropped like withered leaves when spring comes.

He has begun a new novel, a sequel to his *On the Open Sea*, again with the superman, Axel Borg, as its hero.

We are happy, and happiness makes strength. He bears life as lightly as he carried me on our sunny wedding-day, when he insisted on my travelling in his gentle arms from bed to breakfast table, so that my bare feet should not touch the rough boards.

Yes, that was a merry day. He had laid the table himself and decorated it with flowers and greenery which he had gathered while I was still asleep — I certainly had left him time enough.

I slept most unfittingly late on our wedding morn, for the night had been restless. All of a sudden, at dawn, he had brusquely started from a dream, had not at once remembered that he now legitimately enjoyed the company of a young woman, and, in his first confusion, had attempted to throttle the interloper. He had already half succeeded — for whatever he does, he does well — when, at the last moment, something familiar in my protesting voice brought him back to consciousness. Although he soothingly reassured me that the attack had nothing to do with me, but was probably intended, as a mere matter of habit, for his first wife, I did not get to sleep again for quite a while. Black thoughts were unavoidable.

August Strindberg, Heligoland, to Maria Weyr, Vienna

'. . . Once again the unexpected and the sweetest surprise of all. Listen! Everything is for the best in this best of worlds. Happiness beyond measure, that is too much for one who has suffered so much.

'Thanks for all fair and for all stormy hours that we have gone through together — August Strindberg.'

That was a week ago now. Sister had hurried back to her husband immediately after the wedding, her own marriage meant more to her than ours. We really do not take it ill. She is no longer essential to our happiness, not even as a chaperon. We may parade our love openly now. What was immoral a few days ago, now has a blessing upon it. The clergyman's good wife hopes with all her heart that a darling baby may be on the way. The clergyman himself smiles beneficently when he sees us. Congratulations arrive less and less frequently since we acquired an official right to them.

Our home is a lovely little house after Strindberg's own heart, with three rooms, a white veranda, a flower-bed, a lane and trees in front. The islanders are friendly and peaceful and fonder of inns than of churches. Everything is quiet and beautiful in spite of faint rumours from Berlin and Stockholm of money shortage and bad business.

The post calls here only twice a week.

I have been appointed his business manager in Paul's stead; believe me, this is no sinecure.

He is unable to give his attention to tiresome discussions about prices, he is incapable of bearing the atmosphere of vulgar minds. Yet he is not living in the clouds at all, he lives down here amidst reality. Nor is he indifferent towards success. A man wants to know what he will leave behind one day and what will survive him. He is keen on the publication, the sale of his books, on the production of his plays. He has a theory of his own.

'A work of Art begins to exist the moment it kindles — and no sooner.' It is this act of kindling divine fires which conveys to him the triumphant feeling of vitality and immortality.

His eyes are shining while he now tells me of his latest ventures and hopes in Berlin. He has more than twenty irons in the fire, and if he does not at once succeed in conquering the world with them, this is the fault of his being in advance of his time.

He proposes most simple means; for instance: Do you want to force a manager to produce a Strindberg play which he is reluctant to produce? His monopoly of Strindberg must be withdrawn and half a dozen other theatres be given permission to play Strindberg . . . that will quicken the man's appetite.

Is there no publisher who wants to print and pay? All the better. Then at last things will develop as they ought to have developed long ago, for social reasons. Private capital shall no longer hold the right to exploit the genius; the People themselves shall take the place of the publisher and shall produce as well as buy. He suggests selling Strindberg by subscription. Each copy includes a share. The more copies and shares are sold, the lower the price of the book becomes, on the one hand, and on the other, the shareholder, the reader, participates in the profits of the sales. Thus the People become the proprietors of August Strindberg's authors' rights.

'The "Ferkel Round Table" enjoyed it as a joke,' he tells me. 'When I suggested this,' he pensively adds, 'they were of opinion that it would be six times more difficult to sell six plays than to sell one. But my day will come.'

A whole chapter of the new novel is already finished, Strindberg writes for three hours every morning when he returns from his walk, which is devoted to meditation; not even I may accompany him.

He writes without a pause, almost without stopping, does not even read over what he has written, to say nothing of correcting it. It is like harvest-time when the fruit has ripened.

And how warm the weather is — he is already wearing his light suit and a panama, the sunshine justifies it.

So much sunshine! I cannot imagine that it will ever be winter again.

I have been Strindberg's wife now for a week — but if anyone should ask me: What kind of a man is he, who is he? — I should not know. I had always heard it maintained that you know all about a man, once you have shared his bed. I ought to know Strindberg, but it is his greatest charm that you never get to know him. At any rate, I know him just as thoroughly as one knows the world at the end of a week's tramp. He is a globe of all Knowledge, Thought and Emotion. But you cannot nail him down, for he throws over all fixed conceptions. Take his hatred of women; yesterday he

began a poem in which he praises woman's body as the great
wonder of Creation and hymns therein the divine harmony
of the universe — sings of it! — sings of it!

This a man who denies love, who enjoys it in calm bliss,
like a posy of flowers or a ripe fruit? This man inconsistent,
who keeps his promise every hour of the day and night that
he would never bore me because he is always new and
different . . . ? No, there is nothing, nothing that I know
about my husband, save that I am happy.

August Strindberg, Heligoland, to Maria Weyr, Vienna

'Weather Report, issued May 10th, 1893, Heligoland.
Sunshine every day. Temperature, very warm. Wind
unchanged, mild. — The atmosphere shows no sign of
magnetic disturbance — August.'

Has he forgotten his past, and is it thanks to me? Or do
the embers still glow under the new fires?

Yesterday we unpacked the trunk full of his pictures and
writings. The green, budding tree before the window pointed
now to this sheet, now to that, with a long, narrow, shadow
finger. He pulled out two faded photographs from a mass
of papers, importantly, as one lays hand upon valuable
possessions. In the tone of a proud owner, he said: 'That's
how she looks: she is aristocratic, beautiful, slender and
refined.' The pictures were of his first wife and were taken
in Switzerland. She stands under a pergola, holding a knitted
shawl or jacket close round her figure.

'Slender,' he calls it. Worn out and emaciated is what she
is; in the eyes of my twenty-one years, she, at forty, is a
faded and spent woman. There is no human being that I
am so boundlessly sorry for as this woman. I can feel no
jealousy, only a pang of guilt, as if I were a thief. It hammers
on my brain: 'She is old, faded and weary. And the man

who made her so now belongs — to me.' Of course I am innocent, they were parted before ever I came, nothing on earth could have brought them together again. And yet —

But there is a strange thing about it, too. I see her quite as she now is, devoid of charm. But he does not as yet. When he speaks of her, and now again, as he shows me her picture, he does not say: She *was* beautiful, he says 'she is beautiful'. And on our wedding morning there broke out in the midst of our kisses, with the pain of despised tenderness nurtured for years, a defiantly triumphant exclamation: 'She did not think I would mate a young bride!' . . . Does he still love her? I do not ask him. He himself does not know. I therefore remain silent. He takes it for a tribute which I pay to her outward appearance. Satisfied, he lays the pictures back in the trunk and will continue to carry them with him on his journeys.

He takes my arm, beaming, lively and tender as we promenade along the shore. I feel a slight uneasiness, but the sun is as radiant as he, and the future seems ours.

A Scandinavian newspaper announces that William Heinemann, Ibsen's publisher in London, has already set up Strindberg's volume of poems, *Noctambulist's Nights*. Justin Huntly McCarthy, son of the historian, has published a fine article in the *Fortnightly Review* on Strindberg's play *The Father*. Now an enterprising young Dutchman, J. T. Grein, has founded the Independent Theatre in London, a modern stage for international art. There is Robert Browning on his programme, Émile Zola, a certain G. Bernard Shaw, of whom one now hears much — Grein's letter is most inviting, he wants Herr August Strindberg to authorize a production of *Father* and — if possible — to visit England. Strindberg cannot be a Viking if the conquest of that island should not tempt him mightily. But England must wait, says he, we are still busy here.

Three weeks of happiness.

Then, gathering closely until they shadow our whole horizon, clouds.

Strindberg is no longer the same man.

The novel Axel Borg does not progress. The stream of inspiration seems cut off, run dry. His early morning walk, lasting an hour, with which he was accustomed to preface his daily task, stretches out now until noon.

Letters arrive, he reads them furtively. The corners of his mouth twitch and he has taken on a harried expression. Is he worrying about his children, of whom he has not heard since their mother, in quiet and friendly fashion, wrote to wish him a happy marriage? Is it because he has cause to fear that the friends in Berlin, under Aspasia's influence, are changing into enemies? Is it because we suddenly realized that our little capital, which we have incautiously used to pay off old debts, is drawing to a close?

Or — are the mysterious cosmic cohesions, which Schleich attributes to Strindberg, making themselves felt once more? They command a change of air, at least, whenever they are seen.

I watch him grow unhappy, yet he will not take any decisive step. I am the one who first says, 'Let us go to England straight away!' But he agrees so eagerly that I want to cry . . . Scarcely three weeks! Scarcely three weeks.

ALARM

We took passage on a collier in Hamburg for fifty marks a head. It was to land us in the Port of London after two and a half days' passage. I was attracted by the cheapness of the passage, Strindberg by the length of the voyage. The captain, with whom we struck the bargain, was a sturdy, bearded man, half soldier, half old sea-dog, very pleasing to Strindberg. Things began well, but changed for the worse. It was probably the fault of the singeing heat in Hamburg. He

could not bear heat and here at noon the town glowed like
a furnace. I watched his brain grow dulled; he hardly spoke
at all and never gave any answer. He had armed himself,
as it were, against an enemy world. Impossible to persuade
him to name a dish to the waiter as we sat at lunch in a
restaurant. Impossible, later at the café, to persuade him
to change his seat and prevent his hat flying under the wheels
of a passing vehicle. He did not glance at the papers. He
did not glance at me. He never once glanced at the *Alster*.
He merely gazed before him, stared at some torturing vision,
invisible to me, which he seemed to feel, mortal to body and
soul. The sun blazed on the asphalt as we strode towards
Hoefer's Hotel, where we were staying. We were indescribably weary and both of us inexpressibly sad. Thus we
arrived at the large square which faces it. It was no unusual
place, just a stone-paved ordinary space and the traffic was
normal for a fairly large mercantile city. Vehicles traversed
it in all directions, trams rushed by, but it was not difficult
to make way for oneself, and pedestrians were crossing
continually from side to side by hundreds, without hesitation
and without accident. I saw that August Strindberg stood
still with a countenance turned to stone, his eyes riveted in
front of him. I took his arm; put anxious questions; entreated
him; stood beside him — and did not know what to do.
People began to notice us. A woman asked in a talkative
way whether there was anything the matter with the
gentleman? A policeman kept his eye on us, suspecting
something wrong. My husband's face began to twitch, he
fought with himself, combating an invisible power —
agoraphobia! The anguish that roots one to the spot. I
do not know what made it come into my mind, but it was
agoraphobia. I hope no one to whom I mean well may
ever experience it. It seems to be a sister of the Fear of
Death, Horror of Death, of Emptiness — for what is death
other than a paralysis of motion? Strindberg staggered. I

feared that he would fall. But slowly he regained command of himself and turned back. I called a conveyance. We drove to our hotel, one minute away. He lay back in the cushions, his brow beaded with sweat. The attack was over. But how frightfully it had affected him.

He slept. Exhausted. With deep and quiet breath. Recuperative sleep. At four o'clock he awoke well and cheerful, kissed me lovingly and went out. Alone. I let him go. Both of us needed solitude.

When he returned at nightfall, his nervousness was gone. He had brought me flowers. And I was waiting for him with Turkish sweets. Neither of us spoke of the dark secrets of the day. We never do. We scent the precipice too near not to shun it.

Even if it were only for weeks, days, hours — that which was to come, which we felt drawing close, would come soon enough.

VII

GRAVESEND-LONDON

June 1893

WITH QUEEN VICTORIA AND SHAKESPEARE

FORTY-EIGHT hours at sea and still no London. A miserable
sufferer from seasickness, I crouch in a dark cabin below
deck.

Strindberg stands immovably by the captain, who wonders
that this bookworm should know even more about the sea
and ships than himself. From time to time, however, he
dives down into the cabin, takes me compassionately by the
hand and reports, as eager as a boy in Wonderland. He has
been making observations, he is in hot pursuit of the optical
illusions which gave rise to the myth that the earth is round!

I ought to congratulate him, indeed. But I am so exhausted
that I can only afford a weak and wry smile. He gently
pats my brow. Perhaps it would cure me if he kept on long
enough, he is a mountain of strength. But he is already off
again, back on deck. Once more his watch is in one hand,
a telescope in the other. He is about to destroy a dogma on a
£2 10s. trip!

At last the steamer reaches Gravesend. The coast gleams
white in a silvery veil, a shining church steeple rises, ancient
trees nod to us. I have lost all desire to travel and consent
that we should stay here instead of going on to London. It
is really the old captain who has put this latest idea into
Strindberg's head; he is compelled to spend one night every
week here and thinks it both profitable and pleasant to have
good friends available with whom he could dine and smoke
his pipe.

We decide upon a house, No. 12 Pelham Road. It looks exactly like all the other houses, but a trifle younger and better kept. The ground floor consists of a front sitting-room and a back bedroom. Both rooms are spacious and clean as a pin. We ought to be enchanted but we are not. In the bedroom, a shameless married English double-bed with shining brass knobs. It brazenly defies our notions about modern marriage. Beautiful are the old trees which cast shadows in front of the window, there cannot be for us any brusque awakening in the brutal glare of day. But the pretty-pretty furnishing of the sitting-room exasperates my husband. He hates the smoothly-polished mahogany, the rosy shells on the what-nots, the prints after Alma-Tadema and Sir Frederick Leighton. 'Pour cocottes' — he says, disgustedly. He wants to make his escape and I must make him realize that these furnishings are really quite the thing in England. They are probably more or less the same everywhere. Finally, we rent the rooms. A pretty high price is asked for them. — Brass, mahogany, sea-shells, Alma-Tadema and Leighton are all 'of the very best'.

The captain congratulates himself. A deep and roomy armchair is drawn up to the fireplace. He sees himself dozing in its depths every week-end, pipe in mouth, a glass of whisky beside him. He is pleased.

But Strindberg suffers. All I can do, to save him from the splendour of the sitting-room and from the double bed is to rent one more room in the second story, containing nothing but a rickety old table and two chairs. In a corner stands sulkily a lumpy old divan, on which he can take a rest during the day and on which I can sleep at night. Here is a fitting retreat. Here he feels secure, this will be his work-room. The colour and pattern of the wallpaper has long since faded out of all recognition. No curtains at the window, the naked sky looks in. Still, England can never be home to him. There is such a thing as physical home-sickness. Transplanting hurts the roots. Strange earth imparts strange nourishment and new objects arouse new thoughts which break in upon the old.

Strindberg's idea for the new novel has faded out. The rosy pink shells, the polished mahogany, the Leighton and Alma-Tadema pictures, all make mock of the glorious wildness of his dreams. The fairylike silvery veil which shrouds England's heaven and hell and separate both equally from the common earth strangles his imagination.

A pallid, discouraged man comes slowly down from his work-room to the dining-room to lunch every day. Forces himself to eat something, scarcely speaks, even when, in defiance of his recent abstinence, he has tossed off one brandy after another. I put no questions, I know that he cannot write here. And he makes his escape to his researches, that his powers may not lie idle.

He has now turned to geology. I pointed him the way myself, accidentally.

Yes, there is nothing more glorious than the mighty old trees of Kent, its velvety lawns are world-famous. But you must reach them first! Right and left are hedges in endless rows. Half laughing, half in despair, we had begun a race. Strindberg dashed off like an arrow. Burdened with a wife, however, he did not get far, for I stumbled over a stone and fell. I began to be afraid he would show merely vexation. But he gazed so long and tenderly upon the ground where I lay that my heart was warmed. He even picked up the stupid old stone which had been the cause of my mishap and put it piously in his pocket, evidently as a relic; conjugal love could go no further. Arm-in-arm we wandered back home. Neither of us spoke. Each was busy with his own thoughts. An almost religious awe held us in spell.

Only when we reached home did he break the silence.

'Do you know what that is?' he asked me, depositing the
stone in his sanctuary on the writing-table.

'It is the firestone spoken of in the seventeenth century by
Petrus Kalm, the Swedish traveller; he says the folk tradition
regards it as a product of chalk by gradual transformation.
This will prove my theory of transmutation!'

Again there was a tender gleam in his eyes. But — I could
no longer deceive myself. This tenderness was not meant
for me.

Ever since he has been probing into the ancestral origins
and kin of his new friend.

I go reconnoitring in London twice a week. A world of
disillusions gapes between the rosy Scandinavian news and
the grey English reality. It is not true that William Heinemann is thinking of Strindberg's poems. His firm informs me,
politely, but without possibility of mistake, that Mr. Heinemann has gone to Italy without leaving a word that could
indicate any such intention. The firm, of course, does not
pretend to know all Mr. Heinemann might be contemplating,
but that he is not contemplating us — even his firm knows
that.

Justin Huntly McCarthy has, indeed, translated *The
Father*, but his excellent essay in the *Fortnightly* did not prove
an 'Open Sesame!' The Treasure Cave up in the Mountain
had remained shut, and low down in the valley we shall soon
find no more food. Only J. T. Grein proves a tangible
reality. An admirer of the *Théatre Libre* in Paris, born and
educated in Holland and now in business in the City, he is
occupying his leisure hours by attempting to build up just
such a home of modern drama in England. No easy game,
costs money as well. Only hard work in Mincing Lane makes
it possible. But he takes the kind of pleasure in talent that
another man finds in a good cigar. He is determined to produce Strindberg. However, he will not be able to produce

The Father this season. Impossible. We have come too late. 'Next year for certain!' he comforts us.

I heave a sigh. A year is a long time. Grein understands. He, too, knows how long a year can be — where there is no money.

'I shall have to go abroad soon,' he says suddenly at the close of our conversation: 'if you wish to leave Gravesend for London, I should be happy to offer you my flat — Well, well — Everything will be all right.'

Kind J. T. Grein! How comforting this sounds! And yet it is only a little while ago that I myself used to say, well assured and smilingly at any question which arose: 'Everything will be all right!'

In the meantime, Strindberg had penetrated into the mysteries of the various combinations of chalk and into the indescribably complicated questions arising therefrom. As a father who has lost a child tries to benumb himself with work, so Strindberg tries to find in his researches a substitute for the purely creative work which is impossible to him in such a place as this.

Gravesend is about twenty miles from London. When we took train at ten o'clock in the morning, there was not a cloud in the sky. When we got out in London, the air was full of smoky black fog. As we went along Pall Mall, we could see it getting thicker and thicker. Then it descended suddenly like an iron curtain, just as we turned into Trafalgar Square. The one-armed Nelson who had perched in the centre a few minutes before, seemed to have taken wing, along with his telescope. Only his column was there abruptly cut off. The darkness swallowed up more and more of the daylight; some subterranean monster must be spewing up this darkness. Then of a sudden all the lamps were lit and now the whole sea of fog seethed wildly, sulphurous yellow, in a dusky and threatening glow. August Strindberg stood spellbound. Drawn up to his full height he stood, his head thrown back and his eyes aflame:

'That is how I could envision a poet's monument — Hercules, setting light to his own pyre! The flames are his character and his destiny. Hercules the herdsman cannot for ever remain a herdsman and yet be Hercules. A poet must live a hundred lives in order to create live souls. He must go through everything himself, must have risen to every virtue and plunged into every vice. Only the poet-seer can shed light upon humanity's dark, abstruse path — by means of the flame that burns in him, slays and devours him and that he has himself kindled! The life of the poet — a holocaust!'

I shall never forget it. As though consecrated to the fire we stood amidst the uncanny swathes of reddish-yellow smoke and greedy gleam of flame. It was impossible to distinguish the point where the neighbouring streets reached the square, but we felt them cowering in the darkness like the open jaws of wild beasts. We felt as if these maws might open wider at any moment in order to spew out still more bloodthirsty flames, still more conflagrations and funeral pyres.

Strindberg drank in the picture. In the wild glow of the destruction he seemed only to see the resurrection from the ashes.

I cannot understand how England achieves it, but she indulges in thunderstorms in spite of her fairylike silver veil. A storm was to break over Gravesend this afternoon. Hours of oppressive mugginess proclaimed its approach. Strindberg had retired to the attic for his siesta. I sat in the mahogany sitting-room on a soft couch surrounded by rosy shells from the depths of the South Seas.

Letters had arrived after lunch; with them, a book. In

my drowsy condition I had not glanced at the title, but had begun straight away to turn the pages. Now it was impossible to stop, to remember, to lay the book aside. I was caught in the wheels. It was the history of Strindberg's first marriage.

Without the *Plea of One Insane*, he would scarcely have survived his first marriage. He had had to write it down and cast it off his soul before he could recover.

But the crucificial hour, he knew, would break when that which he had confided to the mute white paper in his solitude should lie before him in print, accessible to the whole world! That would be martyrdom!

And he had made me promise him, solemnly vow to him, that I would never read the book.

He was right, I ought not to have read it. It cast an evil spell between him and me. I experienced his love and his hatred for the mate of his early manhood. I saw him embrace her and then pelt her with dirt in front of the whole world. From being his wife, I had become one of the many thousands before whom he stripped this woman naked and whom he allowed to penetrate into her soul. One of the crowd, I too, saw him in her arms and heard his passion. I myself was lost in a far-off distance. I was no longer there at all, only that other one existed.

Then, in a curious change of feeling, quite another kind of terror took forcible possession of me. It was no longer Siri von Essen whom he exhibited, but I myself. No doubt it would soon be my turn. . . .

I no longer had a thought for the boundless suffering from which the desolation of this book had sprung. Reason, kindness and love had grown dumb. Art? The word would have come as a mockery at this moment. I myself was the pawn, I, as I sat and talked and took my breath. Were these frightful accusations true, or were they a betrayal of reality by imagination? If so, they might happen again any day and would then besmirch me too? For the first time I saw Art as an enemy and a destroyer.

I had not noticed the storm, which had meanwhile arrived over Gravesend with blinding flashes of lightning and roaring thunder. When I roused myself from my brooding, the rain was streaming down heavily, grey and leaden. I knew how much Strindberg suffered at such times. He was a most sensitive electric receiver — he could not endure strong currents. His whole being became compound of fear and resistance to electricity. He was capable of hesitating before he turned on the light in a room or went near a telegraph pole. When nature let loose her elements thus, he trembled like a reed in the wind.

Was it not precisely this power of reaction that stood so cruelly between him and life? It was possible, very possible indeed, that Siri von Essen had not committed a single one of the sins of which he accused her, and all his accusations had no foundation in the world of fact, and yet they perhaps had a psychical basis. Perhaps he had perceived what lay slumbering in the deepest caverns of her sub-consciousness — had wrenched it up to the light. Perhaps, his every nerve quivering in contact with hidden powers, he had worked electric telepathy.

When I entered his attic, it was empty. Had he sought my help and discovered me at my disastrous reading? Was he gone, and whither? I was seized with unrest. But just as I had reached the door again, I heard a stifled sound of weary, heavy breathing. It came from the corner behind the divan. Now I caught sight of him—

In order to escape from the yellow lightning flashes, he had sought shelter on the floor behind the table and the couch!

He now lay in a deep sleep of exhaustion. Pale and sad he looked. Verily not like one who has slain, but rather like one whom people have tried to slay, over and over again.

I did not awaken him. I let him lie on the hard floor. I

did not even slip a cushion under his head. He groaned. I stood quite still, stupefied, horrified, not daring to move or make a sound. After a time I crept out of the room.

It seemed to me as if anything would be better for him just now than to awaken.

*

Now we are in London, at Fairmantle House, 84 Warwick Street, J. T. Grein's home.

He has gone away, but his housekeeper, Bobbie Jeffreys, has stayed behind — a pretty, plump Irishwoman. Her hair is rather too red, her cheeks somewhat too white. But the laughing brown eyes, the white teeth and the shamrock are real.

We have a bedroom and the sitting-room in which stands J. T. Grein's large writing-desk.

Around us, hot and sunny, foams Pimlico's ocean of houses. Fairmantle House is scarcely a drop in this glowing sea. There is no silver mist in Pimlico. Mountains of food of all kinds, clothes, old books, household goods and rubbish piled higgledy-piggledy are on sale a few paces from us in the open street market. A sharp and brutal scent of raw meat hangs in the air, of fish, winkles, rotting fruit and vegetables, pitch, salt water and human sweat, exciting and intoxicating. Torches flame and flicker late into the night. Dark figures in fantastic costume flit across the patches of light as in a lurid scene from Dickens. Tipsy beggar women wear great hats with nodding plumes, others have frocks with long trains, poverty has bought up the glories of past fashions from the rag-and-bone man's barrow and trails them through the dust. Bobbie looks after the house-keeping, her provisions kept strictly within the limits of national taste. Three times a week we get chops, three times steak, and on Sunday, the seventh day of creation, there is roast mutton. As accompaniment we have marrow, beans, spinach — spinach, beans and marrow. Salad every day, but without oil and vinegar. Salt is only to be tasted in the tang of breezes from the sea.

Strindberg rebels, he has the Swede's highly developed sensibility to appetizing food and, as every disturbance of his physical well-being puts a brake on his intellectual activities, he regards unsuitable diet as an attack on his genius. The dry, dusty heat, too, is a torture to him. And the narrowness of two rooms which he must share day and night with a woman, and the millions of people in the vast city, all of them strangers to him. He cannot rise above these conditions of life, they tie and squeeze him like a skin grown too tight. And then there is something worse. Strindberg can sit at J. T. Grein's table and sleep in J. T. Grein's bed, but he finds it hard to work at J. T. Grein's desk. The drawers of this desk are full to bursting of other people's intellectual labours. Young Shaw and old Browning have already leapt out of them. Who else besides? They all lie there, each crouched ready to spring, just waiting for his chance. Is August Strindberg to sit quietly by, until other people's dramas shall be born and buried? Strindberg is Youth, knocking at master Solness's door. But here Ibsen himself is only just coming into the world. You cannot very well thunder to an innocent: 'Make way, Ancient!' No, a gentleman must behave, out of consideration for the god-parents. Still less, however, can one remain what one is and what one wants to be — Strindberg, the pioneer — at a writing-table where the battle for Henrik Ibsen is still in progress. Strindberg rattles the bars of his cage. He wants to get out.

Why should he not build as his own contractor? Why not found a theatre of his own, over Ibsen's head? He planned already years ago to marry a new dramatic form to a new art of the stage. Now this plan should be put into execution — and in Berlin; footing on the excellent rule, no great expenditure and continuous takings, even though small.

We sit together for hours and build theatres in the air. If I meekly object that we might need money for this play or that other, he at once has a new idea. He turns the whole art of the stage upside down — from an economic standpoint. Why has he imagination, why is he a painter and poet if he cannot create new scenes as well, bodiless, made only of colour and light, of line and shadow?

The creative spirit of my mate is bearing me upward on its pinions. But money gives us a shove back into reality. One fine Sunday morning, Bobbie suddenly announces that we must lunch out that day. She means to go rowing, rowing on the river. 'A long, long way up. It will be heavenly, right in the country,' she declares.

For our supper she has carefully prepared the cold mutton, sacred to the seventh day of creation. My death sentence. Strindberg is particularly enraged against this biblical mutton.

Faced by catastrophe, I persuade him to follow the example of Bobbie and also be heavenly and simple-lifey with me. I have a varied and educational programme in mind. I want to show him the convent of the English Ladies, where I finished my 'education'. It is not far from there to Hampstead Heath, where the masses wander out to snap their bits of fresh air as well.

The weather is beautiful, exaggeratedly beautiful. Gorse stretches for miles in the sunshine and we wander for miles. Neither of us has any idea where we are. We are tired enough.

At last we see an inviting inn. Strindberg, who has for some time been playing with the idea of a glass of ale, laughs delightedly over the charming name, Dickens Inn. He is laughing too soon. The giant figure of the landlord blocks up the entrance. He regards us darkly and penetratingly and then asks:

'Where did you sleep last night?'

'Where did we . . .!' I repeat, indignantly.

Strindberg stares in astonishment, first at one, then the other. He has not quite understood or did not dare to trust his ears. At last he exclaims in a half-whisper: 'What did the man say?' and I answer, abashed, in a half-whisper: 'He asked me where we slept last night.'

I had no idea and Strindberg still less, that this question, which we regard as an outrageous insult, was due merely to a legal provision. Since the sacred peace of Sunday may not be disturbed, no inn might serve a wanderer with meat and drink unless he were at least three miles removed from his legitimate home or the place where he had last spent the night. Strindberg thinks the question reflects upon our honour. His cane switches through the air. I throw myself between him and the offender just in time.

'Drunk already, first thing in the morning, you ought to be ashamed of yourself, young feller,' shouts the landlord, indignantly and slams his door in our faces.

We wander back over the heath like Adam and Eve driven out of Paradise. The earth really seems to bear thistles and thorns.

And we wander on and on, thirsty and depressed, until the streets are about us again, in the grey of the evening. One bus after another gallops invitingly past us. But every time I want to jump up, Strindberg shakes his head silently. He stands obstinately still. Agoraphobia has him in its grip again.

I prepare for a long wait and let my thoughts roam. At home on our writing-table lie drawings which he made for me the day before yesterday. He will not believe that the problem of aviation can be insoluble. Only a few days ago Leonardo da Vinci's manuscript on bird flight was sold in Paris for thirty thousand francs. Leonardo's prophetic soul had dreamed centuries ago of man's conquest of the air. Strindberg in his turn would like to build an airship. He wants it to be a one-man plane which, in the highest potency of power, would bear not only a man's body, but his very soul, his triumphant personality, rejoicing, jubilating high up. A slim shape it is to have, with delicate limbs. A little machine shall sit where the heart beats. Wings or sails. It is to rest on a great wheel of aluminium or bamboo, the wheel should start like lightning, using speed to upset gravity — until the heart sets in beating, driving forward and upward to the Sun.

Seer-poets have always been swifter than their time. Alas, that time itself takes centuries ere it produces a poet-seer, a Leonardo, a Francis Bacon, a Goethe or a Strindberg! And when at last he is born, he must learn to wait — wait — wait!

It seems an eternity before at last a four-wheeler comes crawling along. The bony old mare takes two hours to rattle us home to Pimlico.

Scarcely have we arrived home than Strindberg begins to look out once more cheerfully for his supper. Alas, the bony old nag has swallowed the last of our ready cash. I have no choice but to fetch the ill-omened cold mutton from the larder. I know exactly what will happen. And it happens. My poor husband gulps down two glasses of whisky neat, thrusts the mutton aside and goes sulkily to bed, hugging a huge astronomical tome. Soon his lamp is turned out, he is asleep, fast and sound.

The street has grown quiet. Only the staggering steps of a drunkard resound now and then on the stone pavement. The lights flicker a dirty yellow through the darkness.

It is long past midnight when Bobbie arrives. A strong scent of flowers accompanies her. Softly she opens the door. She shakes her head disapprovingly as she discovers me lying on my leopard skin on the floor of the sitting-room and pulls me up by the arm.

'Exactly what I expected, my dear, don't I know these men? Come along!'

I have to obey, otherwise she would awaken Strindberg. She has filled great vases with the lovely hothouse roses she has brought with her. She leaves me no time to wonder where they may have grown, she makes me at home in her own bed in the most motherly way.

The Irish linen is smooth and cool and perfumed. It seems like ages since such linen has fondled me. Rest . . . rest . . .

London, and the historic Thames suggested a great idea to him. He began to rummage in his 'Green Bag', this treasure-house of the notes of many years. A flood of pages and slips, observations, quotations, poured forth and provided Strindberg with the material for a new kind of history of the world.

Once before he had shaken the spirit and form used up to now by historians. That had been in 1882, when, in the *History of the Swedish People*, he produced not a chronicle of rulers but the story of the evolution of the race. He had illumined things from below, instead of looking down upon them from above in the customary fashion. He had taken the masses for his hero. This time, however, he went further and what he attempted to link up was two worlds, so far considered isolated. He took hold of history as no one had ever done before — as a result of natural laws. A Conscious Will is apparent and this Will — Strindberg is the first to perceive it — this Will favours certain repetitions and correlations. One might call it a law of the series.[1]

He worked feverishly. Page after page glided full from his pen, one monolith piled upon the other. His prophetic vision roamed from past to future.

[1] When I met Dr. Paul Kämmerer, the author of *The Law of the Series*, in 1924, he acknowledged that Strindberg had set up his theory twenty years before and had worked it out on several occasions.

Strindberg certainly had the right to demand peace and quiet, and it was the only thing in the world which he did demand. But everyday life would grant him none. There was no protection from the noise of the traffic, from the disgusting stenches of the street market, no protection from the dusty heat, no protection from me. The being together, which should have been happiness, had become torture, being forced upon us. He was crushed by my continual presence. I felt ashamed of existing every time I caught his reproachful glance, seeking in vain the concentration only solitude can bring. I was continually set thinking of a story by Gogol. A bachelor has a dream on the eve of his wedding. He dreams that he is already married and sees his wedded home and his wife in it. He sees her everywhere. He looks at the bed, there lies his wife. He goes to the table, there sits his wife. He opens the cupboard, his wife springs out of it into his arms. He draws out his handkerchief to wipe the sweat of fear from his brow — his wife slips out of his pocket. I feel as if I were this appallingly ubiquitous wife. But how am I to get rid of myself?

Our money no longer suffices to buy mutton for us two. After a desolate lunch, rendered still more desolate by the fact that, in order to save, I pretended to have already eaten, he pushed back his chair silently and reached for his hat. Outside the heat was tropical. I was afraid for him and followed him into the street. He was like one who seeks liberation at any price. We wandered aimlessly through the blazing sunshine. I did not dare to speak to him, but merely sneaked along beside him. I sneaked like a shadow. I was the only shadow there, however.

We got as far as Chelsea — wherever is he going? I asked myself. Heaven! — Cheyne Row — surely not to that martyr, Carlyle. He walks past 'Number 5' without thinking of Jane . . . On, on, till he finds a place along the embankment which is open to the water. He steps down to the edge — only when I grasp him by the arm does he turn about, unresisting, hopelessly weary. Thus he goes slowly, with dragging feet, homeward through back streets, without a word.

In the evening he went to bed early, still silent. Silently I cuddled up to him, comfortingly. Hour by hour passed away. His eyes were closed, but I felt that he was peeping, lying in ambush. I dared no longer breathe. At last he fell asleep. His breast rose and sank, painfully restless, he moaned. Then, suddenly, he spread out his arms with a powerful, voluptuous thrust, pushing me aside like a swimmer joyfully cutting through the waves, setting everything aside and suffering no hindrance. And now all was peace and relaxation.

Quietly, without waking him, I stole out of bed.

Next morning, we kissed each other tenderly, as if nothing had happened. He looked refreshed after his sleep, chatted pleasantly and went for his walk as usual. Scarcely was he round the corner, however, than I caught up my possessions helter-skelter, the faithful leopard-skin, all the lace I had, dresses and linen. I threw all these worldly goods into our portmanteau and, heavily burdened, I hurried out. I went blindly in the direction of the shops. I did not have far to seek. At one of the next street-corners the longed-for word 'Pawnbroker' confronted me. As usual in England, the business had two entrances, an elegant, broad one looking on the street, for English pawnbrokers are jewellers, dealers in antiques, gunsmiths, anything you like, for the rich. For those in need of cash, there is a discreet side entrance round the corner, and secret separate cabins. The pawnbroker considered me and my wares with an indifferent eye. He was used to better things and interested only in jewels, old silver or fine porcelain. My possessions did not impress him.

He did not want to take them. But after listening to my urgent prayers, he, as a sympathetic gentleman, gave me five pounds for the lot, including my wedding ring. I believe I told him, in my panic, that my husband must get to the Continent.

I have never felt so immeasurably rich as at that moment when I emerged from the private cabin, minus lace, fur and wedding ring — but with a whole five pounds in my pocket. For now August Strindberg could get away from London, away from this heat, away from the strange writing-desk, from roast mutton, from the double bed — and from me.

We decided that he should go that very same night by steamer back to Hamburg, close to where our friend, the Danish poet, Holger Drachmann, was living. Drachmann was a genius, in finding money. From there he should proceed to the Island of Rügen, which faced Sweden. Paul, the novelist Tavastierna, and other Scandinavians spent the summer there in Sellin. It was green and cool and he would be among friends.

I kissed him out in the street in front of everybody, although one should not and does not do this in England——
But as I lay, comfortable and cool, with plenty of room to spare, alone in the double bed that night, I wept bitterly.

It was our first parting!

VIII

SELLIN ON RÜGEN AND LONDON
July 1893

HIGH SEAS

(Excerpts from Letters and a Diary)

August to Freda Strindberg   *On board ship*
       Sunday night, 8.15

'. . . A heavy sea, as scribble shows. What are you doing? What are your thoughts? To me all things, past and present, merge like a dream and life makes me sick although the sea does not. What tortures me most? That I should have dragged you, dear Girl, into my misery as well. Had you not troubles enough of your own?

'We shall not be in Hamburg until five o'clock to-morrow afternoon.

'What a Sunday I went through! And you?

'You cried, yesterday! Yes, cry! There's no cause for laughing for the present. It was not London alone nor the heat that weighed on me. I daresay it was something else as well. Farewell, *sans Adieu* — Your August.'

*

From Freda's Diary

Thank God, he is sheltered now with the friends in Sellin. It took him eight days to get there, the time it took him in lucky days to write a play. But what good would his staying here have done? No one knows yet, that they have need of us.

And yet I feel it — London has unlimited possibilities. Am I in love with London? I believe so. A new art is stirring, a cry for modernity rings out, but what fascinates me is not its art, but the world that bears it. I often forget that I have a task and only want to drink of London!

*

August Strindberg, Sellin on the Isle of Rügen, to Freda Strindberg, London

'Rügen at last! Where I flung myself head first into the sea to drown my black devils but only half succeeded. Now, to-day, Sunday evening, June 25th, I receive your letters, full of love and tears! My heart aches at the thought of you worrying about me — old good-for-nothing that I am, who eat, sleep and vagabondize with not even enough energy to earn a serious living. What crushes me is the fear that I over-estimated myself when I married you and that — sooner or later — I may leave you in want. I lack hope, and a choking lethargy benumbs my soul, which sinketh into sleep. Maybe I am exhausted by excessive work, sorrow and care. My spring love (*Seconda Primavera* — oh!) shook me awake for a while. But the past sends ghosts, to sow dissension in my life.

'The dread of the future haunts me, and I no longer have the energy to reach out my hand for the fruit which must be waiting ripe after so many years of struggle.

'Just now I am possessed by Natural Science and cannot concentrate upon *les belles lettres*, nor upon my theatrical affairs.

'Here everything is quiet, the sea, the woods, men — even femininity. Everything except myself. What are you doing? How are you? . . . .

'*Au revoir*! But when? — August.'

'Were this cursed summer but at an end, with its suicidal mania and lethargy. I must descend from Laplanders, for I cannot bear the heat.

'This is a d——d watering place, with clothes-changing three times a day and roulette tables. Bad and expensive. And Paul will leave soon, the only being with whom I could speak Swedish and who would lend me a hand.

'Can I be with you soon? I am nervous here. Every day and every night a storm, once the lightning struck close to me. Since then I live in fear, not of death, but of the agony preceding it. . . .'

'Your letters cross and contradict and, owing to irregular delivery, arrive pell-mell. I do not understand the last one . . .

'On my arrival in Sellin I still had forty marks. That's all. But I do not understand what you write about sending money. Are you supposed to support me? I should say no and beg you to keep the hundred marks which are due from Finland.[1] Paul has sold my "Toadstool" to a rich collector, Dahlberg, for that sum. I myself am expecting a little from Sweden and Denmark.

'Was it not one of the motives of my departure, that I did not want to be a burden to you? For the moment I am provided for and have not borrowed any money.

'Tired and dispirited as I am, my life is rather devoid of joys.

'And you mean to stay on through the whole of August? What a feast for scandalmongers. All right, if you wish it: but what about the consequences?

'I am so spoilt by the habit of speaking to you that I cannot write any more. Pen and ink disgust me. I feel landed in a blind alley, with no way out.

'I finished the paper on sulphur yesterday and sent it to Berlin.'

---

[1] Dahlberg, a rich Finn, contemplated buying a painting by August Strindberg, 'The Toadstool', for 100 marks. Fairy gold. It never materialized, but floated on the horizon for months, radiant, and encouraging: in all moments of pressure, Strindberg saw it shining and disposed of it as a life-belt for my benefit.

'What it is that ails me I could not say, but I live only one-half of life. Do what you like, but do not be cruel! Let me, if possible, come back and join you, but not in London. There's danger for me.

'I am sick of soul. Renewed contact with my country, with the past! And you far off! I live in anguish and dread that we may never see one another again.

'Dreams, bad dreams! Am expecting every possible misfortune!

'Am writing all day long for the "Green Bag" as eagerly as though it were my last will.

'Don't know, but it seems to me I have lost you! Let me soon have a good word from you.'

'You write me a furious letter, then you beg forgiveness and withdraw your senseless accusations. All at once there comes another letter, with fierce reproaches because I have not replied. I cannot quarrel by post. And I don't want to.

'Two days without news from you. Yet I do not scold, because the post may have miscarried, or perhaps you are tired or have no news to tell — like me. . . .'

*

From Freda's Diary

Things must change for the better now. Heinemann has come home from Naples. He only went there to meet the novelist Matilda Serao. If he goes so far just for Matilda's sake, how far must he not go for love of a Strindberg?

He is a man of the world, keen, young, easily enthusiastic. Speaks tenderly of his authors, like a bibliophile of his shelves. Very distinguished, almost blushes at the word 'Money'. But he is by no means reckless. Closely observed, he even seems a most careful gentleman. Of course, he is ambitious and broadly hints at a tenderness between himself and *eine neue Kunst*; but he commits no indiscretion; they have progressed no further than Ibsen and have remained obviously platonic — quite platonic.

If only Ibsen does not block our way here, too! I begin to fear as much, at Heinemann's embarrassed hesitation:

'The time has not yet come for a Strindberg edition . . . It is much too early . . . Strindberg must first have a big stage success in England!'

Nevertheless, he seemed neither astonished nor displeased when I retorted with an engaging smile:

'Create one for him — you!'

He has invited me to lunch. This — contrary to Europe, is not in the least objectionable here.

*

August Strindberg, Sellin on Rügen, to Freda Strindberg, London

'Things seem to be shaping well and I am preparing twelve lectures for the Humboldt Academy, Berlin, on the "Philosophy of Chemistry". I am working hard and have come close to the solution of the problem (you know which). Adieu, Literature, therefore, and welcome, Science!'

*

'This is a nice sort of marriage at a distance. See this postcard, with Heligoland on it? That was a different story! But seriously, things cannot go on like this.

'Your good news cannot cheer me up. I am so depressed that I no longer dare to hope. Paul is leaving soon, then I shall be quite alone. And alone I feel everywhere and ever without you.'

*

'Either I must go to Europe, or you must come here. It means Life itself, our whole future, and I don't give a hang for the honour of being played in London. The old suicidal mania has come back, life is so repellent to me that I can take no food. On top of it, the ugly rumours about us keep on growing. People are asking themselves, "What's that . . .?

Married seven weeks and already parted . . .?" Be careful.
A whole life of discord for so little? Put matters straight,
otherwise the avalanche will kill us.'

The glass terrace of the Savoy Hotel looks out upon the
Embankment, close to Cleopatra's Needle, which comes all
the way from Egypt. The surroundings have their effect
upon us. Everything is carefree and my own girlish spirit
comes back. The big restaurant, full of handsome, well-
dressed people, the broad river on its way to the shoreless sea,
the Serpent of the Nile, Shakespeare, music. . . .

Out of the champagne sparkles forth an inspiration. I
suddenly begin to improvise. Why should not our Strindberg Theatre rise out of the big stage success which Heinemann is to create for Strindberg? It may come up against
hindrances in Berlin, but it could be done — and that
infinitely better — in London. The machine exists already.
Grein has set the wheel turning. We only need to give Grein
a chance. Then the 'Independent Theatre' would suddenly
transform itself into a Strindberg Theatre. Strindberg as
playwright and scenic reformer, Grein as a directing manager
and Heinemann's publishing house backing it — that would
be a 'triumvirate' sure to carry off the victory.

It will not be my fault if it does not come about. Empires
were made and shattered, so say the historians, because
Cleopatra's nose was exactly the right length. Mine certainly
cannot rival hers, either in beauty or size — but my ambitions
are so much more humble and legitimate. So I begin to un-
fold my theatrical dreams just as they rush to my mind, and
keep harping obstinately upon that Strindberg Theatre,
although the much embarrassed Heinemann tries to distract
my attention and tells me a hundred anecdotes with this end
in view. The anecdotes are quite amusing. He knows the
whole town and means to introduce me, should I desire, to
every lion, from Herbert Tree to Bakunin. He says neither

'yes' nor 'no' to my proposals, yet he has invited me to lunch again, the day after to-morrow, although as an honest gambler, I have warned him that I shall not spare him the theatre. Nor shall I spare it him. Love of the stage is burning in my blood now. Has it not been my secret wish since childhood, to become an actress?

August Strindberg, Sellin, to Freda Strindberg, London

'Madame Tavastierna arrives here on August 1st and then I must leave. To go where?

'Where is there a spot for me in this accursed world, where the brutes feed on the choice morsels and intellectuals die of want?

'I feel at times as if we were never again to set eyes upon one another. Why? What — I could not say. Our farewell in London was so sad, so full of sombre forebodings. The old suicidal mania haunts me. I long to leave earth and find peace.

'For others that might possibly mean a loss. Not for myself. And I feel that you too, want to get rid of me . . . You want me to desert you, else you would be here long since!'

'As to my demanding an advance payment from the "Bureau", this crime was committed in prehistoric ages. Besides I owned up to you and you merely forgot it in our love-drunkenness. Enough of that.'

'It is possible that my sulphur will summon me to Berlin. A chemical expert read it in the manuscript, enraptured.

'No other news. No money. Dahlberg has stopped buying pictures. Nothing doing.

'I await particulars about the plays which might be considered for London and about the theatres.'

'Nothing new, not the tiniest little thing. Neither from Neumann nor from Dahlberg. I want to know in what magazine the "French Peasants" will appear and whether in their entirety. I now await with increasing impatience the verdict of the authorities on my paper on sulphur. It may cause a change in my life within the next week or so.

'I do beg of you so to word your postcards that they do not expose us to general derision. — And be careful, do not travel *via* Hamburg. One can never be sure whether the cholera is not there, and you know, quarantine. . . . Especially when things are as they are. Adieu, — August.'

*

From Freda's Diary

What has stepped between us?

I write to him so often, so much, and yet I cannot tell him. — This giant city is a new world.

Rich restaurants, caviare, champagne, the smiling Egyptian, — at home, dry bread for which I pay, confectioning hats for Bobbie and the not yet 'arrived' young actresses of the Independent Theatre to whom kind Bobbie kindly sells them. Viennese *chic* which strikes the poor girls as profitably sensational in my make. I am no longer my father's daughter, I am a daughter of Eve now — that is all. It does not frighten me though, it rather tempts me to find out now what I myself am worth . . . If only there were not the anxiety . . . the fear which I cannot explain . . . Always his strange ideas . . . 'I feel as though you wanted to get rid of me . . . You want me to abandon you' . . . In writing thus, is he suggesting to me thoughts and wishes which are in me, but which I do not yet know about?

He wants me to join him. How can I? — Does he not understand that one may found a theatre, but not have the money for a railway fare? — He obviously does not, and he sees it as though our separation was my fault and wish. Does he perhaps wish it to be my wish? Does he hate me so much already that he is looking out for some good cause to hate me? Does his love need hatred as a food? Good Heavens! Have I grown mistrustful, like him . . . Am I stealing his thoughts now? Is he absorbing mine?

He has turned into a business man — all at once.

He forbids me the innocent pet names which so far he has himself patronized and used with delight . . . with which he has himself inaugurated all his letters and postcards up to now . . . Why, all of a sudden?

Now, in spite of the heat, he wants to go to Berlin. Why? In order to be near Rügen. Why? Is the reason called Madame Tavastierna . . .? He was in love with her a year ago, when he was a bachelor . . . He is a bachelor again . . . Is that . . . why?

*

I have been to a few Ibsen performances, Elizabeth Robins playing the lead. She is an American, a thought too literary, perhaps too honest for the world of illusion; but with talent and a superb stage presence. Would be the thing for us. A pity that Ibsen fills up her horizon. Really touching, to what dimensions she expands the artful old gentleman. In *Rosmersholm*, for instance, her long, sensitive fingers clutch a delicate, endlessly long Shetland shawl, which flows disembodied down her long, slender limbs and billows round her feet in a foamy, symbolic, white misty cloud. Illusion! There is no such long Shetland shawl cloud in good old Ibsen. And there is no such shawl in the whole of Norway, much less in a parsonage. Even the most modern Norwegian temptress cannot treat herself to such things, on account of the import duties. The shawl is tremendously effective, but it belongs to Miss Robins and to her alone. She has superimposed it upon Ibsen; it draws its decorative length through her whole conception. Why does she play Ibsen and not Strindberg? Or buy a hat?

I feel like a Nabob, but with bewitched treasures. All around me, they cry for jewels! I offer them . . . and no one sees them in my hands.

Bobbie points out a lean gentleman in the dress circle. George Bernard Shaw . . . 'The coming man,' Strindberg had said, approvingly. At the first glance I merely notice his companion, the most beautiful woman I ever saw. Comes from *Outre Mer*, Bobbie explains. The Virgin forests might account for her. Has travelled *via* Paris, though: she was a friend of Victorien Sardou, Bobbie whispers — now she sits close to Bernard Shaw. Quite a career. Shaw looks like a Whistler harmony in reddish brown. Hair, beard, eyebrows and eyes, all neatly matched. From the chin down, one tone lighter, marron Stuttgart, pure Gustav Jaeger wool. But what a vitality, what eyes! Strindberg radiates, Shaw sparkles.

He comes up to greet Bobbie, but takes no notice of me, in spite of Strindberg. He seems to know that genius occasionally also stoops. To be quite frank, I never altogether understood Strindberg's selecting me, either.

This would be funny enough, and not a bit depressing, if I did not myself experience sometimes this Shetland shawl mania for enlargement, when confronted with nebulous white Nordic horses.

*

August, Sellin, to Freda Strindberg, London

'I have just received your superb letter and rejoice for you, young and ambitious as you are, that you have found an opportunity of using your vitality and talents. But why such a sharp, arrogant tone? I had asked you amicably not to put on postcards pet names fit only for intimacy. That was all and now you openly hand me my dismissal, the moment you appear to have achieved an imaginary success. It is indeed a trifle early to cast me on the rubbish heap and my disgust of life and man increases.

'I forgive you, because I love you and I am ready to return to England as soon as we can lay hands on the necessary money, subject to the conditions that my person be not involved in any theatrical business. . . .'

'I do not feel joyous and your letter of to-day does not promise me the conjugal happiness of which I had dreamed.'

'What are you afraid of? Don't you know that when I love, I willingly allow myself to be maltreated and that there is no end to my patience? I am not surprised that you should feel your nerves in such a hellish heat; but if you do not write at once to Mitzi and borrow money, then I shall.

'You must come here to give me courage. I am so paralysed that I cannot even write a letter, and no letters, no money. . . .'

'So we cannot exist without one another — well and good. The bond is there and one must be careful so as not to grow to hate the bond. If these five cursed weeks have taught us nothing else, at least they put us to a test — and with results.

'I cannot deny that in Heligoland and England I at your side often felt as if in Huldra's spell and you were often cruel as a loving woman is who knows herself beloved.

'You began to despise me as soon as I was weak, that is when I gave way to you, as a lover does. And you hated me when I revolted. And like the majority of girls, you were at times obsessed by the idea that I had not married you for love, but for reasons of utility. Already in Gravesend, I forewarned you. Do not let us be too intimate! To search and probe too much in one another's soul is bad, especially when two souls as strong as ours have met. I gave you more personal freedom than you gave me. You wanted to influence my writing, there were even symptoms that you wanted to degrade me into a commercial farce-writer. And you tried to persuade yourself that I was pretty stupid, more or less a fool. But that I understood, because I understand nearly everything — it was your fight for your ego. You crave power in small matters far more than I do. But no more of it. . . .

'Let us start all over again, wiser by experience.

'I shall be with you in a week's time, I hope, but not in London.'

'Is our position so very dreadful, I ask myself in a quiet moment? Why, you have done colossal business with my manuscripts, you say?

'I myself expect from Christiania and from Stockholm altogether 500 marks.

'No, I believe the disharmony is in ourselves. At first, when you cold-bloodedly transformed the two weeks' separation into six, I thought you had wearied of me and I tried to save myself by bravado, to eclipse you by my scientific research. It succeeded for the moment and I submerged myself in the profoundest problems, so that the 'Green Bag' has got a horrid paunch now. But then — there came an emptiness and a despair so intense that nothing any longer counts.

'I reproach myself with all that you have suffered through me. The past rises up, the lovely unforgettable hours in the Linden Hotel and the sad ones — and I fret my heart out.

'You took pity upon me, and for a loving woman it is only a step from pity to contempt. This caused the lack of harmony. I am over-sensitive as a result of intellectual strain, sorrow and care, and your absence depresses and tortures me. When I shall have escaped from this hell and when we shall have found each other again, I shall look back on these five weeks as the most cruel I ever went through. . . .

'Do you still believe that we shall be happy and, loving one another, be able to take up the battle against poverty?

'Believe me, I am almost at the end of my tether! And I have no faith in your riches! Forgive me and let us re-unite, soon, soon again.'

'So alone as I am, a stranger everywhere — and you write me fairy tales of "father and mother" who love me? — My most haunting fear is the return of the past. There is a dream the most horrible of all — the attic coming back. "Back, back, up under the roof!" I crawl, crawl into exhaustion up the stairs and then I am up there once more, back again. And there stands the old Mademoiselle of my young days, already waiting. She had warned me: "Do not do it, do not do it!" But it was done! And then it came as come it must! Back once more, back!

'Oh! how I suffer in my dreams!

'I begin to long for death. But I do not want to die alone. Near you and in your arms — Not here all alone!

'Had we not vowed never to leave one another! And yet it came to pass so soon!'

HELP!

Freda Strindberg, London, to Max Burckhard, Manager of the Imp. Royal Hofburg Theater, Vienna

'Dear, kind friend: We pay for everything on earth, but most heavily for the good we do and wish. So I write to-day to make you pay for the thousand wishes you sent me at my wedding. You graciously said I had been a nice girl and would be a good wife. Alas, I was not a nice girl at all and that may be the reason why I find it so hard to be a good wife, much as I want to. A good wife smoothes her husband's path, removes the stones which lie on his road and I — I can't — unless you help me. Do help me, I beg, do help me!

'Listen, we are obviously *mal vus* in Germany just now (his first marriage, you know, and the book about it). In order to rehabilitate us, you will have to play Strindberg at the Burg Theater, or at least pretend that you are going to. Our lives depend on it. You may do so without the slightest danger of being daring.

'Strindberg has a drama which is not only respectable, but religious. It teaches Faith. The real Faith, in God and our own work.

'Do accept it for production and if you absolutely cannot, then spread all the more violently in the papers the rumour that you are going to. Somebody else is sure then to produce it, and in that case we can dispense with you, dear Sir.

'Now as to my personal news. I am a grass widow and have started as a promoter.

'On account of the heat and the unsalted diet here, Strindberg was severely attacked by reform ideas and wanted to originate an Art Theatre in Berlin, amateurism rising above the professional humdrum, eager students, talented wayward Delilahs; painters who would not use colours, but lights, screens and curtains — in short, all that's needed to put new life into the adored old thing. Strangely enough, I fancied one could give birth to it better here — and now I want to bring this about. England is asleep as a rule, but when she does take a leap, she jumps with a bound over all obstacles. We are guests of an admirable young enthusiast, who wants the good and the new, but has just arrived — at Ibsen. I lunch once or twice a week with a young publisher; he wants the good and the new, but has just arrived — at Ibsen. The two men would be a power. I want to become the missing link between them. Failing such a link, they probably will never fuse. But if they do, they will reach up to Strindberg. London will have an event, we our daily bread, which up to now is non-existent.

'So while my godly spouse sits in Rügen, I sit here, fabricate hangman's wit (God help me) and take an oath every morning in my bath that I will rather drown in it than cross the seas again without gold and laurels.

'Now you know my part — and yours. That I have stage fright as "the good wife" you have no doubt perceived. Yes, I have most dreadful stage fright! Please take me by the hand and prompt me with my cue: "Don't be frightened — I am here!" As soon as I hear these words from you, I shall take courage. I need it. I thank you for it in advance! Ever your Freda.'

Freda Strindberg, London, to Maria Uhl, Mondsee

'Dearest: No, no, no, Don't be afraid! I give you my word of honour, I am not amusing myself. Fear whatever you like, but not that I am having a pleasant moment. I am simply trying to be a man, as far as that is any good. But — you must now help me, mother. I want you to fulfil your own dearest wish — to meet your great son at last. Ah, that I could have taken him to you myself, it is not possible. He is half way already, in Germany, and I must stay here firm, to look after our interests. He is a racehorse, I draw the plough. Don't be shocked; we are not upsetting the order of nature, I am trying to find it out and follow it. Mother, I am roasting here, Strindberg must not roast with me — you understand. Invite him to Mondsee, at your quickest and nicest, his address is Sellin auf Rügen — Mondsee is cool and care-free. I know, you won't let him wait. See that he gets there before father does. You will be having wonderful times. The chance may not come again, be quick. There's nothing in the world I beg of you so much, and there is nothing you will so much enjoy. It must be. He cannot come here. Because of the heat, you know, that terrible heat. And all the people here speak English, except him! — I kiss you a thousand times, and please embrace my old nurse Resi, and our dog, and the

lake — every big and every little thing — I love you all,
Oh, so dearly! F.'

August, Sellin, to Freda Strindberg, London

'You are surprised that after mating the bird no longer
sings. There you are wrong, for that is the way of things.
As for myself, when everyone else thinks the sun is
shining, I see only the clouds in the sky and feel the coming
lightning.

'This is the position: the mother of my children is in
want and demands for the little ones the 500 M. I owe
her.

'In Sweden a low-class paper has pirated the *Plaidoyer* and
published it under the pretence that it is German literature
and unprotected. The whole country is convulsed with
rage and shame — and rightly. Thus cursed by everyone,
I cannot return home again for years to come. My Stockholm
publisher maintains a menacing silence.

'What right have I to call you my wife, if I cannot support
you and am on the point of letting you support me?

'As long as we were using your father's money, I did not
mind, for that belonged to us both. But after that?

'What a position for me to be in!

'Is it not enough to stupefy a man? And yet you threaten
to leave me alone. That is the worst madness of all! But I no
longer wonder at anything! I have tasted every sorrow life
can inflict . . . !'

'Freda, it will not do for us to live apart! Everything has
got into a muddle! You blame me wrongly for negligence in
letter writing; I blame you. And neither is at fault.

'I did not write to you such lots because I did not want to
sadden you with my worries. What have you to do with my
children, why should I bother you, and so on.

"Come here and see if I do not love you, which is rather difficult to prove in writing.

'I love you, *je t'aime*, these are phrases, but to love one another — that is worth while! Oh, you little sheepkin!'

Freda Strindberg, London, to her friend, May T., Berlin

'. . . What have I to do with his children — ? O, the misery of it! Does he really believe that I have not known for a long while that he is devoured with longing for his babies? He could live without a woman, but not without a child. He is tied to his children as the child to the mother by the umbilical cord. I remember how he once said jokingly that only the man felt true maternal love. However that may be, he feels it.

'Here matters continue a steady course towards success. Heinemann begins to look less at me and more into the future — he is thinking of our theatre quite seriously by now.

'But can he help us as long as Strindberg is forced to deny himself his one great longing for his children? There is only one who can help — She, whose place I occupy — their mother!

'Will she? . . . Perhaps . . . She must know him — She has lived with him for thirteen years . . . all I go through now, she has gone through . . . She must know . . . just as I know now. We are not rivals . . . We are sisters, sharing the same grief! Shall not the one give help where the other fails in strength? I can save us all if they will only assist me now.

'My brother-in-law, Oscar, is the trustee of the children. I must write to him. He must beg the mother to let us have one of the babes — just one!

'In the meantime I sit and write to Strindberg . . . in the morning, at noon, in the evening, at night. Now I beg him to come back, now I advise him to go to Mondsee to my parents . . . but again and again I implore him to keep up courage — courage . . . On my knees I beg of him not to lose courage and to believe in me.'

August Strindberg, Sellin, to Freda Strindberg, London

'Dearest dear: I read your last beautiful letter, again and again. You are sad, dear child, you too! And now that I see no way to you, I am desperate. I do believe you love me and I do love you and yet we are parted.

'You think I want to go to Mondsee by myself?

'No! I only want to be where you are, but not in Fairmantle House.

'Love me always and I will try to live — August.'

August Strindberg, Sellin, to Maria Weyr, Mondsee

'Dear Mitzi: At the risk of falling into disgrace with my beloved Freda and being held in contempt by my parents in Austria, I have decided to write this letter:

'This is how things stand:

'After a month of happiness in Heligoland, we conceived the idea of going to England to prepare the soil for my plays. Freda, Mistress of the Exchequer (probably up in the clouds of our married bliss) assured me that our means permitted the journey; and so we set off.

'In England we fell into the hands of honourable robbers and a month later found ourselves stranded high and dry.

'Unable to speak the language of the country and depressed by the great city and the overpowering heat (besides other evils) I was attacked by a general nausea and on the verge of real illness.

'We therefore decided that I should leave in advance for Rügen and engage our rooms for the summer. Freda was to follow me in a week or two. But instead of herself, letters arrive from Freda which revolve round a theatrical venture too grandiose to be at all likely. And she demands six weeks to get that in order. I have been waiting dolefully for a whole frightful month and suffering hell from loneliness — with the result that she now announces her firm resolve to stay a whole year in London and wants me to come to London too.

'To speak frankly, it would not matter to me whether I live in London or anywhere else, but I fear that Freda has fallen into the clutches of clever adventurers.

'At any rate, and to crown our misfortunes, I myself have had no luck, on the contrary, I have been dogged by misfortune. Unable to write, in despair over our parting, I have neglected my finances and suspect that Freda has had no luck either in her speculations with my manuscripts.

'I am expecting money from Sweden and Norway, but the publishers are asleep or gone on a holiday, thanks to the dog days that are holding every country in their grip — and I can wait no longer.

'Forgive us our youthfulness and foolishness and come to our rescue, if you can! I am mortally ashamed, but the position is insufferable. Set me free from this prison and let me go and look for my little lost sheep. If there are 500 marks to be had on earth, beloved sister, get hold of them for me, and I swear to you never again to reckon with castles in the air.

'I own up that we are both of us a little crazy, but we are honest, we love one another and the future will be ours.

'I kiss your hands and beg you to embrace your parents for me.

'Do not betray a word to Freda, it would cost me my happiness — your brother in spite of all — August.

'PS. Freda tells me that she has "placed" my manuscripts for fabulous monetary results.'

August, Sellin, to Freda Strindberg, London

'Dear, dear child: After I had emptied suffering to the very dregs, energy returned to me for a few moments, and now we may hope anew.

'I hope to hold you in my arms in a week at latest. Oh! Now I live again! And, re-arisen from the grave, I want to live!

'To our meeting! And love me! — Thine. August.'

*

TWO WOMEN

I am madly happy, since his last letter came —— I almost cry for joy, I am so happy —— In a week's time.

If only a mad outbreak of mine does not ruin it all!

In my last letter, in a wild fit of jealousy (poor Mme T!) I flew out at him and brutally tore open his wounds. I could have killed him — for not writing every day. This jealousy of mine is like a blind drunkenness, a savage greed. It had no cause. The post may have been careless — or somebody else had been — but he was not to blame: now his letters of various dates arrive by the same delivery. He wrote! He loves me and thinks of no one else. That is the only thing that matters.

I have hurriedly wired him not to read that angry letter. In my wrath I had treated him to insults his worst enemy would not have used. The telegram will surely come too late. Then I, who would give anything to help him, shall have made his life still harder.

But he will forgive me again. We always forgive each other. And then he will come. He *shall* come. He *must*. Thank Heaven, money for the journey is at last on its way. How glad I am that he does not want to go alone to Mondsee.

What a heap of contradictions! I do want to know him safe with my father — and yet it would have broken my heart if he had gone there without me. Now I shall quickly look for quarters ... In the Swedish colony on Putney Heath. ...

*

Maria Uhl, Mondsee, to August Strindberg, Rügen

'My darling new son, sprung from the heart of my child: Cross yourself, to be sure, but do not be alarmed, it is only your new mother sending you greeting (Mother-in-law is a hateful name and is not to be uttered); greeting you for the particular purpose of inviting you in the very heartiest, friendliest and happiest fashion to visit your new parents.

'She, your little wife, in overflowing fullness of love, has suggested it to us: "Ask him to come," said she, "now is your one great chance."

'With what rapture did we hear these words. Dear, beloved August Strindberg, come to us, come to your home, give us this pleasure, do us this honour. Your new father is longing for your genius, I to soothe your wounded and bleeding heart, we want to take possession of our property, each after their own manner. Come and stay as long as you like and as it pleases you. It is lovely here and your love of nature and art will be satisfied. You need bring no further luggage, only some volumes of Strindberg — and come at once.

'On August 1st, father Uhl will presumably arrive, you could easily be here too by then if you would.

'Make haste, do your packing and a pleasant journey and joyous arrival at the House of Uhl — Mama.'

AND A MAN

Freda Strindberg, London, to Adolf Paul, Rügen

'Dear Adolf Paul: I hear from you to my consternation that August has gone off to my family in Mondsee, after leaving me without news for a week . . . I am worried. I had hoped to adjust matters here, but now I no longer see any hope, any way out for him—for I do not understand anything any more — Freda Strindberg.'

*

From Adolf Paul's 'Memories'

'I accompanied him as far as Putbus. And there, for the first time since he came to Rügen, he was his old self again. His good spirits, joyousness, optimism and love of adventure had all come back. The world lay open before him once more, hell had spewed him out upon a green meadow lush with flowers. Around him birds were singing, the heavens were blue, it was blossoming, sweet-scented summer. His soul could lift its pinions again and soar towards the sun.

He took long breaths like a man who had escaped happily from a great danger, made fun, laughed, was in his gayest mood and had recovered his old high spirits and his light and graceful wit — and his trust in fate and in humanity. The radiance of the joy of life gleamed about him, like the last red glow of the sinking day, when the sun slants once more through the clouds. And there was hearty friendship in his voice, as he gave me his hand in farewell — Adolf Paul.'

MONDSEE AND LONDON

August 1893

SPIRITUAL EXERCISE

THE first news of him that reaches me in London, after a week of torturing silence, is lovingly worded on a coloured picture postcard:

'Greetings from *Schafberg* (Sheep's Mount).'

It causes a noticeable atmospheric cooling-off in Warwick Street, Pimlico. I retaliate:

'Dear August: Best thanks to the *Schafberg* for his kind greetings. Your arrival, however, might have come about without so much secrecy and so many falsehoods.

'I need a few days' quiet and am going — for the present — to my convent in Hampstead. Best wishes. — Freda.'

'Dear Freda: Just received your letter. You write in a way that almost drives me wild... "Falsehoods and secrecy!"

'You urge me to go to Mondsee. I do go, and you scold me for obeying you! You write to your mother that you are going into a convent — (because I abandoned you?) — Isn't it enough to drive a man crazy? — August.'

Quite so. I have gone to the convent. Not in order to escape from marriage, though, but to find my way in it.

To-day I am resting under a big shady tree, searching for knowledge. I admit it is not the Biblical apple tree, only an English pear tree, but that makes no difference. I had rested under precisely the same tree once before already, as a school-girl, four years ago, and then, too, I had been meditating. I had sought Faith at that time and read Chateaubriand's *Génie du Christianisme*. To-day I cogitate over *le génie, tout court* — I am seeking Love. Then I devoured huge quantities of pears, for they were forbidden and that was tempting. To-day I am satisfied to lie in the shade and dream. Married life prevents dreaming.

The tree stands in Maiden Lane, in the garden of the English Ladies. I finished my so-called education under them; it was in their convent that I tried to build up a pious conception of the world. Now my adored Mother Superior, Sister Theresa, has again offered me the old shelter. The house is empty during the Summer holidays; the sisters are at the Mother House, in Ascot. Sister Theresa and I are alone. She finds this is the time for a spiritual exercise, the time to meditate over God and man, Strindberg and myself.

She is right. It is time for me to think.

But does one think here? The grass is soft and cool. There is the hum of a thousand voices. The sun has drawn a veil across its face, so as not to scorch.

Out of the chapel sounds the organ, singing of Love to God. Sister Theresa is playing. She has sacrificed her whole life; she will never belong to a man, never bear a child. Has she paid too dearly? . . . Does one ever pay too dearly?

I fondle the grass, breathe in the earth, which is perfumed with sunlight. My resistance is gone.

'Now, my child,' asks Sister Theresa, some time later, 'Have you meditated?'

'I have been listening to you, Sister — You were playing "God is Love". I can think of nothing, I know nothing, I understand nothing; and I would like to stay with you a few days more, think of nothing, seek nothing, wish for nothing. Then I too might know.'

'That is the way to Faith,' says the Sister.

'But can one live on Faith — in the holy state of marriage,

when there are two?' I ask, without any connection, half crying, half luxuriously resting. 'Can one have three rooms, which one needs, and two beds, which one must have, and enough to eat and drink and just as much nearness and just as much distance as is essential? Does Faith supply all that?'

'True faith builds towers', she comforts me and dries my tears in her motherly way.

What did Strindberg quote to me one day from Buckle, the historian:

'The spiritual also obeys the laws of Nature. All so-called spiritual qualities spring in the end from a material source and chemical relationships are just as spiritual as the sympathies of souls. Only knowledge can enlighten man. And the simple-minded or ignorant can only do harm with their morality, their charity, their protectiveness.'

I consider this. Yes, that goes down to the roots of our marriage, too . . . One must know. In men of genius the genius and the man are two different persons. They are a double personality, and the one watches and vivisects the other while burning in the flames — a willing-unwilling, ecstatic self-immolation. As the two distinct and different persons that they are, each selects a woman according to his needs. The genius needs an unceasing, never-resting storm, but the man, whose entire energy the genius devoured, needs the protective spirit of a mother, that she may dry his moist brows and give him rest. August Strindberg lost his own mother much too early to be able to construct a Saint-Protector for himself out of his memories of her. For that reason, he is unable to resist when this part of his being is appealed to, when the mother appears to be calling him.

How could I worry so, how silly of me not to understand? It was that which drove him to Mondsee.

I might have spared my tearful telegram. It arrived too late and was altogether superfluous. My violent letter had never come into his hands. He had not waited for it or given even a thought to London; he had gone right off to Mondsee. A letter from Mother Uhl has sufficed to alter everything for him overnight and to wipe everthing else out of his mind — myself included.

The call of the Mother! — What August Strindberg has missed all his life long, what the early orphaned one had longed for through many a tearful year, has come to him at last. A mother has called him. He does not ask what such a call may perhaps demand precisely from him; he only hears the unwonted sweet voice, and follows it, believing, happy, turned into a boy again, high-spirited and eager as a child ... while I, suspecting nothing, am waiting for him in London.

I have closed my eyes. The mild air caresses my brow ... I feel weak, as after a long illness — and yet so light.

MY PATERNAL HOME

August Strindberg, Mondsee, to Freda, London

'Dear, wicked litt animal: So here I sit in your room and look out at the Schafberg, but my sheep is not here. Freda, you have suffered so much that you have developed a mania for self-torture, and when you have been torturing yourself, you get better and want to torture others as well. But don't! I can bear anything from you, but others are not like that, especially those who are not so fond of you as I am. And you act so abruptly in your rages that you might render things irreparable here.

'You are afraid to come to Mondsee because you are a daughter here and resent being treated like a child. But do you not believe that my presence and your new dignity as a young matron will make all the difference? Your mother is so kind to me and I am certain that — be it only on my account — she will not in future treat you as a child. Mitzi is no longer here and cannot come the elder sister over you.

'Freda, let me tell you one thing: you blame me for having come here instead of to England. But I let my instinct direct me at the last moment and I was quite right. For it was high time for me to come. Clouds had gathered. Mitzi imagined that we had quarrelled and Father, as I hear, began to grow uneasy. My presence has saved the situation, but we need your arrival to make things quite clear, especially my own position. If you are to be busy in London in the autumn season, it is better you should take a holiday now.'

(*Continued*):

'Well! Now father has arrived! But lo! — he is a fine, young, good-looking fellow, so much like you, and most likely will not look black at us. He kissed me and I felt like a child again. Am I born to be a child all my life long?

'He was so kind to me that my fears are all gone! And your mother seems to love me, so that I was as ashamed of myself as a hardened old sinner.

'Freda, Freda, just come and I believe that everything will be all right!

'Come to your happy — Gräfsvin.'

*

'Dear Hedgehog: You prick when I caress you and you cry because you pricked me. Since you maintain with such persistence that you are not coming, I have no business here either and must leave as soon as I can. But to go where? To England if I were sure that you want me there, which I often doubt, most of all when you do not believe in my love! But where else could I go in this desolate world, in which I am a stranger?

217

'Time after time I ask myself: What am I doing in this house? I am an intruder. Your parents' love cannot disguise the fact. And what do you want your father and mother to say when "people" ask where their daughter is?'

(Continued: three hours later)
'We talked of you at supper and mother praised your beauty and loveliness as a babe; your father joined us and so we all made a pilgrimage to the balcony-attic to look at you, carved, in your bath, Mother with the lantern and I carrying the lamp. (Now I suppose you will say that I treat you as a "fille publique!")

'This evening, Father said to me that you were welcome here as my wife and were to regard yourself only as such. He also said: "August, she is your wife, do not fear that I shall treat Freda as a daughter (i.e. as a minor)."

'Here, darling, everything is so harmonious, and you will find that your position in the family is quite different now. It strikes me that you ought to enjoy the liberty and independence you have grown up to. Don't you, dear?

'I dreamed of you last night, you had come but you wore a black mask over your face. I wanted to take you in my arms — and then you vanished! . . .'

'Freda, Freda — Father is not yet angry, but he might easily become so and when he asks "Now — where is my daughter?" then I shall have no answer for him. Give up the *fata Morgana* of getting rich quick! Let Grein and Heinemann manage their theatre alone. It will always be open to us.

'Father says: "Command your wife to come!" I answer him: "I never dictate to my wife." Whereupon he replies: "Then I shall make her come."

'You roast in hell, but why? Come here, here is neither hell nor paradise, but the old green earth, where the sun shines out of the clouds after rain — Do not wait until father will get really angry; do you not understand how it hurts to see you, my wife, spoken of like a child? I feel like a minor here, too — It is you who abandon me in hell, when it just depends on you that everything be beautiful! . . .

'PS. And so I have been trout-fishing with Father and have been permitted to carry the creel, which used to be your duty. And Father says I am no such irredeemable sheepkin as you, for you always carried a novel along too, and that, at least, I did not do, only a tobacco pipe with Imperial-Royal-Austrian-State-tobacco.

'Well, I have bathed now from your bathing-hut and have been swimming in your lake and have gazed at the Sheep's Mount (with no sheep there) from below.

'But Father says that in Vienna you have made quite a name for yourself as a writer, that your articles are very good, that your style is perfect and that you already have a personal style. That you are a brilliant little donkey; but that all will come right in the end.

'Father and I are great friends. He is quite young . . . not a bit of an old veteran, as you described him. He grumbles, as becomes a married man, but he is kind and your little nephew Caesar and I are rivals for his favours.

'The St. Bernard snarled at me at first, but snarls no longer. The ancient crone in the basement was introduced to me as dear old nurse Resi and I gave her Freda's fond love. She seemed to hate me at first, because I had seduced you even though with legal sanction. But now *she* snarls no more either.

'I am in love with Mother, who gives me not only her loving heart, but so much to eat that I live in dread of a paunch and permanently protest: Freda would not like that!

'But I am deeply sorry that all of you, yes, all of you, are unkind to Mother. Even as a stranger I can put up with her religious ideas, although I frankly tell her that I do not share them. But this refined and sensitive lady ought not to be so humiliated and hurt. I feel moved to tears when obliged to listen to this slaughtering. But I know it is only a thoughtless bad habit in families to stifle one another. And I have often observed how attempts to crush you are made, merely through sheer force of habit. I have told Mother to her face that she does not know you and I might cease to be such good friends with Mitzi if she does not stop bossing you. But you know best how much she loves you and you put as high a value upon her devotion as I do.

'Now you have seen the whole of Mondsee as I see it.

'Once more, I do admire your great qualities, I love you, soul and not-soul — but don't merely be brilliant, be sensible as well and do not devastate our future — *malgré tout* so beautifully started — by mental lockjaw.

'*A Dieu*, dearest, and be with us soon — August.

'PS. Do you know that our portraits were published in Sweden, before I came here, in June; you looking lovely with your hair down?'

'Dear Freda: I have just read a certain letter of yours to your mother, written after my arrival here. Only a hideously jealous person could have phrased anything so vile. You yourself sent me to Rügen and then to Mondsee; and then you complain that I have abandoned you?

'All your pretended care for me is just as treacherous. That you should hand me over to your parents, like a beggar, has caused me to come to the following decision:

'If you are not here within one week, I shall go to Berlin and give a series of lectures at the Humboldt Academy, hoping to be offered a professorship. If you do not arrive in Berlin within a week from that, I shall start divorce proceedings. Only because of my love for you have I permitted you to manage my business affairs for me — Now I am taking things in hand for myself.

'I love you as much as ever, but I believe that you do not love me any more and that is why I am going away from here.'

'Dear Freda: I have just received your letter ... I cannot say that it gave me pleasure as nothing does since we two parted. You are ambitious. So am I.

'But I fancy I know that your ambition is devouring you altogether and will engulf anyone who comes near you. I try in vain to see for you and me a future which would be devoted solely and exclusively to my science. Often I reproach myself with having taken you and your career too lightly, with having under-estimated you. But I did not then know the value of your talent. I had never read a word you had written. Now that I have read your articles, with their coloured sparkling language, I know that you are somebody and that I was wrong to tease you.

'Well, you have been treating me like an idiot — playfully, for fun, in the beginning and finally in earnest. We might say that we now are even; nevertheless, I confer upon you the privilege of telling me all kinds of home truths, founded and unfounded ones, without my having a right to reply.

'Now that I am returning to Berlin, I feel as if I were returning to Darkness, for I am afraid that you will not come.

'I see it all again, this Berlin, the *Künstler Klause* where we played the gypsy, the Neustädtische Kirchstrasse, where our love blossomed in a young sun and thunderstorms, love wild and tender as Spring, sometimes grandiose and so sad at times. The sublime struggle between two souls, wrestling to avoid the unavoidable. Two cells that, in becoming one, must cease to be. And now that is all past.

'Past. Can that be? I regret only one thing — that I did not summon death a few weeks ago, in London, in your arms, my head on your heart. I did think of it, but recoiled from our sordid environment.

'Here I dream of Death far out on the Mondsee. Water, that is so pure. Or on the lounge in the bathing-hut — you know it. But at the last moment, you rise before my eyes and Hope smiles at me again. You are casting away Love to grasp at Fame. But let me tell you this. When the hour comes and fame is yours, you will want to throw it from you, all will be empty and waste around you and you would fain give all your laurels for a wreath of roses.

'If life is generous enough to offer you both, why do you discard one of them, and that the sweeter? I could tell you that the laurel has thorns sharper than the rose's. Is all at an end? And why? A riddle with no answer! You love me, as long as I am weak and unhappy and you hate and despise me when you begin to scent in me the lord and master.

'You hate and despise men. Your flesh desires the man and your soul rejects him. Amazon that you are! Have you found out that I had adapted myself to you, that, unconsciously, I played the part of the weakling and had resigned the role of the male to you? Why? Because otherwise you would not have loved me. And I did want your love! Now that I have lost all hope of winning you back, I feel tempted to lay bare and show to you my hidden motives every time my doings were incomprehensible to you. It would be healing balm to make you see the truth of what really goes on in a Man's soul when under the thraldom of your love. But what good would it do? You would only misuse it! I am the man of the future, so male a man that I do my utmost to conceal it. That's why I play the part of the misogynist. My sex urge is so vigorous that it always leads me on to the good path, where there is an excess of love awaiting me, matched with the cruelty of woman.

'What is it you want? At times, mother-love, gentle, blonde love, sheepkin love? Is that the thing? It seems so to me — and again, not. Suppose you won it, then you would despise it and wish for another kind.

' "Chaste love!" Fiddlesticks!

'You despise me — and rightly so, up to a point. I wonder whether you would love me more and differently if I were to turn into the cave man and show you the brute, the cannibal? You are not in need of intellectual love, you possess intellect yourself.

'Can man and woman continue to live together, once the innermost has been put into words? — So we will let this be.

'Why do I not come to England? On my faith, I do not quite know.

'There is nothing for me to do there. I might be endangering my new profession. I dread my love and that I become your slave once more.

'So I shall go to Berlin. And then? And then?

'Have you considered the fatal results of a separation? Revenge, retaliation! Ruins! Irremediable ruins! If you repair them, they collapse anew. One prostitutes oneself, exhibits one another before the public. The crowd expects a new *Plea*.

'And the revelations and replies! One dies of pain and rises from the dead to slay out of revenge.

'It is all the fault of life, adorable and cruel life — August.'

*

CONCLUSION

This ends the episode of London. I shall leave to-morrow for Berlin. It is written in the book of Fate. The English modern movement will have to dispense with us. There will be no Strindberg Theatre here, most likely no new art of the stage either, for a little while yet. The Triumvirate will never be formed after my departure. The unlimited possibilities have come to an end.

Bobbie wails mildly and is just a tiny bit hurt: — 'Mr. Grein would have been most enthusiastic about it and Mr. Heinemann would certainly have been willing.'

Yes, Bobbie, Grein would have been enthusiastic and Heinemann might have been willing — but not Strindberg. He is a law unto himself. One day, perhaps . . . Somewhere or other he will once more want his Theatre and then he will have it . . . but not now . . . not here. And I have no right to insist.

No, Herr Paul, I was wrong when I answered you, writing to Rügen, that I was justified in demanding of Strindberg that he should come to London and take upon himself what I had taken upon myself for him. We are not made of the same stuff, he and I — I must never, never forget that.

To-day money arrived unexpectedly, my pay from the faithful *Wiener Zeitung*, after it had vainly sought me in Rügen and Berlin.

There is nothing now in the way of my departure. All preparations are made. I have even bought fine Scottish trout flies for father at a shop in the Haymarket. He has been wanting them such a long time. They will appease him.

I do not leave London with a light heart — it has given me much and is ready to give me more.

But it must be.

X

SALZBURG — PANKOW AND MONDSEE

August 1893

A SENTIMENTAL JOURNEY

TELEGRAMS

Flushing

'En route. Fond love. Freda.'
(*Addressed to Strindberg, Berlin, care of Neumann-Hofer. Forwarded from there by letter-post to Mondsee*)

Mondsee

'Are you in Berlin? Don't understand your wire. Answer and I will come. August.'
(*Telegram returned by letter-post with postal comment. 'Addressee left'*)

Berlin

'Coming Mondsee. Stay. Freda.'
(*Wire returned by letter-post. Postal comment. 'Addressee left'*)

Mondsee

To Neumann-Hofer, Berlin
'Do you know where Strindberg and Freda are? Desperate. Maria Uhl.'

Berlin

To Maria Uhl, Mondsee.
'All's well. Freda left for Mondsee. Strindberg arrived Berlin. Neumann-Hofer.'

In Salzburg I take the little local train going to Bad Ischl, where the old Emperor Francis Joseph, the young actresses and the fashionable musicians and journalists of Vienna collect in summer for health and love.

One more turn of the line, and my lake lies spread before me.

Oh thou, my dear, dear lake — happy childhood which once more seems to return with thee —— Was all this new life in the foreign big world only a dream?

Do you and I belong to each other after all — In the end only we two?

Have I not always felt it, that there was something in common between us two, which parts us from the rest of men?

Absence has sharpened my glance — and now I know.

We are serious, you and I, about our heights and our depths.

Naked stone, high summits looking West and South —— but behind you, in the North, there hide peaceful and low pillowed hills and behind them again, flat and sated pastures and fields. That's it.

Father and all of them adore romance, but as a spectacle on holidays and Sundays. The plains behind Thee, with corn and fruit, that is what they cherish for the six days of the week.

Thou and I alone are different.

Father stands in front of the house amongst his roses. His glasses hang quite low on his broad nose, almost over his lips. He gives me an angry look over the rim. No greeting, only the question: 'Where is your husband?'

Cain cannot have been worse startled when the voice of the Lord questioned him about his slain brother.

'With you . . .' I stammer in confusion.

'If he were with us, I should not ask.'

No, August Strindberg is no longer with my parents — not since yesterday. He and Father did not understand my telegram and they quarrelled over the explanation. Father grew excited, violent — and Strindberg had left without an adieu, without his hat, without his luggage, gone off without one word — off without any known aim. Peasants said they had seen a stranger with flying hair marching across the open fields and others declared that they had seen the same man get on board a train. What still others suggested was so weird, but unfortunately so entirely unlikely, that Father had simply driven them out.

Father was horribly upset, although he would not acknowledge it. He said it was Strindberg's fault, but this time Mother contradicted him, bold as a lioness:

Father shouted at his son, said she, as he was accustomed to shout at her. The son had not yet, however, been long enough in the family and had resented it. He had gone quite white when the old gentleman in his fit of anger had called him a fool. — Father remains silent. He would do anything to recall what had happened and knows that no one ever can.

'His trunk is upstairs,' he tells me after a time, when we are sitting on the veranda and Mother has poured me out a cup of tea. 'Resi shall fetch it down at once. You can take it with you' (i.e. 'you had better take the next train, you no longer have a home here').

Not here, but where then, where? — I almost cry out. But I merely nod dumbly. Father is right, more so than he knows. I do not belong here any more. My whole education has suffered a breakdown and the craving for liberty, which it had suppressed in me, has broken out. Between me and my father's house lies adventure. I have starved for days at a time and in between have drunk champagne, proudly and joyously, to the conquest of London. Finally, when reputable work actually offered itself to Strindberg and me, I ran away from it, contrary to all reason, vagabond that I am. And now I chase all over Europe after my beloved one, because I have learned to comprehend that genius cannot count and always remains unaccountable as well.

On that one point Father and I hold the same opinion: Strindberg is a genius.

'You probably do not even know what a tremendous genius you have married, you simpleton,' says Father more mildly after a while. 'I have seen many a great man — from Hebbel to Makart and Brahms, from Richard Wagner to the Magician of the Kobenzl, Baron Reichenbach, the discoverer of *Od* (I could not tell your husband enough about him, by the way), but an August Strindberg I have never yet seen . . . I wanted to make it clear to him that my daughter, as a lady, had no business alone in London. But he did not even listen. His eyes shone as they followed intensely the rings the sun painted on the tiles of the veranda. And when I had finished talking, he had discovered a new law of physics. Such a man has his place on a pedestal. One does not marry such men.'

No further train that evening. I must stay a night in Mondsee. I can be off again only at five o'clock in the morning — to the man who has his place on a pedestal.

'You can sleep in the bed where Strindberg slept,' says Father gruffly, laughing: 'Then you can see the condition to which he has brought my house. Your old flowered pink lace petticoat, which he discovered in a drawer, he laid reverently under his pillow; as compensation he tore all the curtains from the windows without asking permission — "because they keep out the light", says he. Since the house was built, they have never kept out the light for any one. But he took down all three pairs of them with his own hands. Well, he folded them up carefully — that one must allow. No servant could have done it better. Strange fellow'.

Father kept the strictest watch over tradition in his villa. No chair might move a leg without permission. And now this August Strindberg had not only removed the daughter of the house, but also three pairs of window curtains, heavy pairs of curtains made of sailcloth, in the bedroom which had been allotted to him in the first story of the villa.

It is a spacious, fine room, flooded with light from a centre window nine feet wide, looking south towards the lake and the mountains. Other large windows look east and west, a balcony, twenty-five feet wide, spreads on the west, behind glass doors. In winter hundreds of birds come visiting there, and the ailanthus tree, growing beside the wild little mountain torrent that crosses our garden, reaches over with its feathery leaves. The room looks embarrassed at its nakedness, but it cannot be denied that it is a gain. The Schafberg has stepped closer. The sky with the white moon and the ragged black clouds now stares in unhampered. When the wind bows down the branches of the ailanthus, its black shadow fingers fan my face, weird, but beautiful.

Morning comes up red and radiant. Softly, so as not to disturb my family, I steal down the stairs. I want to see the room once more which used to be my nursery. Up to my fourth year, mother had left me here entirely in the care of my faithful old Resi. I gave Resi lots of trouble, for I had a leaning to Christian Communism from my birth and presented everyone who came with everything he wished for, out of Father's museum or Resi's garden.

In front of the east window there still stands the apple tree which had always looked in, full of blossom, every May, and later bore such juicy fruit. When I was little, I believed my guardian angel lived in it. When I grew older, I sat with my sister up in the boughs and we read and nibbled and enjoyed ourselves hugely when we had the chance to drop a hard apple on some passing visitor's head without their having the least suspicion that it was not the vengeance of Heaven upon them. The nursery has now become the dining-room that is used when only the family is present. Guests are entertained in the large Renaissance *salle*. Well, this is past history for me now.

All I take with me is one of Father's roses. He would rage if he knew that I had broken it off. Or perhaps not — ? Perhaps he watches me from his window? Is he standing hidden behind the curtains? I run back into the house and lay the new trout flies on his table. Then he will know.

August Strindberg, Salzburg, Hotel Europe, to Maria Uhl, Mondsee

'Dear, good Mother: I came into your house like a prodigal son and left again like one, without thanks or farewell. I did not intend to leave, but when I passed by the station, I felt the urge to get away again, out into the world, somewhere — no matter where. I was not angry, only miserable, perturbed by the irritations of the last few months.

'And now I beg you to forgive, if that be possible, and to tell Father that I did not leave in resentment. I feel much too guilty to do anything of the kind, since I have brought you nothing but anxiety and unrest.

'Good-bye, good-bye, and may I soon have good news to give you — August.'

*

From a Strindberg Narrative [Free rendering]

Travelling by way of Salzburg and Munich, he was soon in Berlin.

It was evening. He sent a messenger to the (Neumann-Hofer) family with whom his wife had usually stayed. Since she had not come to Mondsee, she must be in Berlin. On the visiting card he had written only the words:

'Where is my wife?'

No human being who has not waited for an hour and a half in the street can imagine how long an hour and a half can seem. But the waiting was shortened by his hope that after a silence cure of one week in Hamburg, five weeks of lonely imprisonment in Rügen and another week in the Seventh Inferno at Mondsee, he would see his wife again.

After six periods of fifteen minutes had elapsed, the

messenger came back with somebody else's visiting-card on which was written:

'She went to Mondsee this morning, to meet you!'

His next thought was: My poor unhappy wife is going straight into the lion's den! Father's anger had already passed all bounds and Mother had said only the day before: 'If she comes now, he will box her ears!'

So he telegraphed to plead that she might be forgiven.

It would be four days before she could return. In order not to remain in Berlin itself, where the papers would have gloated over the details of this wedding trip, he settled down in the neighbouring Pankow.

To kill time, he resolved to pursue his study of the biology of plants. He took a morphia syringe with him on his rambles, to see how sensitive the local plants were to the nerve poison which he used. One afternoon, he sat in a garden restaurant over a glass of wine. His table was overhung by an apple tree heavy with small red apples. This was just the thing. He mounted a chair, pricked the stem of an apple with the syringe and pressed it home; but with undue violence, for the apple fell off. At this moment, he heard shouts on the hill by the woods, and saw a furious man come tearing towards him with uplifted cudgel, followed by his wife and child.

'Got him at last!'

Him? Evidently a long-sought apple thief. He descended from the chair and seated himself, prepared to be arrested and carried off by the police, since he had been caught in the act. It would be impossible to explain his behaviour, for no official would ever believe such a wild story as that he was about to inject morphia with a syringe into an apple stalk.

Meanwhile, the excited landlord took a full minute to run the length of the fence and arrive at the entrance.

He sat there like a prisoner sentenced to death and awaited a whack from the stick as a preliminary move. Determined to die like a hero, he made no attempt to explain and merely thought: This is the most devilish thing I have ever been through.

Was it his well-groomed appearance or the quality of the wine and cigarettes before him, or was it something else altogether which came to the rescue? At all events, the landlord, who had presumably seldom had such a distinguished customer, took off his hat and obligingly inquired whether the gentleman was being waited upon. In the course of his polite reply, Strindberg caught the landlord's gaze fixed upon the morphia syringe, the packet of powder and the glass of water. In the easy tones of a man of the world, he at once explained the situation: 'I am a botanist and was just about to make an experiment when I was surprised in a rather unusual position.'

'Oh, sir, please make yourself entirely at home. Do exactly as you like!' And after a few remarks on the weather, the landlord took his departure, whispering a few words to the waitress which the guest imagined that he overheard and which caused him also to take his leave — with due precaution and care.

'He thought I was one of the inmates of the asylum. That saved me. But I can never come here again', was Strindberg's dismal reflection.

*

When he got back home from his ramble, he found his door locked. Half-guessing, he knocked and spoke his name. When the door opened, his young wife flew into his arms. He found this quite simple and natural, as if he had left her only two minutes before. Now she was his again, and she was gayer, younger and more beautiful than ever — so it seemed to him. She did not utter a word of reproach, question or explanation, but merely said:

232

'Have you lots of money, or only a little?'

'Why do you ask?'

'Because I have lots and want to have a festive lunch in town.'

They were soon agreed upon this point; and this was their reunion. Why not, indeed? Two months of martyrdom were forgotten, wiped out as if they had never been; the shame of a divorce, about which people had already begun to gossip, had utterly evaporated.

'If anyone should ask me what we quarrelled about,' said he, 'I should not be able to remember.'

'Neither would I! And that is why we will never, never part again. We will not be parted even for one day, else the trouble begins.'

Both of them felt this decision to be the summit of wisdom! A memory of Gravesend would return, another of London, where they had not been parted for even a minute and everything went wrong just on that account. But they were in no mood to weigh matters so exactly.

'And your father?'

'Well, he was so fond of you that it made me jealous.'

'But how did he receive you?'

'Why, I would rather not discuss that subject! But it was all on your account, so I have forgiven him.'

They only smiled over this — and over everything else too.

'To-day is a holiday, to-morrow work begins again.'

BERLIN

September—October 1893

THE OLD HAUNTS, AND YET?

ON the very evening of my arrival, we took up residence in two large gable rooms in a family boarding house in Berlin, in the Albrecht Strasse. The building looks across the Spree right into our good old Neustädtische Kirchstrasse.

At the Unter den Linden post office ancient letters were waiting for us. There was even money amongst them, though not very much.

Joy had been waiting for us too. This seemed to us like our good, temporarily stored, marital property and we surrendered ourselves up to our happiness. Friends and acquaintances could not get over their surprise. We were a perfect couple. The wife evidently knew her husband's every thought, the husband his wife's every fault — and yet they loved one another! — No one in Berlin literary circles had ever heard of such a chivalrous husband. He helped his wife to brush and clean her dresses, for although she kept order for him, she was not particularly neat herself. Once the wife of a leading critic had surprised Strindberg on the staircase, running after his ill-dusted spouse with a clothes-brush in his hand.

Strindberg and I have grown nearer to each other. We cannot be apart even for an hour. Recently he left me alone in the evening for the first time. A Swedish friend had insisted on seeing Berlin by night with him. When he came home, he found me sitting in the dark at the open window, bathed in tears. 'Whatever is the matter? Do you want something?' he had asked in alarm, and I, half laughing, ashamed and crying still harder, hung round his neck and sobbed: 'Yes, I want you — you — you.'

I could not have brooked a rival. I have none. His relations with the Ferkel have cooled, if they have not entirely ceased. He seldom goes there and I must not enter its doors. 'It is no place for you,' he says.

From time to time, one or another of the Round Table drops in to see us, bringing the latest gossip. Strindberg is always a pleased audience. If it is something humorous or psychologically interesting, there is a glow and sparkle in his eyes.

However, I can read a certain apprehension in them as well. When Aspasia's name is mentioned, his features darken. It is a long story, sounds frivolous, but is romantic and sad at bottom — Schleich had handed her over to 'Poland' in the same farcical spirit in which he had received her from Strindberg — but between her and the chivalrous Przybyszewski a passionate love had sprung up. They had married. There was no other man between them as yet — but there was alcohol, they both drank now. Heavily.

Strindberg took much to heart the downward trend of their history. He regarded this marriage as a rope with which two people had bound themselves together before jumping into the river, because they did not know what to do with their lives. Strindberg was sorry for Przybyszewski, his talent and his heart. He was still more sorry for the abandoned Maschka and her two children. And he was sorry for himself: he was not mistaken, his favourite disciple had become his enemy.

Without loss of time Strindberg once more plunged into the chemical research work and experimenting which he had inaugurated in Rügen. At the moment, Sulphur was the focal point of interest; he disputed its accredited reputation as an element. From now on, Sulphur (with a capital S) was to play a part in my life, too, almost like a human being. Strindberg was the Saint Francis of chemistry and I, indeed, came to think of sulphur quite as a person. When I got home one afternoon, I knew he had arrived. I knew it almost before I had completely opened the front door. There was something in the air that told me. The look which the maid gave me ought to have warned me. As I entered Strindberg's room, I started back from a penetrating, horrible smell, which one felt seeping into all one's pores and sticking there. But Strindberg's eyes were radiant as he introduced me to a wonderful new friend — Sulphur.

It is hard for Strindberg to live with others without a collision, because his cosmic and tellurian reactions are different from theirs.

About a week ago, I went out one afternoon for half an hour and came back without encountering anything of interest. Strindberg's brow was dark. After the evening meal, he asked abruptly:

'You met Sudermann?' It sounded more like a statement than a question.

'I — no?'

'You met him at 4 o'clock, at the corner of the Karlsstrasse.'

I had been at the Karlsstrasse at 4 o'clock, but had met no one.

'N-no . . .'

'Were you not wearing your green cloth dress (he had not seen me go away in it) and did he not say it reminded him of something?'

'I wore the dress but I did not meet him.'

'Why do you deny it?'

'I give you my word, I did not meet him.'

To-day, however, when I have clean forgotten the conversation, I actually do meet Sudermann, precisely at 4 o'clock, precisely in the Karlsstrasse, in precisely that dress — and the dress does really remind him of something. I am so staggered when he tells me so that I run away at full speed without an explanation. Sudermann cannot understand, thinks the fault must be his and chases after me, calling out apologies. I do not turn round. At last he slows down. He probably thinks me crazy and he is quite right. Strindberg notices that I am upset, puts questions — and I tell him, weeping. But he only gives me a look of inexpressible contempt. Why did I not own up a week ago — ? Again a sign of woman's pre-disposition to lying!

There were other strange incidents of this kind to occur again and again, when he experienced as the present what was to occur later to other people as the future.

*

St. Martin's summer had given us three weeks of heavenly sunshine. But when we began to think of harvest, before the winter should come, we suddenly found ourselves on foreign and barren soil.

The Maytime Berlin, which we had left behind when going out into the world, existed no longer. In those days of old, the name of Strindberg had been spoken enthusiastically. Now one scarcely dared mention him. *The Plea of One Insane* had created an extremely painful impression. With a ruthless hand, it had laid bare, depths into which no one liked to gaze. It was not so much the story of Strindberg's marriage which upset people as the exposition of their own decadence. Slowly I began to see the book in this light.

Then I discovered that it was an achievement and a work of art.

'It is a good book,' admitted the wife of an important newspaper editor, who was visiting us one afternoon. 'It's a pity that so good a book should not be more widely read. But without some rattling of drums nothing really goes in literature nowadays.'

Now it was my turn to agree. Her husband had quite particularly good drum-rattling connections. He could wake the dead if he wanted to.

'I know exactly what ought to be done, to get the book read,' she continued.

I heaved a sigh of relief.

'It ought to be forbidden by the Public Prosecutor as immoral. That would make it in a wink.'

Strindberg stared at the lady, speechless. I could not quite suppress an exclamation of dismay.

'A real inspiration!' I said icily after a while, as something must be said, and moved farther away from her.

She took the compliment seriously and smiled benignly.

Strindberg stepped to the window and flung it wide open — for fresh air!

Our sources of income are running dry; things are at a standstill. We are in bad hands. Our publishing firm, the Bibliographische Bureau, is not the right one for us. Under the title *The Confession of a Fool* the translation of the *Plea* was done in a most vulgar German. The same concern is now to bring out the earlier autobiographical works, *A Bondswoman's Son* and *Growth of a Soul*.

I pay the firm a visit. The head, Dr. Julius Steinschneider, is a young descendant of an old family of lawyers. He is about thirty, dark, slim as a reed; in his dress, appearance and manner, he has a most ridiculous resemblance to an old-fashioned bogus Jesuit by Eugène Sue. He is a gambler. There are times when money is plentiful and oils the wheels. But there are days when no coin of any kind could be found in the house. It seems to have been my luck to come upon such a day. I cannot even get a statement, when I ask for a copy of the agreement, Dr. Steinschneider corrects me: 'Men of honour need no written agreements.' I am obliged to tell him that, when he and I are together, only *one* man of honour is present. He can interpret that as he pleases.

What has come over me? An unknown weariness causes my shoulders to sag. When I complain of all this, quite astonished, my husband smiles proudly — he is not surprised. He knows these signs. He has been a father before.

'That is the way of things. The mother's body has its own conscious will. It chooses the man and it decides upon the hour. It has a psyche of its own, which determines the spiritual mood of the woman, sorrow or joy. Only after woman has fulfilled her destiny and presses a small new life to her bosom, then only it falls dumb. Wait and see . . .' Strindberg tells me comfortingly.

But my blood speaks differently, it has grown feeble and unwilling, like a reveller who has done with joy and will hear nothing of the consequences. Added to this was the fear that we should not be able to support a child. What help was it that Strindberg, who did want it, waved my anxiety aside with a confident gesture.

He not only wanted the child, he waited for it as a simple, pious soul waits for his life to perfect itself. The thought is like a rosy cloud under his feet. Great-hearted and confident of victory, he makes concessions. He has laid Sulphur aside for the time and is now producing gold.

After only a few days, smiling contentedly, he showed me scales of gold, shining with true metallic glitter, which had formed out of the mixture of copper and sulphate of iron with which he had experimented. 'It is "gold",' he explained quietly, 'or rather a hitherto unknown intermediary stage which, properly washed, would result in pure gold.'

This opened up perspectives. Moreover, the change of favourites was to my advantage in any case. One could say of Strindberg's gold what could not be said of Sulphur — '*Non olet!*'

Unwearying, he stands bowed over his retorts, operates with balances, looks up old books and the very newest; the whole room is crowded with books and papers, chemicals, lamps, glass and porcelain. Only the bed stands up above the Flood like Noah's Ark. When he lays himself to rest, lying flat on his back, according to his habit, it is a fantastic sight, like a floating sarcophagus. The realities of the world have melted in the cauldron and go up with the elements in smoke.

Gold . . . gold . . . ! The bills are unpaid, the last ready money is gone.

The skies were grey and cloudy and both of us were sad like the passing summer. Arm in arm we took our way towards the Tiergarten. Where has its glorious magic gone?

Hesitating and stammering, I put a question to him — As answer an angry dark red floods over his face.

We sit silent, as we had sat once before, hand in hand. Now yellow, withered leaves rustle at our feet.

I ought not to have asked him. Any other man in my modern world, but not him. And I would never have asked him, if I were not pursued day and night by that other puzzle: What is to become of us? It has grown upon me, since my condition has sapped my strength, since out of a healthy young woman I have become inert and hesitating. Suppose I should be ill when the child is born, or die — what then? I never thought of such things formerly. Now everything is different — different.

BERLIN

It is night, but I cannot sleep. Strindberg has angrily slammed the door. I should not have asked him. But — what shall we do? I do not know. I am so tired. I am always tired now.

At last I have gone to sleep. I must have uttered a loud cry in my dream — I dreamt someone was suddenly throttling me as on our wedding night.

Strindberg stands at the window, hands in his pockets; he has not yet undressed. He looks me over sternly and nods: 'Remorse . . . ?'

I am so tired that I do not at once understand. I nearly ask him what that is — Remorse! Then I gradually collect my thought. 'No. I am only afraid, afraid . . .'

Strindberg looks ailing. It may be the overstrain of his work. It may be the latest misfortune. The police authorities have actually provided our 'rattling of drums'. They have banned the *Confession of a Fool* and summoned the author under the *Lex Heinze*.

The Lex Heinze is a new law, designed, no doubt, to sift the wheat from the chaff. It threatens all who 'manufacture' announce or commend immoral writings for the purpose of circulation; also writings, descriptions and illustrations which, without being in themselves indecent, are calculated to create a scandal through grossly offending the public sense of modesty'. This sounds praiseworthy enough. Unfortunately the word 'immoral' is decidedly hazy. The authorities seem to make a dead set against reformers. Tolstoi and Hauptmann have just had their trials. Now it is Strindberg's turn. He resents it as an insult to have his clean name coupled with the name of Heinze.

The Lex Heinze has a shady ancestry. It takes its designation from a couple of procurers who figured in a criminal affair and were accused and convicted quite rightly. Frau Heinze had been a prostitute and her husband lived on her earnings. Both were accomplices in the murder of a night watchman.

The news had come to us first as a hint. In Munich and now and then also in Berlin, high police officials had the kindly habit of warning artists and writers who had carelessly come in conflict with modesty that a little journey abroad was advisable. It was a friendly and useful custom. But Strindberg, trembling in every nerve, was the most courageous trembler that ever existed — where he stood, there he would fight.

Then followed the news in the Press: a denunciation had reached the police authorities signed, 'A German Mother'.

The summons arrived in due time. Strindberg himself sent his protest to the *Landesgericht*. His defence we placed in the hands of the lawyer Richard Grelling, who lived in a permanent feud with the Lex Heinze.

A bright spark in the darkness! Max Burckhard has kept his word. He has really spread the news in the press that he intends to produce Strindberg's *Secret of the Guild*. 'A bit of advertising won't hurt the Burg Theater. I am doing it in my own interest,' he wrote humorously to me.

A success at the Burg Theater might banish the shadow of *The Confessions of a Fool*. Strindberg draws new life from the news. But Burckhard (so he informs me confidentially) wants alterations made. He fears that this particular play may be dramatically weak, especially towards the end. Too much of a sermon for the débutantes. One must know those débutantes!

'Who shall talk to Strindberg about this and suggest changes?'

'I will try to speak to him about it . . .' I write in sheer desperation to Vienna. . . .

'You shall receive the new version from me — if he agrees to make one — if!'

No, I have no right to suggest such a thing! August
Strindberg's work can and shall obey his inspiration.

Nor in any case have I the courage to hint at it — not now.
His nerves are lacerated. The shame that has been put upon
him is gnawing at him. And his maniacal dread is awake
again. He is always trembling at the thought of losing his
liberty, whether in a prison or an asylum. It pursues him
day and night. Previous cases have proved that German
judges are better critics than the police officials, but Strindberg will not be reassured. The past holds him once more in
its clutches. Once before in Sweden — in respect to his
Married — he had been tried and had come out triumphant.
But before acquittal he had lived through all the horrors of
prison in his lively imagination. They now torture him
anew. There are times now when he will sit and stare in
front of him, seeing visions of himself in a convict's garb.
There are moments when I shudder at the thought that he
might speak and stammer forth incoherent words.

An angry mistrust has seized upon him. Since yesterday
it has also turned against me. A tiny, grotesque, most
natural happening has been the outward cause. Sulphur
has once more supplanted Gold. But August Strindberg's
unborn child cannot brook the breath of his science and he,
who understands everything, fails to comprehend this one
thing.

He no longer enters my room. Speaks little. He has taken
his business affairs into his own hands. He has written to
Max Burckhard himself too, inquiring whether, and when,
The Secret of the Guild will be produced. Burckhard is unpre-
pared and answers hesitatingly, evasively and clumsily: 'Of
course, everything is going along all right . . . only waiting
for the new version — Frau Strindberg knows all about it.'

Fortunately, Strindberg misunderstands the letter. He
thinks it is a question of a new translation: 'Did you think

your Swedish would be good enough? And don't you know that I have a translation agreement with Brausewetter and can be sued and locked up for breach of contract?' he says angrily. He considers himself seriously menaced, artistically, financially and even legally, all through my fault.

'Yes, indeed,' I stutter, 'I didn't think of that . . .'

His laugh is hard — 'You women!'

I see that his whole heart is in this production . . . I am a miserable coward — I do not dare to tell him the price. It would be a blow in the face.

The more we two become estranged, the stronger grows Sulphur. There will soon be no more Strindberg, but only a slave of this hellish yellow element.

Yesterday morning, Sulphur found that his breakfast coffee was not hot enough. It did not provide the proper inspiration. — He is quite right, but it is not my fault. The maid had brought the breakfast into the dining-room as usual, without giving Strindberg any warning. I was still in bed. Sulphur, however, would not accept the excuse. Strindberg pushed me hastily aside. Then he rushed into the street without hat or overcoat, to reconcile insulted Sulphur by giving him his undivided thought during the morning walk.

When he came home, he shut himself into his room. Instead of a verbal explanation, soon afterwards a long white sheet of paper came gliding in from under the door, like an evil snake, with hateful and extraordinary things written upon it . . . Extraordinary things. . . .

If he wanted his freedom again, the only thing for me to do was to go to my sister in Vienna.

I began to pack my trunk. I could not take it with me, for we had a large unpaid bill, but at least I showed the trunk some sympathy before I must abandon it.

BERLIN

My thoughts begin to grow confused . . . I am weary . . . weary. . . .

It is as though a dark mountain had swallowed me — I see no way out, see no light.

Strindberg gave no sign of life, when I bent questioning and longing over his bed in farewell, early next morning.

XI

BRÜNN IN OLD MORAVIA

October — November 1893

THE ANTIBARBARUS

OUR parting proved that we could not live without each other.

Before I arrived in Vienna two telegrams had come from Strindberg, offering to join me there. . . .

If almost three weeks elapsed before we did meet again, it was because he felt mentally and I, physically, worn out, and because my dear good sister had some home truths to say to each of us, by word of mouth as well as to him in writing.

Now we were nomads without a home and had come to live in the fine old Moravian capital, Brünn, between Berlin and Vienna, chiefly for the very reason that it lay on the way, and also because two grand-nieces of Grandfather's lived there, who might, I imagined, help me over my troublesome time. Alas, in an unkind late autumn garb the town, usually so bright and so attractive, looked like a widow who has grown careless of her appearance; it was black with smoke, its streets filled with fog, oppressive, hopeless. We lived in two rooms, one looked out on to a dismal courtyard, the other on the Theresia glacis. The whole day long the gloomy, leafless trees stared at us, covered with greyish-white hoar frost. In the evening, pallid lights were mirrored in the permanently muddy pavements. We had only one petroleum lamp. By its feeble light, my husband dictated to me every evening in German portions of his new chemical combative pamphlet, 'Antibarbarus', on which he had been working in Swedish all day. His day's work lasted ten hours, yet he showed no trace of fatigue when he laid down his pen.

A wordless compromise had been arrived at. He no longer made experiments, he merely carried on arguments in writing with Master Sulphur, who had remained behind in Berlin. I saw nothing to object to in this.

At first, Strindberg had tried to find his way back from research to authorship. He once more had taken up the Axel Borg novel which he had begun and abandoned in Heligoland. But in the suffocating sulphuric atmosphere of this room, Axel did still worse than when confronted by the mahogany splendours of Gravesend. For two days, Strindberg had carried Axel in his mind, gently and carefully as though he wanted to protect him from assassins. It was distressing how the fires seethed in him in vain. But by the third day he knew it was not to be and, white-faced but determined, he laid Axel Borg to his eternal rest in the Green Bag. He took refuge once more in research. He could not create here but he could think anywhere. Nor did he really wish to produce just now. His thoughts could not endure to be clothed in pictures, they demanded to confront naked the secrets of Nature. Before he should have unravelled these secrets, there could be no rest for August Strindberg.

I had undertaken to keep house. So by day I was Martha, who, in the merciful intervals of humiliating nausea, cooked and cleaned in the smoky little kitchen. But, lo, in the evenings, I was Mary — the other Mary of Magdala — with all her perfumes and ointments, borrowed from my sister's elaborate dressing-table.

I also owned, from my brother-in-law, an enormous, white, glittering inkstand. Strindberg and I went on working together.

And then the bare little room vanished, became unreal and had lost all its terrors, all traces of penury. Rembrandt's

'Man with the Gold Helmet' looked down upon us protectingly. I sat at the table. The little lamp with its pale opal glass shade lighted up the paper and my hand, beyond this it threw only a brief and pallid gleam which was extinguished long before it reached the wall. Strindberg strode to and fro, from darkness into light, from light into darkness. Rhythmically, elastically, he strode, listening to his own words, for hours at a time. Enjoying the strife, confident of victory, the deep, metallic voice went on and on. Often he suddenly stood still, hands in his pockets, as if startled by the truth and boldness of his own vision; threw back his head defiantly and looked expectantly at me. Then his eyes sparkled, large, round, phosphorescent, in glorious wildness. Triumph was in the lines of the mouth, now soft and kind as a woman's. One against all, so he stood there, a light in the darkness, in the dimness of the bare, strange, poverty-stricken room . . . 'War upon the overweening monster of inaction . . . war upon intellectual paralysis . . . Forward, Antibarbarus!'

God knows, it was a savage rending and tearing and being torn and rent. It was a matchless feeling of power as well. The words fell like blows of a club.

The man with the golden helmet twinkled approvingly from the wall.

'Antibarbarus' was divided into four letters, which took the form of discourses of a teacher with his pupil, which Strindberg used to go through daily with me, or, to be exact, with himself. Every objection was dealt with before it had been made. Every misconception had been foreseen and was stifled. It was a crossing of lightnings, a sparkling whetting of thoughts, which clarified themselves, were steeled and sorted even as they shaped themselves in words.

In the First Letter of 'Antibarbarus', Strindberg strove to prove that sulphur is not an element, but analogous in nature to a fossilized resin — that it therefore consists of carbon, hydrogen and oxygen.

The Second Letter, the most important in the book, proclaimed the theory of transmutation, as applicable to all the elements. Here Strindberg affirmed that mercury also was no element, but, subject to fitting conditions, could be transmuted into silver and gold.[1]

In the Third Letter, he cast doubts upon the ruling theories as to the composition of the air and the indivisibility of nitrogen.

And in the Fourth and last letter, he sought finally to explain many of the substances we call elements as combinations of hydrogen and oxygen.

'*The World as it is and the World as I see it*', was the subject.

It was an unequal, an impossible fight, for in the year 1893 he stood alone with his theory of transmutation, the entire body of contemporary science ranged against him. He attacked a Science, ancient and established for centuries, in one of its most rigid dogmas. The Faculty had all the auxiliaries of research at its command, he at one time had not even money to buy a small hammer. Experiments on a grand scale were absolutely beyond his reach.

He is contented only to inspire. He does not expect to reap, he will only sow, that Life may continue to live.

[1] Here we already see the prophetic character in Strindberg's theories. Firstly, modern chemistry has actually discovered in the meantime that mercury is not an element but a composite substance like chlorine, silicium, borax and bromine, just as Strindberg asserted. Secondly, that same body of orthodox science which ridiculed Strindberg's belief in artificial gold, now assents to the possibility of manufacturing it synthetically. Thirdly, it shares to-day with Strindberg the general theoretical preliminary of such production namely, the transmutability of the chemical elements, although it is not long since it opposed Strindberg's theory of transmutation by the conception of the elements as something fixed and immutable. Again, chemistry has entirely adopted the idea of a prime substance as basis of all matter which Strindberg promulgated more than three decades ago, to the horror of all chemical experts of his day. Finally, the physical chemists of our time recognize Strindberg's apparently so daring assumption that mercury is the most suitable material for the attempted production of artificial gold.

'I sit down by the wayside' (he dictates to me), 'to rest for a moment, for I have staggered through the darkness, have groped my way forward, have run against self-contradictions and have stumbled here and there over new, dawning probabilities. Sometimes I have seen a light shine in the deepest pit. I thought I was nearing it, but then it blew out. A thought flew by, I tried to catch it, but it was a bat that fluttered away and vanished in the darkness. 'I am so deep in the mountain that I cannot turn back, for no Ariadne has given me a guiding thread to fasten at the entrance.

'So I rest for a moment and then I shall proceed, in the hope that later, perhaps, someone will come to look for me, alive or dead . . .'

'Alive . . . or dead . . .' I repeat, obediently writing. And then I stop abruptly. I shiver and with lips grown white I stammer tonelessly the last word again. . . .

BODY AND SOUL

To experience is not the same as to know. With experience comes the first real knowledge. In Berlin, Strindberg had once spoken of the remarkable condition in which his spirit forsook the body and de-materialized itself. Now I have seen it with my own eyes.

For a long time past, the intensity with which he worked had had its effects upon his nerves. Like wires which one stretches until they are attenuated to an incredible thinness, every fibre in him is stressed. He tastes the joy of thinking, as another would some material pleasure, to the last drop. I believe the solution of a problem affords him that feeling of life in its highest potency which another only knows in the joy of love. There is the same radiance, when he tells me of some new productive process, some captured intuitive perception, as when he has been lying in my arms. Then the world belongs to him.

I stand in the doorway to his room and call him, it is time

for dinner. He does not hear me. I see him seated at his writing-table. Straight he sits, upright, rigid. I call once more. Again he does not hear me. And only when I drew nearer to him, frightened, and place my hand timidly upon his shoulder, does he turn round. Now I have seen a corpse come back to life. I have seen a dead form to which the spirit slowly returns before my eyes, changing from an inanimate shape into a sentient being. It has taken perhaps half a minute, perhaps a whole minute. Perhaps two minutes — but when August Strindberg has once more become fully August Strindberg and body and soul are one again, I am lying on the floor in a deep faint. I would not like ever to behold this resurrection again. It was dreadful.

He is pale-faced during the few days that ensue — his features furrowed like a field ravaged by an earthquake. It has affected him terribly, but he studies himself as he would study some other man and he is satisfied with the result, does not haggle about the price.

'That was really interesting,' he says simply, with a look of delighted recognition. And that makes up for everything.

But there comes seasons for both of us on lower planes. As it has been from the very beginning of our marriage, the afternoons belong almost entirely to me. Here at Brünn we most unfortunately dispense very often with our customary promenade, Autumn in Brünn is unfriendly this year. All the buildings, even the private houses, smoke their pipes in public, and the smoke lies heavy on one's chest in clots of fog. Once it begins to rain, the soot comes trickling down like black threads. So we prefer to stay at home, close the windows tight and draw the curtains. We light the lamp and I make tea. We sit at the table and then — the whole day we look forward like children to this 'and then' — we give way to our great passion — we go travelling on the map. We go globe-trotting every afternoon now. Free from earthly ballast, unburdened. We fly as no bird, as not even the quickest bullet, can fly. As hardly a magic carpet could take us, together round the world.

He owns an imposing atlas. We open it with a caress on the big table in front of the couch and chair. Then we discuss eagerly where we shall go now and what we shall do there. Of course, at first we never quite agree as to the goal of the journey. At the moment, his main curiosity is prompted by geological questions, whereas my route is dictated almost entirely by the climate. Thus, yesterday we were in Lapland, and he would like to return there to-day, but I have just now a real horror of the snowy wastes and of the sledges which he likes so much. I need the Sun and I tell him so, plainly if apologetically. He excuses his love of snow by a laughing lie, saying that he is descended from the Laplanders.

'That is also why I sometimes drink my inspiration out of human skulls,' he adds, reassuringly. But to-day we are to travel south. We agree upon Rome, that is where we will stay for a while. A German and a Scandinavian colony are there. He knows the leaders of the one, I of the other. His play, *The Father*, will probably be produced this season. That will make us famous in the Eternal City.

'If you think of it,' says he, 'we really have everything necessary to run an important literary salon.' I agree heartily. That suits me excellently. We shall keep house in Rome. There is no doubt that all the conspicuous people are delighted to visit us. We do not need to bother about that at all. Our difficulty is in deciding who shall be admitted to our intimate circle. I point out that one cannot well ignore old Björnsen without insulting Norway in his person. Strindberg, on the contrary, thinks Norway now has younger men and it would end in Björnsen getting a salon and not we. Old Björnsen, he declares, now talks ceaselessly and insists on being always right. All interesting themes and problems are shut out by his sermons. I feel hurt, for Björnsen was a girlish enthusiasm of mine; and therefore — from sheer contrariness — I make out a list of guests at my first reception which consists of Scandinavian and German artists who are all well known for the fact that they do not exactly preach! Strindberg, however, will have no joking where my respectability is in question. His face darkens:

'I see already that you want to surround yourself with a disreputable crowd. I shall not introduce you to any of my friends.'

'Then I cannot invite them.'

'Very well, if you insist, I shall introduce you . . . but as my mistress and not as my wife. You will not have a salon but a saloon in Rome; there you can do the honours all by yourself. I beg to be excused.'

I stand up without a word, with all the dignity which now I shall never display in our Roman salon. Without a word and with a rhythmic sweep of skirt I leave the room. But unfortunately I do not get far. The bedroom in Brünn is too small for flourishes. In this sleeping-car of ours there is nothing for it but to go to bed. Sighing, I creep under the coverlets in the dark. Rome and its thousand lights have faded.

I lie quite motionless and ponder, until all of a sudden a mad fit of merriment convulses me. And I laugh, laugh at both of us.

Carefully the door opens at the sound of these scales of mirth. He is already sorry that he so cruelly nipped our salon in the bud. Now he thinks I am crying, bends over my bed and wants to comfort me. But I laugh happily in his face and he laughs happily too.

He: 'Do you know what I miss in the voluminous Goethe biographies and what would interest me most?'

I: '. . .?'
He: 'How he lived with his Christiane Vulpius.'
I: '. . .!'

He does not live too badly with his Christiane. Sometimes he even calls me Gretchen and joyously trills then from Gounod's *Faust*. But to be happy we need more than happiness.

I believe in my husband. I believe in the unity of creation. I believe in the transmutation of the elements, I believe in the nerve system of plants and that they are able to produce silicic acid and carbonic acid. I believe that sun, moon, and earth behave as Strindberg teaches and not as it says in the calendar; I believe in the whole 'Antibarbarus' and in his synthesis of gold, and that one day men will be able to extract precious metals even from common ones . . . But I know perfectly well that all this will not help us to pay our way.

Did he not write himself, a few days ago: 'I lack money sorely and one cannot live on fame.' Demands for money are beginning to come in from Finland, sometimes direct from the mother, sometimes from the children's guardian, and to fulfil these is not only a duty but a command.

'She is always yelling for money!' says Strindberg, of Frau von Essen, as he mops the sweat from his brow, and tries in his despair to persuade himself that it is a war-cry and not a cry for help. But his troubles make him ill.

What shall we do?

Both of us are incapable of earning money at the moment. We are under the spell of a physiological force — both of us.

I am about to bear a child; he is giving birth to a new man in himself who shall in turn give birth to a new art. They decide for us; we are not the creators at all, we are only the material out of which they form themselves. The child will come into the world when it will. He will write again —

when it will. One must submit and care for and nurture it meanwhile.

This settled our immediate future. There is for us two only one place where food and drink are always to be had in plenty and where one need not work in order to eat. It is the house of my grandparents in Dornach on the Danube.

We call Dornach Schlaraffia — the land of the Phaecians — and I grew up disliking it. Father never sets a foot on its soil, he considers it too vulgar. Sister despises it, because its display is a shameless insult offered by the body to the spirit; she is afraid of it too, because mother and grandmother blindly adore children, and would like at all costs to keep Mitzi's little son there — no matter what the parents want. Every visit causes regular pitched battles for the child. Dornach, in fact, bears a strong resemblance to a bewitched harbour, enemy to Hymen, out of which no ship of marriage escapes quite unharmed back to sea. There gather widows whose husbands are still alive elsewhere and orphans whose fathers are not dead. It has always appeared to me like a negation of love. It is the last place that I should freely choose — but I have no other choice.

XII

DORNACH—THE BIG HOUSE

November 1893 to March 1894

THE PRODIGAL DAUGHTER

STRINDBERG was insatiable in studying ever new phases of humanity? Well, here in Austria was his chance.

The journey itself was a rich experience. Since it was a railway affair this time and no dream excursion by map, we travelled of course third class. In Moravia (in 1893) this takes only people who have very little money but heaps of luggage. Every traveller brings his whole earthly possessions with him into the compartment. They consist as a rule of a loudly wailing babe with a dozen of its elders and whatever else goes with it. Trunks are not customary; huge bundles are wrapped up in patriarchal sheets and feather-bed slips. They stick up to the roof, roll about under one's feet, and barricade the corridors. Some are blue chequered, some red, some were once white. If you look at them steadily, you soon imagine you catch glimpses of hundreds and thousands of small creatures housing in their folds. It is most fortunate that Strindberg takes a scientific interest in all insects as well as in all men. He at once begins to make friends — first with the shy peasants and their wives. With a delightful courtesy, he accepts an apple from a grizzled dame and offers her husband cigarettes in return. Naturally he cannot bite the apple which is hard as a stone and his neighbour does not know what to do with the tiny white tubelets. One usually smokes a pipe or, on Sunday, a Virginia cigar, long and thin, with a straw running through its length, as do the old Emperor and my distinguished father. It is only towards the end of the journey, when the creatures in the bundles also embark on explorations of their own, that Strindberg wriggles uncomfortably on his seat and earnestly remarks: 'My dear, once I lived a whole year among French peasants, but this experience is new to me.'

It is evening when we reach the last railway station, Amstetten in Lower Austria. From here it is an hour's journey by sledge to the Danube.

Our ready money just sufficed to pay the fare. Strindberg grows positively stiff with horror when he discovers on the platform that I have not even enough left to pay the porter who has carried the luggage. And two sledge-drivers are competitively racing towards us already. Everyone in the neighbourhood knows grandfather and his family.

'Who is to pay for it?' Strindberg asks himself as I patronizingly choose the better of the two.

'The driver pays the porter!' I laugh, but Strindberg takes it seriously: 'What kind of an entry will it be, to the house of my wife's grandparents?' 'Mother will see to it. Our grandparents will know nothing about it,' I comfort him. This matter does not cause me a moment's worry. Mother has had to be financially rescued by her mother every day of her life. It is only keeping up the tradition if her daughter also allows herself to be rescued. It is nothing new in the family, as far as the women are concerned. They are all in debt. The more money they have, the more they spend . . . To be sure, when rich people unnecessarily live beyond their means, it is a little weakness. When poor people do it, it is a great sin. We are sinners, he and I.

The wind comes blowing down from Bohemia, icy and cutting. The region is not inviting at first sight. In order to make it pleasing to my husband's eyes, I become historical and my stories go back to the Huns, who swarmed over these valleys under Attila. We are here in 'The Nibelungen-land'. Then I speak of the Avars, who came after them. The Romans, too, were here for centuries and left Roman roads, dykes and buildings behind them. This at once diverts Strindberg's mind from the money difficulty. How unimportant is an unpaid porter, compared with the fact that the Huns were once the dreaded lords of the land. This restores Strindberg's self-consciousness. He has no real community of race with the Huns, but when he is in a good humour he likes to play the dramatic possibilities of such a relationship. Yes, 'his ancestors, the Huns', were conquerors here, and under Gustavus Adolphus the victorious Swedes came perilously near the spot which is to receive us to-day as guests. He was not altogether an intruder here, therefore, he had already a claim on this soil.

Our way leads through a bit of pine-woods, not very large, but much beloved by gipsies who have had their camp here since time immemorial. They crouch about an open fire. Women and ragged children storm towards our sledge to beg. How fortunate that the driver does not stop, it would have been frightfully embarrassing to have to refuse them alms just because — from a purseholder's point of view — we were no other and no better than they.

Strindberg regrets that he has not enjoyed a syllable of their conversation; he resolves to take the next opportunity of doing so. He has been tracing the roots of the old Romany back to the Egyptians in the Royal Library of Stockholm. Now he would like to know whether the Austro-Hungarian gipsy has preserved his language in its integrity. And we drive on through the icy night. 'It is not as cold as this even in Sweden', remarks Strindberg. 'And yet in summer we have a southern climate,' I comfort him, 'figs ripen, melons do well, it is often terribly hot'. He finds this quite exciting, there must be atmospheric reasons for it.

Now the landscape suddenly unfolds itself and the river is

before us, majestically broad between its banks. It no longer resembles a river at all, having covered itself with masses of ice and snow. The sandbanks in the middle of the stream stand up above the water and snow is all over everything. Where the bed of the river is free of spits of land, ice is driving alone in heavy snow-laden blocks. All this glitters under the moon in millions of blue and white sparks. On the other shore, a ponderous, threefold big building rises up with at least a dozen eyes of light behind the windows — Grandfather's house, Dornach.

'Are they expecting us, then?'

'No, they have no suspicion of the happiness awaiting them. In Dornach nobody ever announces the day and hour of their arrival.'

'And so many lights? Are they afraid of the dark?'

I had never thought of that. I looked at him, taken aback. It was true that Grandmother never entered a dark room. She was afraid of robbers, ghosts, God knows what she was afraid of—strange, how he came upon such a train of thought.

The innkeeper on the shore pays the driver, who has paid the porter, and the driver thanks us for the tip, just as the porter had done. Then a shrill whistle sounds; the boatman in Dornach on the other side of the river is warned that someone wants him. We soon hear the boat grating on the pebbles as it is pushed off. At the same moment the lights go up in all the hitherto black windows of the big house: they know now, this can only be the prodigal daughter, coming so late at night. Well, let her come. The fatted calf need not be slain especially for her — it is always ready. 'Welcome home' — So I read the scroll of light in the hearts of the long glittering row and I respond dumbly.

THE BIG HOUSE

Dr. Cornelius Reischl, my grandfather on my mother's side, with his severe lady, Maria, had settled on his large estate, situated in one of the loveliest parts of the Strudengau, between Mauthausen and Grein, to occupy himself with agriculture and cattle, hunting and fishing. They had resided here ever since Grandfather, who had been a Notary Public in Upper Austria, had retired from that position. By great industry and clever speculation he had amassed what the average citizen would consider a pretty considerable fortune besides acquiring some fine house property in Vienna. He rewarded himself by purchasing this country estate. It was a substitute for the hard work to which he had been accustomed all his life long. He could not have endured having nothing to do. Here he fell into bed at night, exhausted from the exertions of a day's hunting, just as he had formerly sunk into a dreamless sleep after a day spent on documents and Stock Exchange reports. Grandmother had been a much-fêted Viennese beauty with cornflower-blue eyes and raven hair. Kriehuber, the famous pastel painter and portraitist of the 'seventies in Vienna, had immortalized her. She was accustomed to reign over men and she reigned over her husband even now though she was bent with age and walked with a cane. Instead of the numerous admirers who used to be at her beck and call, she had her army of maids, all devoutly respectful. In addition to these professional vassals, there was a many-headed crowd of penniless relations who turned up every summer, with children and children's children, at this land of milk and honey. Grandfather went hunting every day and shot more venison, pheasants, partridges, hares or wild duck than would have provisioned a small army. Grandmother had twenty-seven cows in the byre. Every cow had her own milkmaid and every milkmaid had a man. The fourteen dogs and twenty cats helped to devour the bounty, but it was impossible to get rid of the whole. The tables groaned under splendid venison, huge joints, tender vegetables and delicate fruit, of Grandfather's own growing. Most of it ended in the pig trough. In this house they did not understand how to enjoy life or even how to live luxuriously, but one had plenty and was proud of it — one could afford it.

In the building of the big house, too, which was called 'Dornach' after the district, usefulness and price alone had been considered, not beauty. It stood close to the river, secluded from it only by the wide highway and by the 'Treppelweg', a narrow footpath, running at a lower level.

The river was very becoming to the house. Although now, in winter, clad only by leafless espalier fruit trees and clasped in the bare arms of wistaria, it looked just as cold and cheerless as road, stream and forest, it yet commanded the whole region, being its highest point, just as Grandfather and Grandmother commanded all the inhabitants. Originally it had consisted only of what was now the centre; this had been one story high and had eight windows in front and a great balcony of wrought iron. But as the family and flocks increased, a story had been added and two wings, first one to the right, then one to the left — not out of a feeling for symmetry, but in order to shield the house from the winds. These wings were a story higher than the centre, the two wings thrust forward into the garden on both sides like huge blocks from the sky, newly whitewashed, each with six black points of windows like dice. If the whole could lay no claim to architectural beauty, these wings at least lent the house a touch of originality and adventurousness. A broad-branched fig tree stood in the middle of the garden, doing well, in spite of its being so far from its southern home.

This was all in a world of its own. For many leagues all around the land belonged to Grandfather and he could hardly reach the boundaries of his hunt, which also included the Danube swamp-pastures, in a day's march. Apart from a couple of isolated small farmers and a few cottages, no one lived in the near neighbourhood. The food which the estate itself did not produce was brought by the postman every noon from the little town of Grein; letters came twice a day in a great leather bag, along with the newspapers, over the river from Ardagger-Amstetten. This exhausted the connections with the outside world.

Of the family of which August Strindberg was now to become a part, only Grandfather, Grandmother and my Mother were present at the moment. His attitude to these three was as considerate as possible and altogether charming. Between mother and himself he had erected a barrier of friendly respect and he conducted everything personal by way of me. As a hostess, Grandmother, among a number of other good qualities, had one which was particularly attractive to us; she did not require our company at all. That is to say, she was not fond of my husband. There was a reason for this. Grandmother was accustomed to admiration. She still had a set of teeth of unusual beauty and regularity. In spite of her age, only one tooth was missing and she was very clever at concealing this. All the same, Strindberg had remarked the gap at the first glance and, seeing that he did so, 'Urline', as we called her, never forgave him. She would have preferred never to see him or be seen by him; he made her uncomfortable. But Grandfather was sociable and during meals he made us pay the price for bed, meat and drink, in that he talked and lectured without intermission, naturally only on the most serious themes and from the standpoint of a studious reader of the deeper reviews. It was a great delight to him to read whenever rheumatism prevented him from hunting, and it often did. My father used to send him papers and periodicals in such quantities that the old gentleman filled all his leisure hours with them. August Strindberg now received the contents of this reading dished up at lunch and dinner. Strindberg was always courteous, obliging and tolerant, never showed the slightest sign of superiority and was willing to allow the bygone age its little vanities. He also played chess with Grandfather, as one plays with a child. Grandfather always won and I often did not know which of the two exercised the greater skill that this might eternally be the case.

We saw little of the family except at meals. Grandfather lived in the 'royal apartments' on the first story of the centre building, with a balcony. Grandmother lived in the left wing over the stables, for her speciality was the dairy and she liked the smell of well-matured manure. The immense dunghill was indeed worth seeing and we never called it anything but Mont Blanc. Mother and we lived one story higher up, in the apartments of the Crown Prince. We saw very little of mother. She held herself aloof, her son-in-law was still in love with his wife and the child had not yet arrived. Mother bided her time; she knew that it would come. So we two were alone together and were happy. Now we had room enough. We had separate bedrooms. Each had another separate room to rest in and to work in, and this was so glorious that for a long time we were never parted at all and wandered, inseparable, from one room to another. Strindberg's beloved Sulphur and the like also had their separate quarters. Strindberg had turned a large room with two windows into a regular alchemist's den. There his pots and test tubes often glowed over the lamps at night and truly hellish fumes filled the air. For sulphur was still an object of close study, though no longer the one and only. It had resigned, so Strindberg stoutly believed, its title as an element, but although now it was merely a 'species of fossilized resin', yet it continued to exhale the same smell as of old. Had any uninitiated visitor entered, he would have suspected some weird mystery, for the laboratory had a medieval air.

What made Strindberg happiest was Grandfather's library. He found treasures there, venerable works of natural history. Grandfather had once taken over this library as a default payment, after the death of an eccentric old man who possessed nothing but books. Grandfather felt they were better than nothing, but at the time he did not think much of them. And when he saw Strindberg's eyes light up, he shook his head: evidently the race of lunatics was never to die out.

Outside the river roared so loudly that it could be heard even with the windows shut. We had a wide view from the windows, looking upstream as far as the castle of Wallsee. There the Danube rolls broad and easygoing past the wide green meadows of the Naarn, from Linz to Grein; to the north are the flat lands, with mountains in the background and in the far south beckons the snow-white chain of the Alps. Once there was a Roman fort in Wallsee, the principal end and aim of which was to see that the strict Roman frontier laws were respected. Now — remember we are in 1893, the castle has got itself done up for high society. The youngest, ugliest and most pious daughter of Emperor Francis Joseph I, the Archduchess Marie Valérie, has married her archducal cousin, lives here and presents him with a baby every year. Each time the excellent village doctor is called in and this has been the making of him.

At first I had feared the impression the country and the people might make on Strindberg. They were so primitive. But he had the glory of his imagination within himself, and saw everything deep and rich and mysterious. He loved the simplicity of the landscape, loved the bare white walls of the house. He loved a neutral kind of nature, which did not force its especial atmosphere upon him, but left room for unlimited possibilities. Everything transformed itself into a drama in his eyes — an all too obvious romance would have repelled him like an obtrusive stage back-drop. He gradually taught me also to see Dornach thus, so that I can never forget it.

There were evenings when the far-off Styrian Alps glowed mysteriously in the sunset with a coppery glare and the metallic gleam fell far-flung upon the Danube shores and steeped the iron cross on the Kolmütz hill church — across the river — in a flaming red.

CHRISTMAS, 1893

Thus the first Christmas of our marriage came upon us. We determined to celebrate it all by ourselves. I undertook to provide a Christmas tree. In the big house everyone went to bed early, all the doors and entrances being carefully locked and bolted. But Naz, the old servant whose business this was, had helped me to forbidden things since I was five years old. He had given me unripe fruit, and shown me the little new-born calves, or had taken me, hidden under the hay, out to the fields in the wagon and had let me drink sweet cider out of the farm hands' great stone jug. And my good old Naz left the door of the wood-shed, leading out into the woods, open that night. When everyone was asleep, we slunk out like two robbers, August Strindberg and I, to fetch the tree that Naz had felled for us — our own Christmas Tree!

The others had none. Christmas Eve was celebrated here, in accordance with the spirit and habits of the Big House, with pomp and plenty, but prosaically. The family gave each other no presents, they would not think of being so childish. But the table was more overladen than ever. We drank 'champagne' which was of Grandfather's own concoction, but which, in spite of this, had an excellent taste and did not behave badly until afterwards. After dinner the staff received their presents in the Royal Apartments, which they never entered at any other time. Men and women, twenty-seven of them, were called in to receive their Christmas presents, consisting of money, shoes, stockings, pipes, aprons, caps, dresses and other useful articles.

To everyone's surprise, after the general present-giving was over, Strindberg stepped forward, with a shy smile, past the much astonished master of the house, who held the mistaken opinion that giving was a privilege of the rich; and he dealt out his presents too. Each wench received a silver gulden. For the men he did still more. A couple of days previously he had received from my sister in Vienna a tin of Bosnian tobacco, of which he was very fond. This he gave them.

When it was all over, he had to sit down and play a game of chess with Grandfather. This took some time, for the old gentleman was more than usually in earnest and triumphed whenever he could cry 'Check'.

Meanwhile I slipped upstairs to our tree to get it ready. The stem had been fixed into a firm base of wood and it stood straight as a lance in the window embrasure. I had piled twigs around its foot and no decorations marred the glorious green branches; only slim wax candles shimmered silvery white and a tiny wax angel was throned on the topmost point. The table looked splendid. From my mother, who was a great collector of sacerdotal lace, I had begged a cloth edged with real Gothic linen lace. Upon it, in great scented bunches, were the white and pink 'Christmas roses' which my faithful Resi had sent me from Mondsee. She did every year. I loved them so much. In between were the presents. There was a big bottle of Antoine copying-ink, a splendid new eagle-feather pen. Then there were two block frames for Strindberg's paintings and huge tubes of oil colours from Vienna and a bottle of Swedish punch which brother-in-law Weyr and my sister had sent. And a pair of soft slippers were there, on which, symbolically and very badly, I had embroidered a red rose. Brother Sulphur and his kin had their own gift-board, with retorts and lamps for the alchemist's den, mortars and crucibles and such necessary adjuncts to the secret ceremonies. That, unfortunately, was all — and I was ashamed of it, it was very little.

But when Strindberg came into the room and I saw how

his eyes lighted up, I felt like a Croesus. He caressed me with his eyes and kissed the Christmas roses with a look. Then he went to his desk and took out a little pencil drawing, his picture at thirteen, drawn by himself — a little saint, full of a pious faith. This was to belong to me, to me alone.

Then he blew out the lamp. And suddenly it was as though the room was full of the Moon, the Night and Eternity. Behind the radiant Christmas tree, the river glittered magically and the sky arched overhead in deepest blue. The little candle-flames shone like the silvery mirror of the Danube, until they went out, one by one, and left us in darkness, alone with the moonlight and the luminous stream. The invigorating, odorous breath of the Christmas roses hung in the air.

'I have never been so happy,' he said softly.

That evening he told me an ancient legend:
The people of the earth were enduring very hard times. Particularly one poor woman wept and longed for something that she could not find anywhere. The little angels of God in Heaven, who pity the poor and sorrowful, saw this — and they ran away from the Throne of God, into the dark clouds that hide the Heavens from the sight of man. And they stamped their little feet until they had stamped holes in the clouds — men called them 'stars' and in them they catch a glimpse of the Heavens.

DANUBE SPELL

The New Year did not keep the promise that the old had made. We went through grey days. As the Danube fog often shut us out from the light with impenetrable walls, so impenetrable Strindberg's past often stood between him and me. This murderous past had burrowed itself deep into his mind, as the river burrows its bed, and every new emotion flowed down that way and was caught in the maelstrom of memories. The past devoured the present, the Shadow devoured the Reality. At times Strindberg imagined conflicts between himself and me which never took place, but for him they were as real as his plays. It came about then that he would speak words to me that I was already familiar with, that I had already read and heard. In his eyes I wore the garb of his first wife and behaved as, in his mind, she would behave. And he hated me then as he hated her, visioned crimes of which I was guilty (that I had never committed) and forgave me for them and loved me again — as he had loved her. That was the worst of all! . . . Sometimes I no longer knew — was it I at all that he loved and hated or was it the other, still the other, only the other? Or were we both but a poet's fiction, a larvae, out of which she had crept and which I was now wearing?

Pregnant with witchcraft were such days. This was not in vain the 'Nibelungen-land'. Atavism ruled. Then he became once more the Hun, the son of the steppes, who glides like a shadow through the towering grass on moonlight nights, living amidst danger and for the love of it, bearing death and scenting death with every instinct. The spell of the Earth came over me at such times and often I would sit and look fixedly out on the river and the plain, while my wedded mate tore me to pieces in word and thought — and I would ask myself whether in this landscape, these gentle hills covered with orchards, something did not survive of the ancient evil powers of cruel heathen gods.

His distrust fell upon me now. When estranged friends sent news more and more rarely into our loneliness, he would watch me darkly and respond coldly to my kiss. I was bewildered and horrified, but for a long time I could not think what it was he suspected, until one day . . .

Dornach was connected with the outer world only by the post from Ardagger, which was fetched across the river twice a day and carried in a stout brown leather bag that had once belonged to Grandfather. From childhood on I had been accustomed to watch this bag arrive. Then I ran down joyfully to meet it punctual to the minute, with Feldmann, my faithful dog. Never had we raced quicker than now, Feldmann and I, now that I hoped day by day to be able to bring Strindberg good news. The Antibarbarus was being got ready for publication in Berlin. That must put new life into him.

It was a stormy day, ice blocks drove down the river, the post boat was late. And just that day Strindberg was expecting a message and a book, to which he was looking forward keenly. At last the man came into sight through the grey snow. He was still battling with the floating ice. Feldmann and I stood waiting on the 'Treppelweg', although wind and snow were whipping my cheek sore, and impatiently I tore the bag from the man's hand. I opened it on the way, anxious to convince myself that this time the wait had not been in vain; but the bag merely contained unimportant letters for mother and myself — nothing for Strindberg.

He stood on the threshhold of his room as I slowly returned.

His face was pallid and he seized me by the hand:

'Tell me how long you have been doing this?'

He did not wait for an answer, but turned his back on me with a look of unspeakable contempt and locked himself into his room.

He remained in his room that whole day and the next and the day after that. He did not open the door. Neither to me, who begged him to; nor to mother, who implored him; nor to the maid, who hammered lustily four times a day and then had to deposit the meals outside and to take them away again later untouched, four times a day. Deathly silence reigns in his room. Gradually this deathly silence spreads over the whole house. Everyone was afraid — no one knew of what.

Grandfather wanted to call in the police, Grandmother,

the doctor, mother, the priest. I sat with tears of stone, like Niobe. The insult he had put upon me was long since forgotten. I only trembled for him. The evening of the third day had come. No light in his room, no sound. I sat before the threshold and brooded, determined, if nothing else helped, to smash open the door. I wanted to prevent the worst, at least. Or to see the horror with my own eyes. Then suddenly a sound came from within the room like a muffled shot. The report could be heard all over the house. Mother came running in her nightgown, Grandfather stumbled up in his pants. I threw myself against the door with a wild scream.

The excitement was entirely unnecessary — the door spread wide of its own accord — and Strindberg stood invitingly, smiling, all friendliness and very much astonished, in the opening. I fell at his feet without a word. I had fainted.

Grandfather took it ill. Grandmother took it worse than ill. Even mother, who idolized him, thought that this time he had gone a little too far — in what way, no one exactly knew.

But as he sat by my bed, he explained the whole thing in a perfectly lucid fashion; indeed, it seemed so natural, as he explained, that it really needed no explanation; he had simply wished for quiet because he needed it. Since the expected letter had not come — he was expecting some important information from Paris concerning an astronomical problem — he had decided to work out the problem himself without outside assistance. He summoned up his entire energies and — all the better, perhaps, for the little quarrel with me — had thrown himself on his bed, clothes and all. Lying flat on his back, he could always think best. He had brought about a kind of trance, which he had often found useful for the birth of an idea out of his subconsciousness. In this state of trance he had continued until his thought had crystallized. It had been a slow and painful evolution but it led up to a happy result. Now the problem was solved and this very night — as soon as I should be asleep — he meant to inform Flammarion and the Société Astronomique in Paris without further loss of time. The matter was very interesting. The moon . . .

'And the shot?' I interrupted him, still trembling at the thought.

'Shot . . . ?'

No shot had been fired. What we had heard was not any Wild West revolver; only the poor, faithful little bath-tub which accompanied him everywhere! This time it had not been used for two days, while he had lain in the trance; and when, after this unwonted neglect, he coolly ventured to step into it just as usual, to take a cold sponge-down before returning to the outer world, it had revolted under his foot and had protested by a cry of pain — that was all.

There were unwritten laws in our marriage, neither he nor I had laid them down and yet we both respected them. One of them was that we never explained things to one another when we had been parted by misunderstanding or quarrel. We feared the weakness of the spoken word — in its incompleteness, it might fail. Always a silent kiss was my refuge — from him, from myself, from fate. And Strindberg always put his arm about me, kindly and protectingly, as if some third person had threatened us. I was full of fear, he of sadness and sympathy. This strange feeling of impending fate gave to our love something ethereal and winged. It was a death ride over crackling ice and bottomless depths, but these sunny winter days were beautiful.

TROUBLE ABOUT THE MOON

Our asylum began to shake in its foundations.

August Strindberg, who so long had endured the well-meant but trying conversation of our grandparents at lunch and dinner, at which Grandfather mercilessly served up his whole culture and erudition, at last one day, tardily but indubitably, wounded Grandfather's vanity. After discussing many other topics, they had come to speak of Nietzsche. Grandfather had been studying a very dogmatic essay on the Superman, by a fossilized German professor of philosophy, and he was in a mood to dogmatize on the subject himself for the benefit of Strindberg. This chanced, however, to be one of Strindberg's special themes — a theme on which he was a master. He proceeded to refute the old gentleman, politely, but with determination. 'Have you read Ludwig Stein?' sternly asked Grandfather, playing his trump card, for he thought the opinion of a professor at the university settled such matters once and for ever. 'No, but I have read Nietzsche himself,' was Strindberg's uncompromising reply. It seemed equivalent to calling Grandfather a dunce!

Alas, the 'dunce' was the old Imperial and Royal Austrian notary, retired, Dr. Cornelius Reischl, to whom Dornach belonged and who had so magnanimously undertaken the upkeep of the impecunious young couple. And in return he was not even allowed to be cleverer than this presumptuous guest of his! . . . Strindberg, on reflection, would gladly have made amends, but it was too late. Grandfather began to look upon him as an interloper and to treat him as such, displaying his superiority on grounds where it really existed and he could make it felt — in the sphere of finance. By the very next day he had contrived his vengeance and asked Strindberg with a perfidious sweetness, what he was working upon at the moment. Strindberg, usually so mistrustful, suspected no evil and related, beaming with joy, that he was on the track of new discoveries. 'Indeed, indeed — in what field?' was the next question. — 'Astronomy.' — 'Indeed!'

Strindberg went on to explain that he was engaged in taking a picture of the moon. He was photographing it by a perfectly new system of his own, on a plate covered with bromide of silver which he had lying on his writing-desk in a bath of developer, exposed to the moon's rays. Without camera or lens, this would give quite a new sort of picture.

'Indeed, indeed — you simply lay the plate on the writing-desk . . .?'

'That's it — just think!'

This kind of 'thinking', however, was not one of Grandfather's talents. As he always did in difficult situations, he asked Grandmother's opinion. Grandmother's ideas were always clear and definite and had for quite a while occupied themselves with Strindberg's astronomy. She no longer knew exactly what she had learned at school about the matter — that could not be expected of her — but she did know that it had sounded vastly different from Strindberg's statements; and when a man imagines he knows more than his teachers, then he was in her eyes a fool, who would bring home, wife and child to ruin. There was no doubt in her mind about this — and the rest.

With difficulty, they refrained from telling Strindberg so to his face.

But was it necessary to say such a thing to Strindberg? He felt everything, he suffered and began to think of flight.

We knew that sooner or later some kind of blow was in store for us, but we did not want to admit it to ourselves. Just now, scientific ideas rushed in upon Strindberg from all sides. An unknown Flora was waiting for him here. A short time before, in the woods, he had been surprised and delighted to see a kind of moss that he had long desired. Now he was waiting impatiently for the coming of spring. Then there was my cyclamen garden, which I had cultivated since I was ten years old. Near the house a hill rose above the Danube and by the side of the path was a small plateau surrounded by hazel bushes. Here I had planted beds of cyclamen, fetching the finest bulbs from wherever I found them. This had been my pride. He did not yet know the Alpine cyclamen, but found it contained revelations. Both of us were looking forward to the day when they would bloom.

And then geology! Upstream lay a large granite quarry belonging to a certain Anton Schlipitzka and his son Fritz. But the problem of geology also depended upon the attitude of science towards the problem of transmutation. Before that was solved, there would be no order in geology. Geology, petrography and mineralogy of the future — that was all one study.

Then, suddenly, it seemed as if the Heavens were resolved to comfort us. We went for a walk every afternoon at four o'clock, along the road leading to Grein. To the left it was bounded by wooded hills and rocks, to the right the Danube rolled on down below in its broad bed. Thus, unexpectedly, we saw 'IT' for the first time. That is, Strindberg saw it, I could only see it after a long search. It manifested itself as a small black point on the face of the Sun. Strindberg at first believed it to be a high-flying balloon, until at length it occurred to him that it might be a planet — probably Mercury. He fondly nursed this thought, but we would not say with certainty that it was Mercury; indeed, he expressed doubt. One thing he knew, it could not be Venus. The last occultation of Venus had taken place in 1882. There was not to be another until 2004. No, it could not be Mercury, either (it was larger than Mercury, Strindberg thought, and probably about as large as a Jupiter moon) and it seemed to move between Mercury and the Sun.

The discovery of such a new heavenly body would have been of so much importance — not for a poor ignoramus like me, to be sure, who was as little excited about it as about the gold — but for serious astronomers, that we determined to keep IT to ourselves for the present. 'Otherwise one exposes oneself to all kinds of attacks by sceptics.' But we gave IT a beautiful name — Odin. Whatever it may have been — even if IT were only a poet's dream — we saw Odin.

*

Unfortunately, Grandfather was soon to be in luck. The proceedings against *The Confession of a Fool* in the Berlin courts were to take place in March and the defendant was now served with a summons. The bailiff presented himself at the Big House; and as a preliminary Strindberg was called upon to report himself at the police station in Grein. Grandfather was in the garden when the policeman from Grein importantly turned up and inquired after one August Johann Strindberg. Never since Grandfather's house had been his house had a human being lived in it who was 'wanted' by the Law. Grandfather, as notary public, was wholeheartedly on the Law's side and blindly and relentlessly condemned all those who came into conflict with it.

Strindberg argued that he, as a Swede, had no obligations towards the police officials of the little town of Grein, but Grandfather's voice assumed its menacing authority:

'You will go and present yourself to the police to-morrow,' he decreed.

Strindberg, taken aback at this insult, grew pale and went upstairs without a word.

In Grandmother's big drawing-room, which normally was only used when tiresome visitors had come or when solemn reassemblings of the family were necessary, the family held council. The decision reached was that Strindberg must leave the house. As an act of mercy, I might be allowed to stay — in consideration of my condition.

'Without my husband? You don't really mean that?'

No, they did not really mean it. Grandmother had foreseen that I would resist, she had a suggestion to offer; some time ago, she had bought a small hut — not much better than a hovel — out of the profits of her dairy-farm. It faced the road to one side of the Big House gardens. It was only one story high and was built of grey stone, but she had not minded that. A bit of ploughed land belonged to it and Grandmother had an immediate use for it as she was in difficulties where to keep a young Italian donkey called 'Lumpi' whose call for independence made him unpopular with man and beast, for he let neither cows nor milkmaids alone. Lumpi had not been long on the estate, having come as a gift from son-in-law Weyr, and he, being rich and successsful, was held in high honour. So Lumpi had an extra stable built for him near to the cottage. Patient old Naz was appointed his body servant. What about this hut, politely called a 'cottage' — could we perhaps live there? We should then have a roof over our heads and the family would be rid of us, mused my resourceful grandmother.

Dampness trickled from the walls and the interior yawned empty and dismal. But I threw my arms about Grandmother and thanked her enthusiastically. Everyone drew a sigh of relief; they had expected tears and angry words.

I hastened back to Strindberg, stole up the stairs and opened the door softly. He did not turn round. He sat quietly, without a movement, in front of a table covered with written papers, scientific works in big piles and the bromide of silver plate which had photographically registered the picture of the moon without camera or lens. The roaring of the river sounded monotonously from beneath us. The evening glow flickered redly on the little church on the other side of the water.

'August!'

He did not turn round. Only looked in front of him; stared at the round hills. I went up to him, he did not hear me. I put my arms round his neck — he started; I thought he would have fallen. It was an awakening, but not from an ordinary sleep (his eyes had been wide open) — it was forced, painful return from another world. The same phenomenon which had horrified me in Brünn was manifest again. His soul had broken bounds and deserted the body. It was a long time before he came to himself. . . .

'Everything has turned out for the best,' I said at last, 'we are to have a home of our own. Grandmother will lend us the house, Aunt will find the furniture. Mother the linen. And then — the child will come to us soon.'

The hut did not strike him as poverty-stricken, nor damp, nor dismal, nor unhealthy. It seemed to him glorious, beautiful beyond compare. It stood a little raised up from the road. At our feet was the river, behind us the dark masses of the forest, a field spread out to the right. An old pump stood under the pear tree before the door, it had not been working for a long time, but it looked most decorative. The roof was of thatch and a grave-looking crow flew up from it slowly as we entered. Lumpi screamed shrilly for joy and bade us welcome — I was the only person with whom he had really made friends.

The same evening Strindberg departed for Berlin, to hurry on the printing of 'Antibarbarus'.

The farewell from the owners of the Big House which he was to enter no more was cool and formal. There were only a few hours left in which to get ready for the journey. He scarcely took the time to give me a little book which the post had only just brought.

It was printed in Karlstad, Sweden, and in it the most important leaders of northern literature had manifested their faith in Strindberg — England, too, was represented. All of them magnificently, nobly enthusiastic. The title of it was *The Book of Strindberg*.

The book became my friend and my support.

'Let us thank God that he is gone,' said Grandmother. 'The man is out of his senses, a lunatic! Fancy, he actually believes that he knows better than the Academy! Who, pray, is August Strindberg? I for one, never heard of him before he married you.'

To this question the 'Book' replies: Who is August Strindberg? Let Knut Hamsun tell her!

'August Strindberg is the most important author of his country, perhaps of our times. He is a supreme genius, a brain on horseback, charging his own way, leaving all others far behind. He is a live challenge to everyone and everything and is everywhere at home. He is the heaven-sent event in Nordic literature, the man who has imbued it with a new life. He is a hero burning with the sacred fire, a worshipper of beauty, yet ready to sacrifice it without hesitation to the welfare of humanity. He is a Seer, shedding light upon the future and penetrating the shadows of the present.

'He is a fighter against the evil powers. One, who would fain banish misery from the world. He is a radical reactionary, who wants to cut short the false path and go back to make a new beginning, who will not progress further with over-development, but wants man to return to the primitive instinct, to retreat from hyperculture back to nature, until the straight way lies plain and unhindered before our eyes once more. . . .'

'Ah, grannie . . .' I say. 'There you have Strindberg . . . before he married me!'

But she has fallen asleep.

FRIEDRICHSHAGEN, NEAR BERLIN, AND DORNACH

March 1894

LIVING CORPSES

August Strindberg, Berlin, to Freda Strindberg, Dornach

'Dear Freda: After a horrible journey *via* Prague and night in hotel, I arrived in Berlin on Easter Monday. Everything was shut and I had no money. On Tuesday I pawned my wedding-ring and my watch. Hildebrand had not collected the royalties from Kürschner, we wrote a bill of exchange. Lidfors, who had delivered the script in time, had not been paid either, and when I insisted that he should be, it came to words.

'The day after, the present Manager, after telling a score of lies, gave me to understand that 'Antibarbarus' had better appear in autumn instead of now. Then the real fight began and I threatened to publish the book myself. Finally, after indescribable scenes, they gave me a promise for April 1st, and I went to Friedrichshagen to read my proofs in peace and here I am still. Most of the text is now actually set up and the book could be ready next week.

'You see that it was high time I came and it seemed to me that the "Bureau" is on the point of going bankrupt. The translation of "Letter IV" is good, by Lidfors and Scheerbart, a German. Typography hideous.

'My lawyer was despondent. Things looked black . . . then I arrived at the crucial moment. Since the Prosecutor had concentrated his attack on one main point, namely:

"The book, with its broad details, was written with intent to arouse the sensuality of the reader," it was easy for me to prove the contrary. I requested my cousin Oscar in Stockholm to confirm the fact that he had received the manuscript of the *Plaidoyer* into safe keeping in 1889, in order to whitewash my name after my death, which was expected at that time.

'This will prove that the book was not written for publication and still less with the idea of pandering to voluptuousness . . . and so on. The case is as good as won and the book must be released.

'I am not having a pleasant time here, alone and short of money. But I congratulate myself on having come. To have stayed away might have cost me the summer and perhaps the future. Printing here is going on unusually slow and I am not certain whether I can leave next week. This procrastination of the "Bureau" is a mystery to me.

'As for Dornach . . . after the last events, I have rather unpleasant memories of it. I do not know whether it will be there that we shall meet again. Love.—August.'

Berlin, alas! was a disillusion.

Once more spring was at the doors. Once more, the soil was busy germinating. Strindberg had come storming out of his solitude; like a whirlwind of impatient young rested and hoarded-up energy he entered, carrying with him loads of achievements. Joyous, proud, the same as a year ago — he stood before his disciples and waited for them to open their hands — even as a year ago — to receive what he had to give. But they did not open their hands. What he had given them a year ago sufficed the ordinary mortal for a lifetime. Since then they had divided his mantle. The awkward thing about Strindberg's mantle was that it was too voluminous and too heavy, as a whole it oppressed people. But it could be used to advantage in separate, detached bits which could conveniently be handled and held tight. The many disciples had all become petty masters, each cleverly building his own tabernacle.

Strindberg felt disgust and sorrow. You cannot steal an idea alive, it dies at the touch of ruthless hands. Had he not said once that the thought and the work of art took on real life only the moment they struck a spark in others? He could beget, but the seed must find soil to grow in. Hence his need to assemble disciples about him — people who had faith in him.

Now he again lived in Friedrichshagen, where Lidfors lived. He was to have been Strindberg's scientific legatee, Peter, the Rock. But Peter, too, was a weak mortal. He lay as before in Aspasia's bonds — and he must choose between him and her.

Aspasia, now Dagny Przybyszewska, had founded a salon in Berlin. The younger literary world went there, to proclaim in trumpet tones, freely borrowed from Strindberg — the creed of the Great God Pan. 'Pan' also was to be the name of a new literary art magazine. As moneyed people were at the head, it would take on an impressive form.

Aspasia's salon consisted of one room rather shabbily furnished. It could not conceal that it had a past. A deep cleft showed for over a yard parallel to the window like an ugly scar, although Przybyszewski's books now filled in the cavity. There was only one table, facing which the two chairs the room could boast were placed. Over it hung the lamp, which, as an accentuated symbol of a deliberate, obligatory voluptuousness, was draped with a disreputable crimson shade. The chairs were nearly always occupied by the two oldest friends of the house, Munch and Lidfors, drinking in silence. But guests made themselves comfortable, just as the books had found their niche. The intellectual riches made up for any other lack. The salon was very inspiring. Aspasia danced enchantingly, Stachu played the piano ravishingly; he often played the whole night long. In order to keep the neighbours from protesting, the instrument had been inventively isolated and dampened with cardboard. Toddy flowed in streams here, as once at Hansson's and nobody knew or asked whence it came. Neither did anyone ask where the ideas came from. No one was disturbed by the fact that they had originally belonged to August Strindberg. They fluttered about as if in their own home — Aspasia was their young mother.

If one of the faithful or the Lady of the Manor herself, she most frequently, felt their hearts tighten in consequence of the never-ceasing flow of toddy, the suffering one would silently withdraw from the room. If he or she failed to reappear after a reasonable lapse of time, one knew where he would be found — not far off. Protectingly he was fetched back into the midst of his peers.

Strindberg would have liked to rescue Munch, whose qualities as a painter he greatly admired, the foolish Pole, who sank ever deeper into the swamp of alcohol, and the still more foolish Lidfors. But they were the prey of love.

Schleich, on the contrary, was full of enthusiasm for 'Antibarbarus'. He recognized the wealth of enlightening ideas, fertilizing suggestions. But he also had fears, he knew the experts and the public.

He advised Strindberg to submit his gold samples (our flakes of gold on parchment), to recognized authorities for analysis. Strindberg was ready to do it. An analysis was what he wished for and needed. The probability of encountering prejudiced opposition did not affect him. In spite of all his pessimism, he was a boundless optimist. Or rather, he was so great a pessimist that he regarded evil experiences as unavoidable and did not trouble to go out of their way.

Therefore Schleich and he set forth with their neatly gold-sprinkled sheets and laid them before the respected professors Liebreich and Landoldt for examination.

They were politely welcomed. But Liebreich contrived to put off his testimony to some uncertain distant date and Landoldt's opinion was negative on the spot. He stated that copper (which had been a main ingredient) was no longer present; in fact, that it had been transmuted. But he continued to deny the possibility of what he himself had stated.[1]

There was no return to the Past. Strindberg and Schleich had gone to the Schwarze Ferkel to recover from this meeting with Science and indeed the very first glance at the creature over the entrance had been comforting. There were children now! Next to the fat old mother pig dangled two small pig-skins, which had been sent from their ancestral home in Armenia and carefully stuffed. But unfortunately the proprietors, Herr and Frau Türke, were of opinion that one should provide for one's progeny. They had enlarged the tavern by a room on the upper floor, expensively fitted up to suit a worldly crowd of gay young army officers and correspondingly dear. Strindberg's Ferkel had become one of the sights of Berlin. It began to smell of commercialism.

The good spirits refused to appear. Even merry memory turned into a disillusion.

[1] The conversation is reproduced in Schleich's book of memories.
'Landoldt: "Out of what is this made?" Strindberg: "Out of copper". – "What is it supposed to be?" – "Gold." – "No, it is not copper, neither is it gold. I do not know what it is – I have never handled such a substance." – "Then perhaps it is a something between, an intermediate stage."
'Here I would remark' (says Schleich) 'how little Strindberg insisted that he had made gold, he only insisted on the idea of the transmutation and mutability of metals. He was not seeking gold, but a new law of nature.
'Landoldt: "No, my dear Sir, if you can ever bring me the proof that one metal can be transmuted into another, I will bow to the earth before you and this little leaf of metal will prove you to be a great chemist." Strindberg bowed with proud irony as if taking some of this immortality on account and said: "Who knows. Perhaps we shall both live to see it". "Not we!" sneered Landoldt and ushered us out, a pair of fools.'

They ought not to have come to the Ferkel. It was no longer the old animal. It was altered. To take an exact view, it seemed that its great days were over. It had given birth to progeny and now it was dead. And since it was really dead, August Strindberg felt as if it were a ghost, which would haunt him for a long time to come.

The 'Tallow Dip' began to glow anew, was spirited into realms of myth and achieved a form. It had been a creation of his imagination, now it threatened to cow him. It crouched on his shoulders and gripped him tight — a living corpse.

A cleft had opened between Strindberg and his former intimates. Between him and Lidfors it became an abyss.

They rode into town one morning from Friedrichshagen. The whole time Lidfors kept his hand in his pocket. Strindberg sat opposite him and did not take his eyes off him. He, too, now kept his hand in his pocket and this hand grasped a knife. If it should be necessary. . . .

Things had become impossible.

*

I received letters, one from Schleich, one from Neumann-Hofer, another from someone I scarcely knew. Evidently they all felt uncomfortable, wished to warn me and did not dare. Strindberg himself wrote little. It was not necessary — I knew so well — all had failed.

When I sit alone now in the evening, I see him with my mind's eye . . . with hard lines round his mouth and a tired, disappointed look . . . He does not speak. What use——? I want to protect him and try to comfort him.— 'It isn't really so bad,' I say to him. 'It can't last. There will be a change, there must. Why, you are Strindberg. . . .'

DORNACH—THE HUT

April to end of May 1894

OUR HAPPIEST DAYS

Iт had been no easy matter to make the hut — our 'Häusel' — fit to live in. From its birth on, it had never served any but the very poorest as a dwelling and had stood empty for over a year; dirt and dampness had eaten their way into the walls. I went to work at once and it was astonishing what I achieved in the first few days with the aid of lime-wash, soap, swab and scrubbing-brush, although the old well which was rusty and rotted finally gave out altogether. However, things were soon so far in order that Strindberg could come. Come he must. At the moment, there was no other corner of the earth ready to shelter him. Only after he should be at peace with himself and his problems once more would he feel free to face life again anywhere.

But it was longer before he came than I had expected. Sun set and rose again, my birthday came and went by unnoticed. Was it really only a year since our bridal day, really only one single year?

I waited for him all day long, I waited for him at night. Endlessly long days — until one morning, at 3 o'clock, a noise mounted through the darkness from the river. A boat worked its way towards the shore. Then came hushed voices. At such an hour, it could only be he. The boat grounded. In the grey light of dawn, the Flying Dutchman climbed up the bank. August Strindberg had come home.

Strindberg's narrative[1]

'Their hut of grey blocks, its little windows barred with wrought iron and framed in sandstone, was a perfect idyll. It suggested some cloistral abode and was covered with creeper. The walls of the rooms were whitewashed, and had no wallpapers; the low ceilings had heavy beams, grown black with age.

'He occupied a small room shaped like a regular monk's cell: long narrow, with one single small window at the narrow end. The walls were so thick that flowers could stand on the window-sill outside as well as in the embrasure inside. The furniture was old-fashioned, fitting for its surroundings. Here he housed his library; he had never felt so much at home in his life.

'Now, though, it was time to prepare for the coming of the child. Husband and wife painted the window-frames and the doors. To the right and left of the entrance outside they planted roses and clematis. The garden was dug and seeds sown.

'The empty white spaces of the walls yawned void. He painted canvases to fill them up.

'When all was finished they sat down and admired their handiwork.

'It is glorious! Now we are ready to receive the child. How glad it will be to see so many pictures on its very first day.'

'They waited and hoped; in the long spring evenings they talked only of him (or her); tried to guess which it would be, spoke of its name, tried to imagine what the future of the child might be. The woman's thoughts mostly turned about the question of whether the child would be fair and resemble his boy, whom she loved. . . .'

*

Now began the most glorious joy in all our life together. For the first time, August Strindberg was his very self,

[1] Autobiography.

without compulsion. We were free, delivered from the
oppression of other peoples' atmosphere. He now created
surroundings after his own heart and lived in his own way.
In the early morning he went for a walk in the quiet, silvery,
fragrant Danube marsh-pastures; in their long grass he
met only the fleet heron and shy water-birds, flowers and
creatures of the wild. There nothing chained down his
thought. Just as silent and still was the monk's narrow cell
of stone. There he sat hour after hour in the midst of his
books, with a medieval cap on his head, his short brown
wooden pipe on the table beside him, in a loose jacket, like
a Dr. Faust, permeated by the suggestive influence of the
dress and the surroundings. Through the bars of the window,
spring's fresh green fingers beckoned invitingly and the birds
often came to his table and even hopped upon his papers,
when he tempted them with dainties. He kept a luxurious
birds' restaurant and knew exactly what each guest would
prefer. He knew their notes; and established the fact that
the oriole of the Danube sang differently from the oriole
of the Seine — 'Gidleo, zitadidlio, gigilio, gidiagidiglio, gid-
leah' — whereas in France he only sang 'flyoflio'. From his
cell, through the open door, he could hear me coming and
going over my housework, as I cooked, scrubbed and did
the washing. It was not easy, for, the well having failed us,
all the water had now to be fetched in buckets from the
Danube, up fifty yards of steep, stony ground and I had no
help. But this life seemed heavenly to me and there was no
shadow on our companionship.

Like me, he loved the brown, warm earth, flowers, plants
and trees. He created a blossoming garden where a wilderness had been. He worked on the field that ran down hill
from the woods, dug and planted it in the sweat of his brow.
It was a merry picture. Years ago, my father had been
presented by an explorer with an English tropical suit,
probably the first ever seen in Vienna. He passed it on to

Grandfather Reischl, who had hung it in a cupboard and showed it occasionally to visitors thought worthy of the honour, as a curiosity. Mother had now contrived to have the suit descend from Uhl's father-in-law to Uhl's son-in-law, thus providing at once coolness and the exotic note. Soon the little bit of land around the hut contained a wide choice of international products. Strindberg had planted practically every flower and vegetable that could endure the climate. And as a good landlord he knew exactly how all this gentry liked to be lodged and fed and that plants are most particular not only in respect to the food for their roots, but also in respect to their neighbours, that they do well in certain company and in others wilt and die — just like that higher animal, man. He knew everything that a man knows when he loves.

He laughed at my surprise over his knowledge.

'In the garden and in the fields you learn more botany than from books,' he said. 'That is why we will now proceed to reform the falsely-directed lore of plants a little from our hut eyrie. Above all, it would be proved that plants are by no means so very different from animals. They possess the five animal functions, nourishment, digestion, circulation, respiration, propagation. The processes of life are the same in the whole of nature, only their intensity varies. The plant has a circulation of juices comparable to that of man, it has a heart which acts as a pump. It sleeps and wakes, it can be intoxicated and narcotized; it is a mechanician and a chemist. Its method of propagation is strikingly like that of animals.'

This time Strindberg's fever for knowledge has seized me also. Chemistry was too remote for me, but now there is no discrepancy between us. Both of us love flowers passionately — he and I. We could spend hours bending over them. He narcotizes them with morphia like human beings. He can put them in a state of catalepsy. He knows every sensitive place they have and all their vital spots.

Spring is not yet far enough advanced. Up to now we have not many specimens at hand for experimental purposes. After the birth of the child, however, we mean to make a thorough study of the nerves of plants. Impatiens, of which mother already sent him the seeds last autumn, is now to play an important part. From it he expects a number of revelations, the *Impatiens noli me tangere* is one of the most sensitive souls. 'The Beautiful Viennese' — thus the Viennese grower christened a vermilion *Impatiens Holstii* — 'is so easily excited!' he teases, with a meaning look at me.

'You mustn't use the Beautiful Viennese for vivisection,' I beg of him. But he really has behaved most cruelly to a hyacinth. He wanted to study her nerves; to this end they must first be coloured with osmium. Once treated with this colouring, even the finest nerve-fibres, otherwise indiscernible, could be seen under the microscope. Before they would allow themselves to be coloured, however — the nerves must be swollen up and this could only be brought about, he surmised — by subjecting the plant to abnormal excitement. How can one over-excite a flower? Strindberg knew all too well the usual cause of over-excited nerves, a thorough annoyance does it as a rule. Was it a question of thoroughly annoying the hyacinth? He knew how to go about it. Do her roots like water? He let them dangle near the surface of the water in her glass, and as soon as she stretched down to reach it, he drew some off — until the horrid Tantalus torment brought about a regular swelling. The nerves of the poor offended thing were now actually visible owing to the colouring matter and their existence easy to prove. It was a great success, but finally Strindberg himself agreed with me — it was not the way to treat a noble flower.

It was not possible for him to avoid studying me also. One evening he begged me for a little service in connection with my approaching accouchement. The general conception was that 'Bringing forth children' was the punishment

T   289

for eating the Forbidden Fruit in Paradise. But Strindberg did not believe in the pains. He believed that childbed is still part of the joys of 'sin', all of which are not done away with. Ignorance on the subject was only due to the fact, on the one hand, that it is hard to draw the line between utmost joy and pain; on the other hand, woman is prone to lying. Since no man had ever set a child in the world — up to now — there existed no real trustworthy evidence. He hoped from me, as his wedded wife, that I would help the Truth to victory at last. Of course, I readily gave him my pledge. Who would not like to combine the useful with the pleasant?

This was a true idyll. Even between Strindberg and the crow there has gradually developed a friendship based upon understanding and shared meals. The solemn and solitary bird gave an open and arrogant display of the fact that he was a philosopher and a woman-hater, if not, indeed, a Strindbergian. We called him Pythagoras.

Between the donkey Lumpi and Strindberg, relations remained formal. There was mutual tolerance, but that was all. Perhaps Strindberg would not have put up with Lumpi at all, but Lumpi had an inimitable way of constituting himself my protector on all walks. He must be one of the party when I left the house. Whoever dared approach me, he flung up his hind legs so wildly that the oncomer remained at a respectful distance. Strindberg appreciated this in his wife's donkey. He could entrust me to him.

CERTAIN RICH YOUNG MAN

Spring came, soft and mild. We were sitting together one afternoon in the monk's cell. Suddenly he stood up: 'Now the messenger will soon be here with the post, he has just pushed off the boat from Ardagger.'

The shore is too far distant for anyone to be able to tell

with the naked eye what boat is pushing off. And the window looked out at our Mont Blanc, as we call it, not over the river. Nevertheless, he was right; the messenger had just pushed off from the farther shore. My field-glass confirmed it, as I hurried out to look.

'Are you expecting letters to-day . . .?' I asked, hesitatingly.

'No, but your sister is sending you the layette for the child. . . .'

There had never been any question of this. I knew nothing about it, he had never corresponded with my sister. But the baby linen came, just as he had said, by the messenger, in that very hour.

Such 'supernatural' occurrences interest Strindberg as phenomena, but do not particularly surprise him. 'Through our nervous system we were bound up with Cosmos as well as with Tellus,' said he, and for people with refined senses this meant a more or less developed relationship to all creation and to all humanity.

Strindberg follows closely the development of the embryo within me and makes me a daily diagram. Still more closely, however, does he follow the development of the intellectual seed which he has sown in his 'Antibarbarus'. The book went forth into the world weeks ago, clothed unassumingly in yellow paper. One copy he dedicated to Friedrich Uhl in Vienna: 'To my good father-in-law from the prodigal son and author . . . "A failure still and now perhaps successful".' To his friends and to well-known scientists (among them Haeckel of Jena, the father of Monism) he had also sent the book accompanied by warm words of introduction, like a beloved son who must go among strangers. And now, day by day, we waited for news from the outside world.

The first reviews that found their way to us were censorious and uncomprehending — the earliest and sharpest from a Swedish newspaper which had until then been friendly to him. Its notice was disdainful and sneering, with little sly stabs and personal allusions, as well as references to subjects that had not been touched upon in the book. It could only be by someone who knew him well. Strindberg could not believe it at first, but soon he knew that the writer was Bengt Lidfors. That hurt twofold. We knew since his last trip to Berlin that Lidfors now belonged to Aspasia.

Financially, we were in a very bad way. Postage and chemical experiments were costing more than we possessed. I had got to the point when I set a '?' (to be interpreted as a negation) behind the word 'assets'. To put it plainly, we were subsisting largely from pilfering. It no longer sufficed for me to starve myself in secret, honest purchases or even debts would no longer supply meals for Strindberg alone. And yet we had a right to live. Every morning, when day was breaking, I crept forth to poach. In the 'asparagus garden' the first shoots were ready for the gentry's table. Grandmother kept an Argus eye on the treasure, although there was enough for a dozen families and it merely rotted and went bad. Feldmann, most savage of all the dogs, kept watch that no one should have a chance to make use of it. Feldmann would tear any thief to pieces. Therefore, Grandmother could not imagine how it was that every day a number of the earliest and finest sprouts were missing. She forgot that Feldmann and I had been friends since he was a puppy and that her grandchild was now in want. Feldmann, however, did not forget it, and carried the basket up to our door for me. And sometimes it happened that I fell on his neck, laughing and crying. We had a secret, my faithful hound and I. My parents must never know, still less my husband.

But I admitted to myself that our future looked black.

Then, one morning, there is a fanfare of silver trumpets, like a fairy tale. I stare at the newspaper, which has just arrived.

'Do read that. Is that possible? . . . A certain rich young man is said to be living in Paris . . . Albert Langen is his name . . . Comes from Cologne . . . Has millions his parents made in sugar . . . And he's throwing them away now, founding a publishing house . . . to encourage talent.'

'Impossible!'

'Knut Hamsun says so.'

'In that case it must be true. He is a fine fellow . . . Unless Hamsun has gone off his head?'

'What would that matter? The more such men as you and Hamsun go mad, the more infallibly you write the truth.'

And now we have a heated argument, toss up a silver gulden — heads or tails — to see what books we shall first offer to the certain rich young man and which of us shall write him a letter. And at last we agree, Strindberg shall select six books for him as a start and I am to compose the guileful letter.

Long days go by. The rich young man apparently is in no such hurry as we are. Then, at last, when we have already given up expecting it, the answer comes, polite, wearing gloves. Mr. Langen is so sorry and apologizes! He had been most desirous and quite determined indeed to make his call in person, as would have been proper, to tender thanks for the kind letter and the six books. But he had been suddenly prevented — now he begs our pardon and inquires most ingratiatingly whether Herr Strindberg has not perhaps other works in addition to the six already sent which would perhaps be equally suitable for publication in Paris. He is less interested in single books than in the complete works of an author.

He need not pine. We send him six more volumes; although not yet the complete works by a long way, anyhow this is a whole dozen.

Ever since that day, we live on the expectation of Albert Langen's forthcoming cheque. We live very well on it. Immediately we think of Strindberg's young children. At least one of them ought to share our new life and our new prosperity. I want Hans. Strindberg does not agree with me. He votes for Karin, his eldest. 'Karin has talent for teaching,' says Strindberg. 'She is sensible and will give you the least trouble in your present condition ... You could even learn Swedish from her and teach her German. Then you can translate together, as soon as the child is born.'

The letter was a mistake. Of course we were both blinded by our sudden glimpse of Fairyland, but one cannot expect real children between the ages of 7 and 14 to be so childish!

August Strindberg receives an answer from Finland which does all honour to Fröken Karin's good head and her love for her mother, but which strikes her father to the heart. Fröken Karin is of the opinion that if we have enough money to share a princely life with her, we could also send her enough to lead this princely life at home with her own folk. She cannot understand why they should then have to economize and even want for things.

This logic is irrefutable. But it kills Strindberg's firmest faith. This faith in the immortality of the man through his child and in the child had been for many a year his light-house flame in the night, guiding him in stormy seas. Now it has gone out.

This little Miss, who thus admonishes him — can she be the infant he once carried in his arms, whom he had so loved, for whom he had sacrificed himself and his talent and who had once adored him?

The child — what is it? A human being up to its ninth year; then it is no longer a child. The children he had worshipped had indeed ceased to be children as soon as they no longer smiled up at him, showing their little white first teeth — he must needs mourn them as dead.

The child as the continuance of one's personality, as a soul's eternity? No, that was too questionable an idea! He would no longer hear of it.

The disillusion was as bitter as love had been sweet. The cherished link between him and Life was broken — or loosened, for a while at least.

He buried himself in his books for the rest of the day and for the following days. When he appeared again, he was another man. He had pledged himself to a new religion, the Nietzschean cult of the Ego, the preservation of personality, the propagation of the soul by means of POWER — POWER — POWER!

I grew faint at heart. How ill I have chosen the moment to make my début as a mother.

THE EXPERIMENT

At last the hour drew near after which I should not need to beg any other woman for her children.

It is just such an evening as our other beautiful endings of the day. Joyous, still companionship. I am resting, tired but glad at heart. Strindberg, too, has hard work behind him. He tells me of it now; one of his lunar photographs has come out particularly brilliant. He has immediately sent it to Paris, to Camille Flammarion. It will shake the very foundations of the old coelestography — Eureka!

At ten o'clock, proudly satisfied with his solution of a problem supposed to be insoluble, he wishes me 'Good night', and retires to his attic. Dead tired, I fall asleep, but not for long. The moon, which Strindberg fancies he has despoiled of its secrets, glares pitilessly down at me, while I toss in uneasy dreams. Suddenly a wild pain awakens me. I am afraid of being mortally ill. I have imagined childbed as something different, more Maya-like, according to Strindberg and Buddha. I drag myself upstairs.

But my husband carries me down again to my bed as quickly as he can. Then he wakes old Naz. This is no easy task. Only after Strindberg has smashed the door and cursed him into waking, does he arouse. But then he hurries to fetch the *sage femme*.

The midwife was a thoroughly experienced and efficient peasant, respected in stable and sleeping-room alike at the farmhouses of the countryside. Neither woman nor cow had ever perished in her hands. But respect for science has cost more than one mortal his life — it nearly cost ours. Doctor's orders had been that he wished to be 'present when' — therefore the child must wait for the 'Herr Doctor', the physician from Grein, to arrive. As the doctor, unfortunately, had looked upon the wine when it was red that night, there was nothing to be done, thought she, but to delay the delivery until he should once more be able to stand on his feet. By all possible diabolical arts, she actually succeeded in circumventing my child's desire to come into the light of day. I writhed in agony. The peasants passing on the highway heard my moaning and shook their heads. They warned the Big House that there was obviously a sick cow in the hut and that it was being wrongly handled: 'People that don't understand about cattle ought not to be allowed any,' they declared, legitimately indignant.

Only Strindberg assuaged my suffering. Now, too, the healing current streamed from him to me. I clutched his hand fast and never let go of it, never for a moment during all those dreadful hours. It must have been a rack to him, his face was as white as mine, but he did not escape. Again and again he smoothed my pillows, kissed my brow, held me. He did not rest, did not spare himself, took no refreshment. An angel from heaven could not have been kinder.

Then something happened, something so unexpected that
I could not comprehend it. After a specially wild cry of
agony, wrung from me by fiercest pain, I lay exhausted.
And at this moment, he bent over me and said, quietly,
earnestly, so softly that none could hear, but urgently:
'Do not play-act, child; I know well enough that it is sensual pleasure for a woman, not pain.'

The effect was magical. For a second it seemed as though
he were right. My lips, about to yell, gave forth no sound.
I lay still, really felt no pain and stared at Strindberg,
incapable of thought. Hardly were the words spoken,
however, than it seemed to me as if I had only dreamed
them; he took me in his arms as before, helped me into a
more comfortable position at cost of his poor tired self,
dried the perspiration from my brow and smiled as before,
friendly and encouraging.

My body described a wild curve. A loud complaint broke
from me, as though against Man, Nature and God in the
name of all women. . . .

A weak wailing mingled with my cry. A daughter had
been born to August Strindberg.

*

Father's eye takes your measures with a satisfied pride,
little one! You are a success, in spite of my troubles and your
lengthy hesitation. They say you weigh full 9 lbs. and that is
a highly respectable weight for a first-born. And now,
having bathed you, they lay you in a soft bed, in your cradle
with the white veils and blue curtains. Now everything,
everything is well. I cannot remember that it was ever
otherwise. The sun shines in upon us, so warmly. Sleep,
child! Now your father is also going to rest. How we have
tired him, you and I. You must not mind the cloud upon
his brow. Behind the great, high forehead sits the Unknown.
He is always there and when August Strindberg declares
himself ready for happiness, he becomes envious and

demands his share. Thus he was present at your birth. He watched its phases coldly and scientifically. For him we were an object of study. What you, baby, are to your father, that is the Idea to the Unknown. He is all spiritual urge, just as August Strindberg is all father.

Now we are alone, child. Only the sun comes in by the little window. Now he has given you a first kiss. The white blossoms of the pear tree outside are showering down. And the bees are humming a lullaby. The sun to-day is the colour of honey.

DORNACH — THE HUT

June 1894

WIFE IN MAY

THREE days have passed since the birth of the child, the fourth is closing in. Strindberg sits at my bedside, we are deep in discussion. The little girl must at last be given a respectable name; she is still being called 'Mouse'. Baptism, however, is not only a responsible, but also an irresponsible affair. Why should a person be burdened all his life long with a name given him by someone else? We ought to have considered this serious matter long ago, but we expected — Axel, our son. Strindberg wants Elizabeth; I do not, this saint suffered too much. My favourite name is Ingeborg; but he insists on keeping that for me alone. His favourite name is Gretchen. But a daughter of his first marriage is already called so. 'How would you like *Kierstin?*' he asks. 'Goethe did not find it so far from Gretchen to *Christiane.*' — 'Christina, Queen of Sweden,' I agree. 'Well, some day then she can choose for herself whether she wants to be "Christel" or "Christina".'

One hour after. The sun has gone. The child is awake and dining lustily. Mother has come to take the night watch, for we cannot yet afford a maid. She likes the name Christina-Kierstin and transposes it at once into Austrian dialect, calling the little one 'Cherstic'. Strindberg disappears horror-struck.

Her son-in-law has scarcely climbed back to his books before mother starts talking to the point. 'Choosing names is all very well, but bestowing them is the Church's business.' 'In due time.' 'At once, otherwise if the child should happen to die, it would go to Hell.' 'I shan't let it die.' 'Is that for a mortal to decide? It will certainly die if it is not christened. It must be brought to church in Saxen no later than to-morrow.'

The parish of Saxen is an hour away upstream. The only available conveyance is Grandfather's hunting gig drawn by Cupido, an old temperamental cavalry horse. It was always something to survive such a trip. The gig jumped like a ball along the stony and uneven highway in Cupido's wake. A cold wind used to sweep the Danubian plains in May. To expose the child to this ride would ensure its premature entry into Paradise. I therefore refuse to permit the christening until it shall be stronger and the summer nearer. Mother will not hear of worldly considerations — her religious fanaticism forbids. She has soon worked herself up to such an indignation that she rushes out of this abode of sin and leaves me and the child to our own devices. The door bangs, the child cries. I wish to soothe it and struggle to my feet, but my strength fails.

The child screams louder and louder, but in vain. Nobody hears it, not even I. When Strindberg comes down later to get a book on the planetary system which he has forgotten in my room, he finds the child screaming in its cradle and me on the floor unconscious.

Mother returned before nightfall. It was too late, however. I had fever and from then on I could no longer nurse my child.

This was the ruin of us. I will not overrate myself, not even as a mammal. Perhaps any other healthy cow could have taken my place, if only one had protected her from the pernicious influence of sentimental literature. But this was neglected and the cow was a failure.

The doctor had prescribed strictly dry fodder for the

selected cow, as the grass was largely marsh grass and even
the calves suffered from flatulence. Mother, however, who
was sensitive and kind and in her youth had read much
George Sand, feared that the dieted cow might feel hurt and
suffer in her feminine pride — *'la vache incomprise'* — as
Strindberg says. She ordered that juicy green grass should
be secretly placed in the manger.

Thus the cow was spared heartache, but the child grew ill
and remained ill. It suffered. It screamed, screamed till its
poor little face was amber-coloured, screamed day and
night. Day and night I walked the room with it. It would
not allow me to lay it in its cradle. It cried as soon as it
missed the protecting warmth of its mother's body. It looked
at me then with its father's huge, accusing eyes, which
seemed to know everything and to forgive nothing. And it
was as fragile as though all the sins of the world were upon
it; if it must bear but one more, it would die. My heart
broke at the sight of the misery to which I had given life.

It reminded me of the wicked spell in a fairy tale. Spring
had vanished overnight. Everything which had been coming
into bloom, now stared us in the face, murdered and
murderous. No one looked after the garden. It turned into
a desert. The radiance fell from the hut: it was again a damp,
dark peasant's hovel in which there was only one single room
that could be heated. Here the child lived, and when it
rained the child's diapers hung there and dried.

It needs countless numbers. From every tree in the garden,
where there had been blossoms, these diapers now dangle. I
can never wash enough. If it were only less tiring to carry
the water up the steep ascent! I got up too soon after the
confinement. I have no strength.

There is no Gretchen and neither is there a Christiane
Vulpius any longer. Strindberg must renounce my care of
him and put up with the questionable services of a wench
who comes for two hours every morning, makes coffee — bad,

worse, worst — and is ill-tempered. He must eat the food, often grown cold, which is brought to him from the Big House. He has no companion any longer to share his inner life and soothe his outer life.

The monk's cell, too, is lost to him. There is a never-ending coming and going, child's wailing, women's voices. He emigrates with instruments, books and papers to the first floor, where so far only his bed has stood.

Man and wife are no longer one. Now there is an 'Above' and a 'Below'. Each is possessed by the fury of the parental. Each wildly shields his immortality — he, his creative work and I my child.

Each is savagely jealous — I of the Spirit which is estranging him from us, he of his own young, which has robbed him of his mate.

ABOVE AND BELOW

This designation, 'First Floor', is a preposterous fraud; it consists of two attic rooms with whitewashed, thinly bluish walls, without curtains and no shade. One can sleep there, but not live. But he would gladly have moved still higher, he envies Pythagoras on his roof. He envies every tramp who passes by. Full pockets, empty pockets — who cares? Far worse it is to suffocate in this room, so narrow that it cramps his spirit and where the 'Eternal Feminine' has closed up every door and window — plastered it up tight.

His thoughts roamed back to another, far-off summer when he had not yet been a famous man, but free. They had lived in a students' camp, in Kymendö, near Stockholm, in the Scharen. He, Hjalmar, the amateur comedian; Lundin, the dashing young officer; Leopold Litmanson, the violinist — and a few more, whose portraits he later on had drawn in his 'Red Room'. Those had been happy days — often with not one shilling in their pockets — the world belonged to them. Ah, to be free once more, to forget all about the hateful 'Eat and drink, drink and eat, worship of hard cash' of the Big House.

The most gifted of the lot had been Leopold Litmanson. Leopold, with his independent red mane, who was obsessed by his fiddle as he was himself with his ideas. They had called each other Brother, after the fine old Swedish custom between sworn friends. Since then they had lost touch. Litmanson had made a wealthy marriage and lived near Paris, in Versailles, gave concerts now and then and was a man of position.

Paris! Here thoughts of past and future meet: was he, Strindberg, really sentenced to remain here for life, with Paris calling?

The unquenched buoyancy of youth once more bubbles up in him: let him be caged, he defies reality and them. While they wail or scold or wash or cook or count below, he sits now at his window, watching the river flowing down to his sea.

All of a sudden, he finds himself writing to Litmanson, in the spirit of old, the more ferociously gay as he is the more desperate. He jokes, he rhapsodizes, brags and romances, boastingly defiant of reality and striving for power — that last drink of the Dionysian under whose foot all other hope has crumbled. It is his way to fight defeat.

He writes to Litmanson now, almost every day, tries to speak the language of old, to reach his friend where he is most sensitive, set him in motion and, through him, effect his escape. He also writes because he wants to forget his surroundings, or to revenge himself in words for all that he suffers.

But above all he writes because he must cry out both his aspirations and his misery to a human soul, and there is none present, none. He has progressed on his Way toward Truth, he is about to unveil nature and find God — but his mate has failed him and his love has almost died.

⁕

August Strindberg, Dornach, to L.L., Versailles[1]

'We shall soon be fifty and have danced away our milk teeth and ought to be thinking of our end. But I cannot help it, I must laugh when I look at Life and its tricks, damned nasty tricks at times.

'That is why I write to you again to ask whether you are alive and kicking and would like to have me stay somewhere near you this summer as we did in our old Kymendöe camp. I want to learn French, as well as a Swede can.

'Verily, I have grown damned big; there is a bust of me in the Finnish National Museum and two full-lengths in wax-works with a tremendous bush of hair and picturesquely trampish clothes . . . I was hissed in Naples and produced in Rome; judged worthy of an *auto-da-fé* by Sarcey in Paris, etc.

'I have been married twice and have remained a mono-gamist. Have unmasked the whole Universe. — Neverthe-less, Ekström is the greatest of all us contemporaries; he has 6000 Kronen in the Bank and dines with Prince Eugene in the Gothic Room at Berne, where the Red Room used to be. He has lost his front teeth but wears a fur collar on his over-coat.

'Anyhow, if you are living near Paris and if you want me, be so good as to answer by return.'

'. . . Do you know of anyone who would correct my French a bit without manicuring my prose and pruning my claws, which must not be touched? And who would not deduct the postage from the payments and has a clean, clear hand-writing? I should be in Paris by now if I had the fare. Österlind, 177 Boulevard Pereire, promised it me. But I

[1] All quoted letters to L.L. are excerpts from the unpublished originals.

have been expecting it in vain for ten days and dare not dun him so as not to envenom his kind feelings. Do you happen to know him and will you remind him of it? The mischief is that my law suit in Berlin begins to look unpleasant, while in the university town of Göttingen they menace me with arrest for heresy. As you see, my life is still as stormy as it used to be. There were fine interludes, enchanting idylls, but at times it is hellish torture. I am often weary of it. I have had everything I wanted of life and much beyond. Do you remember how I wished to write a play in French at Kymendö? Now, twenty years after, a play of mine is being produced in Paris. "What Youth dreams of, etc." Please be so kind and let me hear on all points. — Cordially, your old Eagle.

'PS. — A telegram received to-day from Lugné Poë justifies me in considering Paris as firm ground.

'Now I do not happen to know how you are situated and I wonder whether my proposition will offend you — or would you like to be my Paris representative and begin business, which might become a huge matter, now at once. . . .'

'I have still another suggestion. You with your fiddle can easily sling the case on your back and tramp or bicycle ahead. Listen: In Hungary, near Totis, lives Prince Esterhazy. He is so infernally rich that he keeps his own orchestra, a theatre, library and stables with about a thousand horses. And he has wine, a whole subterranean church full. This prince saw my *Creditors* in Berlin and went crazy about the play. (I never set eyes on him myself.) *Cavalleria Rusticana* and *Creditors* are to him the summits of modern art. Let us go there as *Fin-de-Siècle* Buddhas (the Troubadour furnishing the coin). We arrive incognito and are then discovered. You become Conductor and Court Composer and I the Princely Librarian and Alchemist. . . .

'But do you happen to know how the Hungarians play the fiddle? Not in D minor, but always *rubato*, like the howling of men. I had dinner one day at the Hotel Bristol, Berlin (of course I was not the one who paid). Champagne perfect and I in the most exuberant spirits. All of a sudden, I heard a noise from an adjoining room. I thought I must have got the Northern Lights in my ears. It sounded like people who cried and moaned and then laughed and snorted in between. It was a Hungarian band playing for Krupp and his friends who happened to be taking a 50,000 Thaler meal there.

'That's a fine proposition. With not a trace of asceticism. Taking to the High Road as in the good old days when the singers and fiddlers went on their knees to the nobles and not to moneybags as they do now.

'You might walk straight in, beg for a position in the orchestra, give them a test — and become a God.

'But you must first provide yourself with a suggestive scalp, a yellow Northern one by all means which haloes round your head, and a blond moustache. Or you might play the Spaniard, with an interesting pointed little Henry IV beard.

'Hungary is flat and the roads along the Danube are excellent for cycling. . . .

'Then there is still another spot that we might try. In Österlind's bathing resort, Finisterre, in Brittany, Zola's publisher, Charpentier, is staying (through us he is to receive the St. Olaf's order) and Sarah Bernhardt is there too. That might be the right place for us, if only I could rake together the funds for the journey.'

'Come, let us have a speculative look at my pictures and see whether they might not sell in the Scandinavian Club? I am sending them off to-morrow. I am also sending you a parcel of ivory Bikupa manuscript paper to keep in stock. Mind you take good care of it. And my winter coat. We shall sell the pictures cheap, about 100 Frs. apiece. Although I sold some in Sweden last year for 1000 Kr. I had an exhibition there, was slated, but not by advanced artists.

'The funny thing is that I was the first to paint symbolic landscapes and lived to see how the whole band of realists turned with the wind. — A.S.'

Mother means so well, would like to see us all safe for Heaven and makes Hell for us all. She wants to coerce Strindberg — or bribe him — into having his child christened according to Catholic rites.

In addition to all other terrors, another Thirty Years' religious war breaks out between the Catholic Big House and the Protestant Hut.

Strindberg was well disposed towards the Catholic Church. He was fascinated by the figure of Mary, Virgin and Mother. The stronghold of this Faith, which admits no questioning, seemed to his tortured mind to promise liberation from the martyrdom of doubt. He would not have opposed the child's being christened and brought up as a Catholic, but he would not hear of any coercion in spiritual matters. Still less could he forgive an attempt at bribery. Mother had held out to him a return to the Big House for himself and his wife and child, and perhaps Mondsee if only he would. . . .

She does not know Strindberg!

When she appeared a few days later with a complete document drawn up by grandfather himself in superb legal phraseology, requesting the priest to christen the child according to the Catholic rite, Strindberg bluntly refused to sign it and sent a letter to his mother-in-law amounting to a declaration of war.

August Strindberg, Dornach, to Maria Uhl, Dornach

'Dear Mother-in-law: We Protestants are tolerant and pretty easy-going in matters of creed, but we do not sell our faith, still less our children. This time you have judged me falsely. Since we are now exiled and I cannot create any source of income before Autumn as long as I stay here, but will not burden the house with my presence now that the child has come, I shall go out into the world for a time to earn my bread, so that I can fulfil my obligations to my family.

'I have one more motive for departure, with which you will no doubt concur, the fear of setting another child in the world, which would effectually seal our ruin.

'You have reproached me with not loving the child. But I am not the mother and the feelings of a father are not of the same nature as the feelings of a mother, as long as the man is healthy-minded.

'Besides, you try to shackle me to this child and yet before its birth, Freda already made arrangements to separate it from me in case of her death. And what efforts have you not made to tear the child from its parents? So you demand that I should bind myself with bonds of love, in order to be lacerated later on?

'That is about all I have to say to you.

'I shall not demean myself to arguments — August Strind-berg.'

Father and Mother Uhl could not endure to live together, but they wrote to each other on every day of their live-long parting. This was father's conception of marital duty and loyalty. This letter from her son-in-law was also sent by Mother Uhl to Father Uhl, to share with him in sorrow as in joy. Friedrich Uhl, however, could read more into these lines than a mere family quarrel. He shuddered when the grim farce which Life enacted between the To Be and the To Have took place in the presence of a genius. And Friedrich Uhl understood that his own child's happiness was at stake.

Red with shame and full of wrath, he telegraphed to the

blind Danube folk: 'Kindly leave the gentleman and his wife alone!'

*

Father's thunderbolt had its effect. For a time all was still on the Danube.

But alas, Germany was also still, a stillness which gradually resembled that of the grave.

'Antibarbarus' had won no victory. It had not even been recognized as a battle-cry. The newspapers were dumb or lukewarm. The scientists whose support the friends of Strindberg had sought to secure for him sneeringly denied his truths. Haeckel alone was encouraging, but in an uncertain fashion and within definite limits. The others would not allow that creative intuition had seen a goal to which there was still no path and damned a knowledge which so far experiment had failed to establish as a fact.

The unnatural stillness around him grew threatening like an unseen danger. There were hours when he could have roared aloud, only to rend this stillness. The effort to kill him had been vain. Were they now trying to bury him alive?

He had lost Berlin. It belonged to the enemy.

But it really was impossible to kill Strindberg without his rising again somewhere.

Paris was the seat of culture, art and the theatre. To be produced on a Paris stage was accounted the highest international acclamation. No Swede had ever yet achieved this honour.

Well, August Strindberg's *Julie* had been played by Antoine in Paris in 1892, and it had broken Ibsen's French record. Now Strindberg's *Creditors* was also to be performed. As one of three authors' one-act plays, each trying to remodel the stage.

Lugné Poë, the founder of the Théatre de l'Oeuvre, a

venture which was rightly considered the most modern play-
house in France, stood godfather. He himself played the
part of Adolf. Herman Bang, the famous Danish author, had
staged the play.

This 21st of June could in no way be called a still and
peaceful evening. It was no mild ebbing of a season in its
last throes. There was a wild fight at the very beginning.
People sprang up on their chairs, screamed and cat-called,
came to fisticuffs the moment the curtain had gone down on
the unsuccessful symbolism of Henri de Régnier.

When Strindberg (last on the bill) finally took the stage,
the audience was still in the mood to rebel. But he over-
powered them — ravished them.

From an article by Herman Bang

'No name is so much storm-shaken at this hour as his. But
this will not last. The storm will pass and, high up — above
the heads of all — the name of Sweden's greatest man will
glow in letters of fire — *August Strindberg*.

'Genius cometh tardily to its own. The more tardily, the
richer, the more untrammelled, the more versatile it is. The
day when the entire Strindberg can be surveyed and
valuated, has not yet come. But even had it dawned, I
should not be adequate to this task.

'So I will speak only of an episode, for the reason that I
was myself a part of it, of the outburst of enthusiasm which
blazed up and bore the name of August Strindberg through
all the great countries of the world. I heard it swell into a
hurricane, a frenzy, in a Parisian theatre, when the Théâtre
de l'Oeuvre played *Creditors* for the first time. Preceding it
a play of mine, *The Brothers*, had been given: it was a
miserable failure. Strindberg strode all the more gloriously
over my defeat, as a volcano smoulders above the place laid
waste.

'The high tide of excitement which greeted his work on this occasion was the baptism of his world fame. Again and again since then his name has broken through and it will force its way on and on, borne on the admiration of the peoples.

'This, I think, is the fact which every thinking Swede must never lose sight of — his fame is that of his native country. The scarlet about his loins becomes kingly, the standard of his country. Greet him, you! Greet him, while the day and the night keep silence. For the centuries will speak.'

*

Once on a time in Stockholm, years ago, a boy was born as son of a serving-maid, and he would not thrive where the sun did not shine: but little enough sunshine was his.

Now, all at once, he has himself become a sun. Even though he is only a small human sun — still he is large enough to shine over all Europe and reflect his fame over his own beloved country.

Paris, city of cities, does honour to August Strindberg! This was not only Life, this was Immortality.

He came down from 'Above' and brought me one telegram from Paris after the other, like tidings of victory from a battlefield. After the dress rehearsal: '*Triomphe*.' — After the first night: '*Grand triomphe*.' In the course of the next few days he brought whole bundles of reviews, letters and telegrams down to 'Below'.

How radiant he was, how every nerve in him vibrated!

But 'Below' had become a vale of tears, where only weeping was heard (for the child was sinking) and no sun could be seen through the tears.

*

August Strindberg, Dornach, to L.L., Versailles

'... Do you know Nietzsche? No? — Ah!

'*The Secret of Life?* Will-power to dominate humanity.

311

'*Happiness?* — To be able to grow and to rule.

'*Unhappiness?* — Not to be able to rule, and to be ruled.

'It is happiness to be staying — as I am — in a peasant's hovel on the Danube, amidst six females who think me half-crazy and to know that at this very moment in Paris, the centre of intellect, five hundred people sit as quiet as mice in a hall and are foolish enough to expose their intellects to my vigour. Some of them revolt. But many of them carry away my stallion-seed embedded in the grey matter of their brains; they go home, pregnant with my ideas and the seeds which fertilized them continue to spread and sprout.

'Six months later I happen to read a French book, a French newspaper — and recognize my children. Ha! That is my grain growing.

'That is happiness. . . .'

'. . . Your eyes were opened early, just like mine. But your scepticism devoured your aspirations. I was lamed for seven years by such scepticism; until, like Kant, I set up a categorical imperative and postulated for myself. "It is all a mass of rubbish," said I, "but let us assume that for the moment, some of it is less utter rubbish than the rest." I invented poets, leaders, reformers, citizens and lords (like Zeus, I alone begot a whole Olympus), engendered fools and cheats, saints and child-like souls. For this continuance I lived. . . .'

'. . . What threatens us most of all?

'The annihilation of our personality, the thought that we shall perish, disappear. That is why we have this hellish unrest in us, for now is the time we must transplant our souls if we want to save them for immortality. A child is a too problematic means.

'Do you see now that ambition is the soul's attempt at self-preservation? . . .'

'. . . Are you again combating a crisis, as I am? — I am always ready to leap off, when I notice that someone is trying to touch my wings. And I am always ready to strike my tents when the atmosphere begins to be tense . . . *And that is the case now.*

'The flesh was your "fatality" and the family mine. But one must be able to go through everything and rise above everything. Forward, on! . . .'

*

'Here I stand now and must come to a decision. Either descend to the Philistines, grow grapes and cabbages, become an heir and overeat myself — or Excelsior!

'Listen —

'Yesterday in the *Journal des Débats,* the following books were announced: Fr. Jolivet-Castelot: *La Vie at l'Âme de la Matière. Etude de Dynachémie.*

'Claude Hemel: *Les Métamorphoses de la Matière,* — Société d'Editions, 4 rue Antoine-Dubois. (Both.)

'Dear friend, buy them. They cost 3.50 frs. each. I haven't a *centime.* Read them first and then send them to me. You do understand, don't you, that they are of the very greatest importance to me?

'I am ill.

'You ask, what I want of you — *I need someone who has faith in me! —* A. S.'

Our refusal to have the child christened made bad blood. Superstition began to concern itself with us. We had a bad reputation. The master was no Christian, but a 'Protestant'. What else he was, no one exactly knew; but there were whisperings. Did not the black crow, that Bird of Hell, follow him on his walks? And in the evenings, did not one even see Old Nick himself in front of the hut, the beast that looked like a horse and yet was none? The gentry said it was a donkey.

One knew what that meant. Had anyone ever seen a donkey in these parts before? The oldest inhabitants could not remember ever to have seen one. At Easter, pious peasant women had come to sell the young mistress consecrated eggs, in the hope of earning an honest penny and of bringing the mistress once more nearer to the Church. But the young mistress had declined the basket, shy and embarrassed, with the excuse that she had no money. That was the first time anyone had ever heard of people of the Big House having no money. Something was not as it should be. And the reputed ass had kicked out frightfully with his hind legs, so that it was only by a miracle that the consecrated eggs could be rescued and did not have to remain on the spot — unpaid for.

The master was given sulky looks or heard a malicious laugh when he encountered any of them along the road.

Pythagoras lives high up. Pythagoras lives on the roof. The roof must be surmounted.

Strindberg arose. High above the roof-trees of men. To heights whither even Pythagoras would no longer be able to follow him. He might be cheated of his Great God Pan, but no one could prevent him from swinging himself upward above Pan and Naturalism into the midst of Supernaturalism, as he called it, and through his researches building up a bridge from the visible to the invisible world.

In Grandfather's library he had met again the Gautama Buddha and had heard from the Sublime one that the seeker after God needs a monastic community and that marriage, with its everyday and petty earthly cares, is lowering to the intellect, which can only reach the summits in the pure sphere of complete detachment. The really spiritualized man — is he not always one who has renounced all possessions and fled the world?

He was weary of the battle of the spirit with the national economy of the nineteenth century. Franciscan ideals swayed him more and more, while the spirit of Christ and the spirit of Buddha wrestled within him and both of them strove against the flesh.

Green and cool, untouched by the grey dust of the broad highway, *Kolmütz Hill* rose up in a gentle slope on the opposite shore of the Danube, crowned with its little church that shone whenever sun or moon was visible. Here Strindberg began to dream an ancient dream anew — the dream of a monastery where the spirit alone should rule. Everyday life was not to penetrate its walls, woman should be banned and earth should not exercise its power through the child.[1] The walls of the cloister should protect the inmates from temptations of the flesh and from defilement. It was a dream of light, purity, love and reconciliation. It was to be a lay monastery, professing no creed, for scientists and poets. Everyone had the right to his own faith and also the right to have none. The purpose was to educate supermen, by means of asceticism and meditation and the practice of learning, literature and art.

The monks should become beggars and wander over the land penniless as once in the days of Luther: 'Grant alms to the travelling scholar!'

It is a moonlight night, silvery and magical. Strindberg and I are sitting together on the bench in front of the hut. It is a long time since we have sat together thus. The child is asleep. It has not slept for several nights and I am so tired and exhausted that my waking hours are like a dream. He speaks tenderly to me, as he has not done for a long time, seeks my soul, fondles my hand — so small and soft, says he, that not a hardness can be felt — and then he looks across

[1] The monastery in *Damascus* is the Benedictine monastery of Melk on the Danube, which Strindberg saw shining in the sun as he rode past it on the water. But the first inspiration for the monastery idea was given by the little Kolmütz Hill, near Ardagger.

at the hills beyond the river. His thoughts now chant aloud, quiet happiness envelops me at the sound of his voice. In spirit he already sees the monastery on the hill, full of the quietude which only that pilgrim finds who lives his inner life for himself alone — that he may become perfect, a man fully awake, one who has cast aside the wheel of being.

It sounds like beautiful church music, at the moment I cannot comprehend its meaning. I am so weary, the sweet accents send me to sleep. . . .

Suddenly I start awake. I am leaning against the wall. It has grown cold. I am alone.

He has gone. Bitterly disappointed. Up 'Above'.

We are both alone.

*

August Strindberg, Dornach, to L.L., Versailles

'. . . Think of it, when the ape retreats, Buddha appears. Is that not infernal? How unjust that three should not equal five! Can I alter that?

'The position of woman as a stunted intermediary stage between the child and the man is now fully established and becomes a part of biological handbooks.

'I have recently enriched the material by an extremely pertinent observation. The house cock with his gorgeous plumage is the preliminary stage for the golden pheasant. The hen with her spotted, ash-grey or black and white feathers resembles a stage lower, the hazel grouse. And all young chicks at first resemble the hen.

'That the pheasant is a higher stage than the hazel grouse can be proved embryologically, physiologically, etc., for the present you must simply believe it'.

(See: '*Of the Sociology of Woman*', by August Strindberg.)

'. . . I am now at work on my book of essays, *Sapience* (A Book of Wisdom), with such wild energy that I feel the approach of epilepsy. But I need help. I am writing direct in French: besides the new essays, the book is to contain the best 'Vivisections' from 'Printed and Unprinted' and they do not exist in German. I do not know any Frenchman conversant with Swedish. If they were done in a fortnight's time, the whole book would be ready and Ollendorf or Charpentier or someone else would take it.

'Can you, will you? — have you time?

'My soul is so shattered by all the wretchedness of life that I need quiet in order to hunt up all my various pieces and join them together once more.

'This, you must know, is the position. My marriage is about to be dissolved. 'The cause: about the same as the first time.

'All women hate Buddhas, maltreat, disturb, humiliate, annoy them, with the hatred of inferiors, because they themselves can never become Buddhas. On the other hand, they have an instinctive sympathy for servants, male and female, beggars, dogs — especially mangy ones. They admire swindlers, certificated dentists, braggadocios of literature, travellers in wooden spoons — everything mediocre.

'And women's love: see *Creditors*.

'English physicians have recently established that when two children of a family sleep in the same bed, the weaker draws strength from the stronger.

'There you have marriage: the brother and sister bed.'

THE HOLOCAUST

With the heat had come a drought. Not a drop of rain fell and the water in the river grew less and less. Three-quarters of the bed of the stream lay bare; stretches of white pebbles on both shores. In the middle the expanse of the sandbanks. There was an unwholesome smell of washed-up molluscs and decayed fish. Wherever one looked, there was a white glitter as on a Golgotha. 'Above' no longer had any horizon. To the south-east it was cut off by our Mont Blanc, our manure heap, already being piled high, ready for use in autumn. To the north-west the trees which had let free the peep into fairyland in spring had now become a wall—thick with white dust from the white highway which crept lazily along until it lost itself in the distance in the white bed of the stream.

Strindberg suffered like one who dies of thirst. The heat robbed him of all vitality. And just at this moment, he was working on a new book and had also engaged upon a new problem — to prove that plants possessed a nervous system.

Only a few weeks ago in Berlin he had declaimed long lectures to his friend Schleich, maintaining that there was not the sharp distinction which is usually drawn between animal and plant. The plant cells reproduce themselves by a division of the quintessence, just like the animal cells. The wood fibres of the pine tree with their alveolar dots represent the heart muscles of the mammals. The sclerenchyma of the nutshell corresponds with the connective tissues of the bones. He had shown him that the plants were vessels containing valves, veins and lymphatic ducts. That there was no lack of muscle fibres. Schleich had agreed, inasmuch as: the boletus resembles to a hair the myielin nerves of the vertebrates. He had also shown Strindberg a splendid syrup mixture which caused plant fibres to appear almost transparent. But even Schleich would not believe that plants had nerves, because it was an established scientific fact that they had none and because, in his opinion, they did not need any.

Strindberg now dyed them purple with chloride of gold and black with osmium, put them under the microscope and wrestled with nature for secrets that humanity — if it had ever possessed them — had lost a thousand years ago.

He lives in a fever. These plant nerves cost human nerves and brains. The work exhausts him. He does not resist, he himself adds fresh fuel to the pyre. He needs such a spur; the more sensitive he becomes, the more receptive. Still more so, when he suffers. He has tried it before. He throws himself into the flames.

He was now on the road to truth. Certain obstacles were still to be overcome. Nothing should hinder him.

One disturbance threatened. New proceedings in Berlin as a result of his lawyer's appeal. He was once more summoned and was to produce his evidence — the correspondence with his cousin — that he had not written the *Plea* with the idea of publishing it. This time the judge was Brausewetter, who was said to be abnormally severe. Strindberg fell into a kind of obstinate rage. He would not let them tear him away from his researches again and drag him to Berlin. The *Confession* must be released. Neither as a man nor as an author did he feel any sense of guilt. He had merely lived through such a marriage as is usual in good society, had suffered and described the experience. Now let people find their own way after they had lost it by their wrong education of women (the root of the evil), their false emancipation and their habit of turning natural laws topsy-turvy. They could do it without him. He had done his part and it was over. No, he would not go to Berlin again.

'You are certain to win the case!' I comfort him.

'Win a criminal case? One is convicted or acquitted. But one never wins it!' said he.

He reported himself as ill.

*

August Strindberg, Dornach, to L.L., Versailles

'What fate now awaits me, I do not know. But I feel "The Hand of the Lord" upon me. Some change is impending, upwards, or straight down into the bowels of the earth. Who can tell?

'I am once more a victim to superstition. I hear the voices of crows at night in my garden and children weeping over on the opposite shore of the Danube; I dream of bygone days and feel a longing to fly, in some lukewarm medium, neither air nor water, dressed in white garments. To hear no human voice, never again to feel the humiliating sensation of hunger, to have no more enemies, neither to hate not be hated any more. (See: weakness, weariness, surfeit.)

'Prison might attract me, but that which comes before? — brutal lawyers, probing my soul and asking me questions which I will not answer — No!

'Here I sit, waiting for some outside impulse which shall set me in action.'

*

'. . . You still seem to intend to try and force order into the great disorder. But this great disorder is there, holding its rightful place and it is glorious in its freedom. I do not dare to write down the dangerous order which begins with X and ends, in Greek, with XX, and which is the secret of Creation. Have you read my *Open Sea*? I sent it to you in German, to make sure.

'Nietzsche!——I!——The cult of the Ego!

'That Nietzsche's brain should have gone to pieces is no more asonishing than that a wooden garden tub should fall apart when the roots in it spread too luxuriantly. In my childhood we once had to surround a wooden tub in which a Persian syringa was growing, with rings of iron. But it burst in spite of this.

'The French philosopher, Comte's, brain also burst — afterwards — you see he thought more strongly and intensely than the other fellows, whose beefsteak brains could easily be jammed into a bone case. . . .

'Do let me see the two books, or I shall die — I am so poor, so poor. — I beg of you. — A. S.'

*

He was ill. Unrest drove him on, fear plagued him. Cowardice and foolhardiness wrestled with one another to possess him. Overwork did the rest. The spiritual conditions broke forth as physical illness. Everything hurt him, he no longer knew where the pain came from. Shy, sombre and taciturn, he went about.

He avoided the child's room — and he avoided me. In his look burned a reproach which I did not understand and no longer attempted to understand. I had no powers of resistance left. Most of all he seemed to avoid Feldmann; this was comprehensible, for the poor dog, until then so beautiful and silky, had presented a sorry sight since Mother had accidentally scalded all the hair off his back with boiling water.

Suddenly Strindberg began to complain of pains in the throat. He might as well have complained of scarlet fever, there were no local symptoms whatever. But I sent to the near-by Grein for the doctor, a simple soul, who had been treating patients for decades without bothering his head much about questions of life and death. Anxious to please and embarrassed, he professed, after a long and vain examination, to have discovered an insignificant flush in the sick man's throat. He obligingly wrote out a certificate and ordered a mild lemonade gargle. As he was about to leave, however, Strindberg asked him to accompany him upstairs — he must speak with him in private.

They remained together for half an hour behind closed doors. When the doctor came down, he looked horrified, scarcely dared to glance at me and ordered, with unwonted energy, that the gentleman should be kept in strict quarantine. He must stay upstairs — one never could tell. I must not leave the child to go to him. He must be nursed exclusively by my mother. Then he pressed my hand as though a most terrible prospect were before me and rushed off down to the street below and into his trap as quick as lightning, without a word of explanation.

Whatever could Strindberg have said to him?

The moral effects of the prescription showed themselves soon enough. The lemonade gargle descended upon Mother's head the same evening as she sauntered under son-in-law's window to see if his light were still burning and whether he perhaps needed anything, but this did not improve his condition. Day by day Mother reported that he was sitting silently at the window, dressed only in the Flying Dutchman. He refused all food. He looked like a ghost.

On the third day a thunderstorm broke. Thunder alternated with lightning flashes. In the fear of my heart about my man, I defied the doctor and the quarantine. I placed the screaming child in its cradle and ran upstairs.

Over the Dunube, the sky was a poison-like greenish-yellow, bright with hail. A lightning flash struck the water. Our house trembled. I tore open the attic door. There he sat, just as Mother had described him, grey as if turned to stone, haggard, pale, wrapped in the grey mantle, which he wore right over his shirt. I shall never forget the picture, nor his face.

Hate and despair burned in his eyes as he caught sight of me. 'Verily, women do not love Buddha,' he spluttered forth, 'they love only vagabonds and dogs — *mangy* dogs.' And like a man who is choking, he grasped his neck in both hands and then, with an indescribable gesture of disgust, spreading out all his fingers, he showed me his poor palms. No doubt partly in consequence of the chemicals he was always handling and partly on account of his nervous condition, his hands were a mass of eruption and bloody matter was beginning to form.

That, he said, was my doing . . . The 'leprous' dog!
'Leprous!'
At first I did not understand and blankly stared at him, stared about me, questioningly — until, all of a sudden, comprehension burst upon me.

Test tubes full of preserved plants stood on chairs and

tables. He was surrounded by great heaps of books and papers. On the desk lay two books newly arrived and a half-finished sheet of parchment. It was plain that he had stopped suddenly in the midst of his writing — halted by something new and not yet conquered.

L'Âme de la Matière, one of the books was entitled.

The manuscript was headed 'Esotery'.

So once more the gruesome battle had begun between the Unknown genius and the rudimentary brain of man, forcing it in defiance of death, to seize the buried treasure.

'Leprous . . . leprous . . .!' He fancies he sees the miserable wretches of the Orient cast out of the fellowship of men, isolated in a desert . . . Emaciated and in rags . . . Ringing their bells, to warn others of their presence . . . he fancies that he too is one of them.

I also have lost all sense of reality, have sunk into the sea of sorrow. I no longer know what I am doing . . . Suddenly I am on my knees, kissing these poor hands, weeping . . .

Had he come back to himself? Had he returned from his world of shadows? Where memory, present and dream were all one? Was it pity for me? Or had his thought suddenly ripened as a result of this shock . . .?

He was transformed as by enchantment. He stroked my hair comfortingly. He spoke loving and soothing words. He carried me down to my bed and laid the child beside me.

He had regained his strength. The old divine radiance of creative joy after some perfected work streamed from him.

I closed my eyes. I could no longer bear to see this deathly radiance. It kills the man I love!

DORNACH—THE HUT

July — August 1894

TWO IMMORTALITIES

QUIETLY, without anyone hearing us, I steal out of the house with the child at dawn. An unspeakable sense of horror possesses me. I must get away. The child has had a good night. 'It is going to get well,' I say to myself and I feel a certain access of courage at the thought that the flight will save the child from these weird influences — Away from here, away! It is no longer reality that I am fighting. I see the Pyre of Hercules flame.

I must get away. I can think no further than this.

In Ardagger I take a room in an inn.

But I do not occupy it alone. Before we arrived, hundreds of fat black flies were already there. They do not find it necessary to emigrate; buzzing and humming surround us. This is just about how it goes on inside my head. First of all I must get some rest. The child seems to feel the same need, she is asleep. Now I see plainly how thin and pale the little face is. Such a short time she had been in this world and must suffer so much pain.

News comes from Mother. I have not told her the reason of my flight. Only that I was going. Rejoicing in the sensation, she interprets it to her own liking and advises me eagerly not to return to the heretic until the child has been christened. Does everyone live blindly in a world of his own, has no one understanding and pity for another?

Since I am now here, I will consult the doctor in Amstetten. Perhaps he knows more than the good old man of Grein.

He would not need to be a genius for that. Perhaps he can help the child.

The doctor cannot come until next day. In the meantime, reports from Mother arrive every two hours. After my departure, she begins to besiege the fortress. Now it is easy for her and she is not refused admission — he is longing for me.

Human beings are so strange. He is already longing for me — and I am already pining for him.

Mother writes that he is vivisecting my flowers like a savage and in between he is continually watching the shore where I am living. He keeps watch by means of a big field-glass, which mother has brought him out of Grandfather's arsenal. And with touching thoughtfulness, she sends me a gold opera-glass inlaid with mother-of-pearl, a relic of my beautiful grandmother's days of glory in Paris.

The morning passes and Mother writes again. Nothing now hinders my return. Strindberg has agreed that the child shall be christened (after Mother had lied to him that the midwife already gave it an emergency Catholic baptism one day when it seemed particularly ill). We are now being impatiently awaited! I must not remain apart from our domicile another night. On account of my reputation. And then — if only on account of the flowers, it is imperative that I return. He has already sacrificed eleven Beautiful Viennese to his experiments. Only one is still standing and that one looks a picture of misery; he has successfully paralysed it, chloroformed it just like a real human being.

Attached to Mother's letter is a slip of paper from Strindberg to say that after new and most interesting experiments, he is on the track of the nervous system of plants. His experiments have been successful beyond expectation.

The doctor from Amstetten has called, a quiet, simple, trustworthy man. He shakes his head pityingly. The child needs mother's milk, otherwise it is doomed. And here it is not quiet enough, he says, I should return to my own house and see that I get a wet nurse at once. It is the only hope left. I have returned to Dornach. Strindberg and I both wept. He for joy, because he had me once more. I, because nothing on earth can ever make me joyful again, if my child should die.

August Strindberg, Dornach, to L.L., Versailles

'. . . I hover between an extreme of joy and discomfiture. Yesterday, when I read the two books which it was so very good of you to provide me with, I thought for a moment that there must be a God who had sent me these baskets of strengthening food for the soul.

'I found my thoughts in them. The one says bluntly: "I believe that one can make gold." But both the authors are children compared to me. Jollivet Castelot uses up far too much power in his transmutations. I wrote to him and offered to collaborate with him. It would save him a great deal of labour and expense.'

'. . . I am not depressed by poverty, although my letters must often lie about for a whole week, waiting for stamps. I gather wisdom from an old encyclopaedia of 1840 and torn-up papers in the lavatory. But I have so much experience and material for study on scraps of paper and in my head, that it grows as I walk about or lie in a dark room.

'I am anchored to life by the thought of my "Antibarbarus"; the exoteric section is ready in the manuscript. The esoteric is complete in notes — on a thousand stray leaves and scraps of paper.

'Everything is contained in it, a new system of physics, astronomy, eveltography, the physiology of growth, and finally — homologous with them — a science of man.

'But I am pursued by the fear that I may come too late. The Cloister? Ah, yes . . .'

'. . . But there is my past to consider. I have moments in which memories — all my strange and weird experiences — assemble themselves as in an accumulator. Then the tension is so great that I think it must burst, but it does not. What remedy is there? "Diversion" says the lore of electricity, translate: "Work".'

'. . . Set at the head of a biological institute, I would change the face of the earth, the climate, the fauna, the flora . . . Well, well, perhaps I would even be content with less.

'But that one has never achieved one's proper place — that is the tragedy.

'And then there is that cruel discrepancy between the man I am and the man I am supposed to be by those around me; the lack of proportion between my powers and their field of action; there is the shame over duties unfulfilled; the hatred and persecution of the unjust; there is the gnawing, eternal torture, the obtrusiveness, of matter. I am ill, neuropathic, and oscillate between epileptic attacks of furious urge to work and general paralysis. — A.S.'

*

It is an eternity since I wrote a letter. But to-day I must write to my sister and beg for help.

The Amstetten doctor seems a capable man, his diagnosis was therefore crushing to me; the child could only be saved if it had a wet nurse at once. It would no longer suffice to feed the cow on dry fodder: the little stomach had been so weakened that it must have mother's milk. It could not endure anything else. One had only to look at the poor mite to know that what the man said was right.

I did what I could, without loss of time. I started across country at 5 o'clock next morning, going from village to village to look for a wet-nurse. In scorching heat and always across fields, over stubble and stones, taking short cuts. Calling at every house. Looking for the newly-born whose mother would be willing to desert her own flesh and blood for so small a reward as I could offer.

There are hardly any new-born babes in the region, and the mothers the poor little things had! The whole night I had been reading about breast-fed babies and had made a thorough study of what medicine demands from a good wet-nurse; the breasts, teeth, glands and so on. Not one of the women that I saw made even an approach towards satisfying these demands. But they could nearly all be bought. Horror seized me — horror of these wretched human bodies, of this misery which did not know how miserable it was, of these souls and brains, still more wretched than the bodies they house in. And how I tremble when I think of my child! How afraid I am and how disgusted, that it should be suckled by these pendulous and unclean breasts — as a last resort. I had already wandered on foot for six hours when at last I met a young girl, beautiful, cheerful. I could have kissed the girl because she was so sunnily beautiful and cheerful. I asked her if she did not know a woman who was nursing a baby. She laughed; she herself had a child by her lover and of course she was nursing it. She was willing to take mine to her breast instead of her own. She had a goat at home in the pen. And she would go with me at once.

There was no train, boat or vehicle to be had.

We punted ourselves down the Danube, hugging the shore, on a wooden raft.

It was ten o'clock at night when we arrived. Strindberg sat at my bedside like a statue and held the child in his arms. He had secured the doors for the night with bolts and bars against storm attacks from the Big House. But he was despairingly uneasy. When I threw my arms round him and the child together, we both laughed so hysterically that the child was wet with our tears. I tore it out of its father's arms and laid it in those of the stranger. She had firm, white breasts. I glowed with satisfaction at the sight, and I had become such a perfect slave-handler in the course of the day that I displayed them to the child's father like a costly beaker full of nectar. He threw me a reproachful glance — but the child drank. It drank shamelessly, without hesitation, greedily, it smacked its lips. And then, perfectly content, it went to sleep on the stranger's heart. I put them both into my bed and remained sitting beside it. The child slept half the night. I felt sure that it was saved.

Then came something horrible: as early as the fourth day the milk grew less and now it threatens to dry up altogether. The girl had concealed from us that she was again an expectant mother. My child goes hungry.

I need money. That is why I am writing to Mitzi. Another nurse must be got. I must go to town. There are none to be found here. I shall need fifty gulden to look for the new nurse in town, pay her something on account and bring her home. I cannot expect any payments from the *Wiener Zeitung* before the 1st of the month. I dare not appeal to Father and, without orders from him, the paper will not pay in advance. It will be difficult for Mitzi to get the money without her husband's knowledge, but I have only one idea — rescue.

*

The child is saved. Mitzi wired money. I went to Vienna. I was lucky. There was a tremendously overstocked market and very little demand. — The woman was in her twenties and had brought her second child into the world so as to be able to take a position as nurse. She knew her worth. She came from Iglau, a Czechian village full of wet nurses, and of a wet-nursing dynasty. Under normal conditions I should never have been able to satisfy the financial demands of such a select personage, but on the very morning of my visit, she had been told, with a view to lowering her price, that she was ugly, which is a great hindrance to a wet-nurse getting into a really fine household. Naturally she did not believe it, but she felt insulted and wanted to prove the contrary by securing a position immediately; so that after a little bargaining, we came to an agreement.

The doctor now gives us hope. But the child herself gives us still more hope; the poor little thing is now quieted; it no longer cries, it breathes evenly in its sleep, the weak little body is free from fever and the smile with which it snuggles contentedly into one's arm after its plentiful meals brings tears of joy into my eyes.

August Strindberg, Dornach, to L.L., Versailles

'Yes, the child is saved. But two nurses and a maid — this will be the end of me and I shall have to emigrate. I am so tired that I wish I had the strength to roll down hill into the Danube. But the Danube is so dirty, and I long for the glass-clear waters of Kymendö. I have a fresh solution of cyanide of potassium but I do not know if it can be relied on, since I have made it myself. And the revolver is so rusty and in-secure, for I have played about with it for so long. — Therefore, the book, the book! Will you really translate it? Then I am saved, for I shall find publishers at once in France and Germany. . . .'

'. . . The little wife is spinning plots: wants me to go to Berlin!'

'Just try to understand, as a woman she was bound to hate me as soon as she had read my writings. As my wife, she loves me. An intermittent current, with alternating effect. Ah! That is why one can never rely upon a loving woman nor upon her love. "My beloved wife — who hates me." Hatred and love! All is one. The same source of energy. Sometimes positive, sometimes negative electricity. But one and the same!—A.S.'

Peace has come to us too. Mitzi is now financing the household. I believe Papa is behind it. He has come to understand the state of affairs to some extent only now. He has imagination, but no one in the whole family has enough imagination to conjure up an author's life as it really is. I would rather die than explain it to them.

The child's convalescence has cured my feeling of paralysis. Strindberg breathes sighs of relief. He is no longer alone. I live again, have free time for myself, can put his room in order, dust his books, clean his instruments. I can cook for him again. I cook badly, not fit to eat. But he finds my dishes delicious. When he sees me doing housework, he feels at rest. I really think he then believes once more in the regeneration of the world. He lives for humanity and, like one possessed, he tortures himself with fear of the threatening decadence of mankind through female emancipation. It gives him no pleasure that I should have to wash dishes, he would be glad to give me a whole troop of servants. Yet he is radiantly happy to see me doing servant's work with a glad heart — being a servant like his mother. Then she is I and I am she for him.

But we have regained our evenings together and our quiet companionship. I no longer go to sleep with Buddha's sayings in my ears. I must make much of the very fastidious nurse, but she, in her turn, makes much of the child. And the child no longer disputes with God and the world from morning till night. It crows joyously, early in the morning. Its Father's heart swells with pride and joy to hear this melody; such music is nearly as necessary for his work as hot coffee. He once more credits the child with his immortality.

*

August Strindberg, Dornach, to L.L., Versailles

'. . . Since 5 o'clock on Saturday afternoon, believe me, I have gone through emotional experiences —! Well, after all, just the same as formerly in my first marriage. But they never fail to produce a certain effect.

'A long letter to you lay ready then, too. In short: since at the moment I have two families and cannot provide for either, I must try my luck as begging monk. The art of growing new roots!

'They grow well.

'Thanks for your present! So I shall not have to make a hurried escape, leaving my travelling bag behind!

'I am coming, positively. I am only waiting for the letter from the gold-maker, Jollivet-Castelot, who is young, rich and has a laboratory! . . .'

'. . . I wonder —

'Since my depression has gone, I once more experience a *faible* for the "Jig".

'Lord, what is Truth and what is Purity?

' "Jig" is a feeling of power — it is everything!

'Perhaps "Jig" is the Highest.

'I shall never get away from it — '

WITH THE SWALLOWS —

The oppressive mugginess has gone from house and garden, Autumn is approaching. In spite of all combats, Strindberg can look back upon a rich summer. His botanical experiments have made decided progress in the last few days. It was certainly very bad for the 'Beautiful Viennese'. He is really sorry for them, but radiant with triumph as he shows me the corpses of those that were tortured and murdered during my flight. The fact that the balsams, living in the park and woods among other flowers, withdrew their yellow flowers, which had been unfolded in the sun all day, under their leaves at night, inspired him with the successful idea of seeking the centre of energy at the joint of the branching stem, the point at which the leaf thrusts forth.

If he should really have succeeded in establishing that plants possess nerves and nerve-centres and that the sharp division which learned men have assumed to exist between plant and animal does not exist in nature in this wise, then he will have pointed out vital errors in the botany of his age and will have prepared the way for new developments in research.

Strindberg wants to get away from here to Paris. He cannot found his monastery there just now, there are no funds to start it with. But this urge is less pressing for the moment since we got the wet nurse. He has a book as good as finished, to be called 'Sapience'. And then — one can do a thousand other things in Paris besides founding and instituting monasteries. Litmanson has a house in Versailles, where he begs Strindberg to be his guest. He is negotiating with magazines, theatres and publishers. Lugné Poë wants to produce *The Father* at the Oeuvre. Flammarion of the Observatory has noted with great interest those same studies on moonlight which so horrified Dr. Reischl and spouse. He invites Strindberg to read a paper before the *Société Astronomique* in person. Honours enough.

The days go by gently and joyously now. They are like our very loveliest. A gift from heaven, falling in our laps in the aftermath of summer.

How grateful is a garden! The red roses and the blue clematis which Strindberg planted with his own hands in spring against the grey stone wall of our hut are all in bloom. The old trees have borne fruit. The vegetables are flourishing in the field. He can now pick flowers and harvest his crops. Will he soon be able to pluck the fruits of his other labours?

News comes from the monastery of Paumgartenberg, upstream close by — the *Agave Mexicana* is in bloom. Strindberg does not neglect to make a pilgrimage to see her. He regards the phenomenon as an interesting case of a plant prolonging its life on account of its blossom-time. It wants to fulfil itself. In its own country it blossoms in its eighth year and then dies. In our cold climate it lives as long as a hundred years, because the blossom does not show itself earlier. Freezing in a strange land for a hundred years! What does it matter? Now the Agave Mexicana can die — she has borne flower.

August Strindberg, Dornach, to L.L., Versailles

'. . . Well then, in a week's time I shall have settled down as a journalist in Paris. But I must live hidden away in Versailles and never show my face, for I am very shy and would only compromise myself and you with my shabby clothes and my shabby French.'

'No, do not do any advance advertising for me; it is true that Sweden hates Strindberg; but I will not scold at Sweden, otherwise they will never erect me a statue when I die and besides l'art *d'être martyre* is cheap and mean . . . "Jig" is the famous negro dance. They excel at it.'

'. . . Keep quiet about my divorce. I am leaving here good friends, taking the farewell of the emigrant who is setting forth in quest of work, in order to rid the house of Ballast.
'What will happen afterwards — A.S.'

*

The broad river under the slope on which we are sitting flows past in the moonlight as pallid as molten lead. I am driven to think of the maelstrom, from which there is no escape.

What was it that had slipped between us, tearing us apart so cruelly, creating so much hatred, making us so blind that neither of us any longer saw the other one or even himself in a true light? Perhaps it was the being too near, the brutal, untrammelled intimacy of family life.

Strindberg looks thoughtfully before him, then he begins to speak hesitatingly. He thinks that natural laws can usually be applied also to the spiritual life of human beings — and this was such a law:

'If any object approach too near the magnifying glass, it becomes indistinct. One can also lose the real aspect of a beloved being, if he approach too near. That which is too close to one loses contour and colouring. Only when it retires farther off does the picture again become perfect.'

He feels that I start back and quiver and he puts his arm about me protectingly. 'In our case, the child also had something to do with it,' — he comforts me, 'there is also a physical repulsion as soon as a third body is propelled between two others.'

'And the parting — ?'

'It can heighten the attraction between lovers. The farther removed, the greater the pain.'

He kisses me tenderly and kisses me long. He is only going on ahead, he tells me, and I am to follow as soon as the child is strong enough.

And yet my heart stands still for a moment. I cannot take my eyes off the Danube, now once more flowing so broad and whirling on its way. . . .

Bright-coloured and cheerful, full of all the pageantry of autumn, was the evening that Strindberg departed by steamer from Grein for Linz, in order to travel *via* Strasburg to Paris.

Parting was as hard for us as if it were not a question of a couple of weeks and the voluntary experience of a Paris visit, but of hard trials without end which would last for years, if not for ever. He loved every flower here, every pebble. He loved the Danube pasture, the river, his garden, he loved the Kolmuetz church and the Hillock-of-the-Skulls-of-Huns.

He could not cease looking, looking, when the steamer passed the Häusel and the Häusel faded away —

He loved the Häusel. He loved his little child. And he loved me!

VERSAILLES, 8—10 BOULEVARD LESSEPS, AND DORNACH

August 1894

NEW SOIL

HE had come from the mountains and low-lying valleys, from the pastoral shores of the Blue Danube. He had left behind him — not without a deep sigh of regret — his unplucked grapes, his tomatoes and melons about to ripen and his roses which were budding anew. All that was gone now, gone. — Then he had spent forty-eight hours in wrong, slow-moving trains, in third-class compartments, crowded with poor folk growing stiff on the hard benches, who stirred his wrath during the day by their relentless prattle and during the night his pity by their helpless fatigue.

After he had slept for sixteen hours in a regular bed, he had awakened in Holy Versailles, sole inhabitant of a big empty house that had three stories, three kitchens and fifteen rooms, one of which had been hurriedly furnished for his benefit with a bed, a table and other indispensables.

He had written to Litmanson on the way, begging for a day's seclusion, which would enable him to bridge over his immediate past and future. This was their hospitable reply. The house was their property, adjoining their own, 8 — 10, Boulevard Lesseps. He might either take his meals with them or have them sent in. One could not push consideration further; there may also have been a trace of cautiousness about it. Mme Litmanson belonged to a highly respected strictly bourgeois French family. Whatever bohemianism there once had been around Leo Litmanson, found no access to his home. Strindberg's rhapsodies had therefore been somewhat startling to Madame Litmanson, who could not guess that he was the last patriarch and that his letters were contrary outpourings of despair.

Having only one husband and two daughters just growing up, she looked upon quarantine as a means of family defence. But, with the respect which the French have for the artist and for art, she was proud and pleased to shelter the prominent guest. She helped her husband to translate *Axel Borg I* ('The Open Sea') and the volume of *Vivisections*, the essays which were to form the new volume *Sapience*. She also proposed that there should be a fashionable lottery arranged among her friends with Strindberg's paintings (the proud collection which had ornamented our hut) and if that came to nothing, in spite of eager expectations, it was merely because of the season and the artistic backwardness of Versailles society.

This was the stronghold from whence he could overlook the Paris which he had come to conquer. Genius may not mean bread, but it does mean a visiting-card; he was known. The king-makers were waiting, who took their absinthe at the Café Néapolitain in the afternoons and with their novel feud against cold intellect, had already created a movement tending philosophically towards occultism (of which Papus was the uncrowned king) and artistically towards the Théatre de l'Oeuvre (whose creator was Lugné Poë) who called on a Burne-Jones and a Toulouse Lautrec to merge their Vision with the poet's Word. There was the mordant critics, Henri Becque (himself the leading playwright of France); there was the fastidious Catulle Mendès, superbly handsome Parisian poet of Spanish-Hebrew descent, whose first wife, Judith Gautier, had been the model for Richard Wagner's Kundry. There were Henri Bauer, Desmoulins, all with power in their hands.

VERSAILLES

Paris was a Parnassus full of gods — and it was open to him. But the man from the Danube hesitated at its doors — He was growth of the soil. This was hothouse. He could live here, owing to his unlimited adaptability.
Would he thrive?

RECONNOITRING

August Strindberg, Versailles, to Freda Strindberg, Dornach [1]

'The fatigue after the journey, the general emptiness, pondering on this and that, have worn me out. Have retreated within myself. At my time of life it is not pleasant to play the guest in the house of friends. But now things brighten, I intend to set up as a painter.

'Litmanson is arranging a lottery with the pictures I sent to him from Dornach. After that I shall paint new ones and exhibit in the capitals of the North.'

'It may come about that I shall soon be rightful owner of three thousand francs, if so, I shall rent a furnished cottage with a garden and ask you to come, but for the immediate future without the child. Firstly because she cannot yet stand such a long journey without her wet nurse, and then there is so much business to be settled, work for us both, I need your help and count on it.

'Langen arrives soon. Litmanson has finished translating the Essays for *Sapience* and the new book is nearly ready. Things look well and you may be able to come earlier than we had dared to hope.

'Since everything which goes by the name of happiness now depends on money, I do nothing except write business letters — August.

'PS. My melancholy is gone, but I feel paralysed. Come and let us settle down quickly, make the most of propitious

[1] The letters published here are excerpts from the unpublished originals.

339

conditions. With my nerves upset, I am unfit for any venture or decision.'

*

'One week of absolute quiet, Dornach quiet, and my nerves are ultra-sick. The unaccustomed climate, food, the change, the journey, perhaps the last three months with sorrow, worry, care, emotions, humiliations — all of it probably preys upon me.

'Here the situation changes every day and improves.

'Langen arrives on September 1st and is eager to see the *Plaidoyer* which is revised and ready. Loiseau did the revisions. Money therefore is in view! Won't you come, take an apartment and get everything ready, so that the child may follow later on?

'The publisher Ollendorf, to whom I paid my regards by letter my arrival, wants to speak to me, he insists; which means that he wants to tell me something. I shall call on him to-morrow. It might be that I am to get money for *Creditors*. The trouble is that I cannot write here; the volume *Vivisections* does not grow — except Mr. Litmanson's translation of the parts already finished.

'*Resolve:* Get ready by September 1st, if you think parting with the child will not crush you. I must know how you feel on that subject before I take steps in the matter of lodgings.

'The Scandinavian Club in Paris has asked me to give a lecture, they guarantee me five hundred francs. I hate lectures, but with you at my side I might. There are two Scandinavian Societies here, by the way. . . .

'I should advise you to write feuilletons for French papers. Madame Séverine stuffs *Le Journal* with boresome, well-paid articles. . . .

'Did you read that the Chemists' Congress in Oxford has just established the existence of a new gas in the atmosphere and has even isolated it from nitrogen, just as I had foretold

in 'Antibarbarus'? This does away with the old lie about
the composition of the atmosphere. Things move quickly.

'Castelot pays me compliments on the "Antibarbarus", yet
remains — *a Pas de Calais!*

'Called by post to-day upon Zola, Poé, Antoine.

'I am dying by inches. Nothing interests me any longer. It
will all fulfil itself, but what is the use of waiting? . . .

'*Report:* — General Paralysis! As a result of yesterday's
dinner with Oesterlind. Preceding it Café Néapolitain with
the publisher Charpentier, Catulle Mendès, the critic, Papus,
leader of the French occultists and the editor of the *Journal
des Débats*, who wants an interview; Zola's intimate friend,
Camille Desmoulins, will write it.

'. . . He has invited me and plans a Strindberg banquet
which I intend to call off. There you have the Café; without
the café nothing, with it everything. . .

'Tell me something about the hut, the garden. In the east
window in the dining-room stands a flower pot with no
flowers in it. I cultivated gold in it. Look after it. . . .

'You have sold melons? Sell the whole hut and come!

'Are they now glad to have got rid of me?

'This week is to decide!'

'. . . Just heard that someone has discovered that the moon
is not a satellite of the earth, but a planet which revolves
round the sun. All this merely to show you that new things
are coming up in all branches of natural science and how
instinctively wise it was of me to have my "Antibarbarus"
printed. Let the old people hear of it — they wanted to have
me examined by an alienist! And tell them too, how happy I
feel! Like a sane man who was imprisoned among lunatics
and at last got free!

'. . . Yesterday, dinner at the famous Laurent's, Champs
Elysées, with Langen, Henri Becque and Langen's literary

adviser, Sven Lange, who knew me from Copenhagen. Langen lives in Paris in grand style, with a valet and everything to match, has definitely decided on the *Plaidoyer;* people know about it here and are keen on it since Cherbuliez's review. Now he is looking for a conspicuous Frenchman to write a preface. Becque is to revise my French.'

'By the way, Langen paid Georg Brandes six thousand marks for the Shakespeare.

'Becque revealed himself as a jolly fellow, witty and amusing and said charming things to me about *Creditors.* He had gone to the Première like everybody else, prepared to hiss the Scandinavian, but confessed himself won over. He knew exactly what I had written about him and laughed heartily. When I got home, I found a letter from Zola, who is keen to shake hands with me. Now I am going to try and sell a number of canvases and establish myself as a painter and sculptor (of busts).

'Your letter arrived this very moment! About the little one! What bad luck, and what vicissitudes this baby is encountering! I am now waiting full of anxiety for further news and fear these worries will make you ill. But what can I do? You do not follow my advice. . . .'

*

'I have now read once more all the letters you wrote to Versailles and my general impression is that you love your child above everything and were born for family life.

'This, then, is the dilemma; if you become a newspaper woman, you will have to put the house, the child, your housekeeping and me in the second place and once you get in touch with the artistic crowd, you will lose your splendid taste for home-life. The troubles and cares of an intermittent housekeeping will fill you with a horror of house and baby-tending.

'Besides, life will be more expensive on account of visiting theatres and exhibitions, on account of Paris, in a word; for we shall be obliged to live close to the city, where the sales people are exploiting the tourist and have become rotten, artful rogues.

'The cursed theatres are another calamity! — never over before midnight and then there are no more trains to be had! Besides, a young woman moving alone among these cynics without a chaperon — well, you know!

'So I have another suggestion to make: give up the idea of a regular position, write now and then, when you are in the mood for it; accompany me to the *grandes receptions* and write your book reviews at home. Or, still better; write books. What you lose is all to the gain of the household, myself, the baby and particularly, the budget. I shall do bad work if I have to keep an eye on the servant, the child and the cooking. And above all in the evenings, missing our sweet hours of repose and heart-to-heart talk, I should seek consolation in the Café. So let us settle down in some village close to town, but quiet and simple, and let us promise that neither of us will go into society without the other. Emancipation is unknown here and an emancipated woman is looked upon as no better than a cocotte.

'. . . My finances are improving, but, if that wife of mine does not keep watch, they will soon be exhausted. This does not mean that you are to become a serving-woman and stay at home when I go out, but still less does it mean that I shall stay at home while you go out . . .

'You want to study the drama? Did I make any studies before I wrote my plays? . . .'

'. . . Alone in this huge Versailles house, I have full leisure to muse about our future. Mr. Litmanson and his family went off yesterday. I was in Paris all day, with just the

343

same effect on me as before. The air must be poisoned. I am overcome by an inexplicable restlessness, my nerves are on edge, I had to run away back to Versailles. Shall I be able to stand Paris? And then: what do I want of Paris? I shall gradually endanger my energy and my brains and there are moments when I should like to flee still farther away — home to Sweden!

'Then, again, there are moments when I want to return to Dornach, to be with you and live on the money I have earned here as a painter. Shall I until the little one is stronger? We can live on it in Dornach like a Prince and Princess. . . .

'With money one can get books, magazines, newspapers, all the little pleasures that make life enjoyable. Picture it all, fireplaces in fayence, beautiful lamps, curtains, carpets and above all, nurses! And then a glass of wine in the evening; our beautiful evenings — only you and I.

'Here you are tied to the house, will have dreadful servants. Will be cheated on every hand. Famous men will gabble at you in restaurants for hours until you are dead beat and bored, instead of your enjoying their good books at home in peace. You are expecting inspiration here? Not a pennyworth. If the baby is here, you won't get out of the house all day long. In the evening you will be fatigued and won't want to go away from the child and the warm bed.

'Own up, isn't it true that want of money was the fatal cause of most of our domestic troubles?

'Besides: here a dirty, wet autumn is waiting for us! Noise of trams, shouts of street-criers, rattle of trains, barrel-organs, bad tobacco, watered milk.

'In spite of everything, I miss the Danube. It was after all a home. Here — the streets.

'Think it over!

'Do you wish me to return?

'I have everything I want — and I want to desert it all, just to get back to you and live a cat-and-dog life with you. Remember what I once said, even an unhappy marriage is better than no marriage at all. It's too quiet here. Nobody worries or annoys me. I am thirsting for a good wedded row, in which you shall get the upper hand without contest! Call me, beloved master, and I will arrive — an ass laden down with gold.'

'. . . Langen's friend, a young Danish painter, expert and collector, has acclaimed me "Master-painter" after seeing the "Alpine Landscape" and he has sold it for me. He is so rich that he wants nothing for himself, he has a portfolio of original drawings by Rembrandt on his table, worth twenty thousand frs. Owns a Velasquez, a Hals, van Steen, Fragonard, Corot; has hunting grounds in Fontainebleau, a vineyard with Château, furnished, near Bordeaux, where we may live gratis.

'He is a bachelor with a mistress from the Alcazar d'Eté (Mlle Polaire). . . .

'Come and start me going, the sooner you come, the sooner the little one can follow . . .'

'You know that marriage by letter is not to my taste. Baby need not be left with your mother. There is auntie. Think it over and be quick. . . .

'My friend here says I certainly ought to exhibit in the 'Champs de Mars. "Alpine Landscape" is a masterpiece, he says, but "Swamp Pastures" is no good. O God, what is any good? What is?'

*

'. . . We have had luck for the first time since our marriage! You can come with the little one and you shall get a nurse here.

345

'Monsieur G., the Dane — (there, you see, these Scandinavians! Norsemen, Barbarians!) — has a flat in Passy (52 rue du Ranelagh), four rooms, kitchen and servants' quarters, which he will let us have free of charge until the first of October. It is less than two minutes from the Bois de Boulogne. After October 1st we pay nine hundred frs. annual rent, that is, if we want to stay on. Grétor leaves the furniture in for us.

'Besides this, he has bought himself two more pictures, for five hundred francs. In all, that makes nine hundred francs for the four canvases. And he guarantees me a yearly income of six thousand francs as an artist.

'He wants to arrange a Strindberg Show at Durand-Ruel's, with twenty pictures, and says that he will sell them for a thousand francs apiece. "Why! that is a fairy-tale!" I told myself. But his friend, Sven Lange, a Dane, a blond youth, assured me that it was quite serious. Well, let us deduct one-half or three-fourths of it! A famous German critic has also seen my pictures and is going to write of "Strindberg as an Artist". They all admit there is something new. And if nobody else does, G. will buy the pictures himself . . .

'I have seen how he lives, Boulevard Malesherbes, two stories, a kingly studio with Gobelins and so on. Besides, he really has great talent for portrait painting, is a Boldini pupil, moves in society, keeps open house for everybody, has three best-beloveds, a valet in livery, etc. . . .

'Tell me how much to send you so that you arrive happy and healthy in Paris, but without the child.

'Ah yes, you see, this is the way of it. I love the child, but I am afraid. Twice already you have been on the point of taking her away from me. I have suffered so much that I will not suffer any more. I love like a father; you love as a mother does. There lies the difference.

'A final decision; be welcome with the little one under my fatherly roof and be my wife, your child's mother. In this case: no jobs for newspapers! A little house (hut) looking on green trees! Quite near the Bois.

'And so to Paris!'

ON THE DANGER TRACK

August Strindberg, Passy-Paris, to Freda Strindberg, Dornach

'. . . Slept in Passy to-night, 52 rue du Ranelagh. Five rooms with kitchen, superior decorating; comfortable. *Rez-de-chausée*, with outlook on fine garden — but no sense of home. I cannot at all imagine what our life here is going to be like. It is all so unfamily-like, so unappealing, with no warmth in it. You and the child have three rooms for yourselves and a kitchen. I have one room; the dining-room we share. But it seems to me that all is not gold that glitters and I have misgivings, for more reasons than one. A pity we must decide so quickly. The outlook is good, but things are a little precarious. Let us annul our battling letters and you answer this one.

'Gilt mirror over the mantelpiece, furniture of carved oak, lustres, modern paintings of considerable value, royal porcelain, all the gorgeousness of wealth is here and is repellent to me. A hut, that suits me! . . . Don't be angry. You see that you and the child are all that interests me in life and gives strength to my ambition. Freda! I scent something foul here. But branches! Branches! One can jump on any branch — momentarily.

'Between ourselves, G. is no idealist! No such sheep as I!'

'. . . What's the matter now, to set you squeaking like a caged young pig? To-day four letters and a telegram.

'Nay, Freda, nay, you are living in youthful mirages and phantasms about Paris, the golden city! But remember! You are a mother now and the child will prevent you from

having a lively time of it! And to be shut up à *deux* all day
in a human crowd is worse than in the country.'

'. . . Have painted five pictures. Yes, but the money is not
on the table yet! Money! If we should run short of it here,
we should be lost. A new time has come and I feel astray in
this world of mammon! I lose myself and want to escape.

'Why do you insist on Paris?

'Think: To be bound by a whole year's lease! What may
not happen in that time?

'I feel uneasy, weary, shy as a wild bird in a cage! . . .

'So I sit solitary here in Passy and paint, without paying
any visits as usual.

'If this lasts much longer, I do not know what I shall do.
Alone, morning, noon, evening and night, in five rooms and
one kitchen.

'In the country it would be sublime, here it feels like a
prison or a madhouse.

'I was in the Bois de Boulogne. The ground was sticky as
the spit of tobacco chewers. Man and women on cycles;
policemen, horsemen.

'I could weep for my Danubian meadows.

'What a horrible autumn after this frightful summer. Last
beautiful spring will never come again, Freda, never! —
"C'est la vie, quoi?" . . .

'What will come now? Probably I myself shall come . . .
to Dornach, and if I do come, you must know that I have
good reasons for it! Enough by letter. More by word of
mouth! I paint better there than here! In order to pacify
and edify the Big House, I shall previously send you money.

'Here it is so cold that I am sitting in my overcoat! Have
bought you a fine coffee machine with a porcelain mortar.

'Would have sent you money in answer to your wire, if I
had not finally resolved not to remain here. Patience! my
hour will come, though perhaps not in a year's time! But

when it does — and then the little one will have grown big!
Au revoir!'

'. . . Two days and two nights alone, not speaking a word,
not hearing my own voice! In the centre of Paris.

'Listen! there is something fishy about Langen too! and I
am coming back to you.

'A *fille de joie* atmosphere, which does not suit us! . . .

'I live in a *fille de joie* home, which stinks of perfume. The
lady is in the country. The Dane has quartered me here
in her name and as her friend. If the police should come and
demand papers and explanations, it will be a pretty how
d'ye do.

'The Dane wants to make me out the friend of the lady
whom I have never set eyes upon.

'I: No, thanks. The police and the concierge might take
me for *M. Alphonse!*[1]

'Becque, who was present, whistled and laughed:

' "Mais vous voila donc installé en Parisien tout a fait." . . .

'Much obliged for the honour!'

'To-morrow ten new pictures will be finished and I shall
send them off to Sweden. Why I do not keep them here?
That I shall tell you some other time. . . .'

'As soon as you receive this letter, wire me where to find
you. I shall come. Would prefer Schliersee. Dornach may
be closed to us.'

*

'Freda, mark what I say! There is danger for us here!

'I am a sheep in that I usually believe other people to be at
least as honest as myself, but my animal instinct seldom leads
me wrong. And I hear, remember, sum up, see and think!

[1] *M. Alphonse*, a well-known play by Alexandre Dumas, with a kept
gentleman as the main character, whose name grew to designate the type.

'Loneliness and an ascetic life rouse and sharpen the senses!

'Only this much! The pictures were purchased a week ago. I saw the letter myself. The money was to arrive next day! Then a day later . . . and then —

'It is not yet in my hands! I have a suspicion as to where it is! . . .

'It is three weeks since we parted in Grein! And what weeks! In Versailles, brrr! In Paris, ugh! No, child, the world has got worse since my young days.

'So let us live in our own little world, let us work and believe — that we are better! — Where shall we meet?'

'The position fluctuates continually. Now Passy is *passé*, done with. The Dane is furnishing a house for himself. The flat is let. Perhaps I shall go to St. Germain to-morrow, to look for something quiet and countrified.

'To-day my tenth picture will be finished. Send me, *The Red Room* in German.

'What happened to the melons, grapes, tomatoes? . . .

'Just have patience. The longer we wait, the easier it will be to travel with the little one, who is recovering. Do you want to go to Schliersee? We shall not get Mondsee of course from our amiable father. With money, Mondsee is ideal.

'Now comes a letter from a professor of natural science in San Francisco to say that "Antibarbarus" is good and is confirmed by other chemists.'

'The ten pictures are finished.

'The Dane again guarantees me four hundred francs a month as a painter.'

PASSY-PARIS, 52 RUE DU RANELAGH; 14 RUE DE L'ABBÉ DE L'EPÉE

September — October 1894

WHEN PARIS BIRCHES ARE MAKING GOLD

THERE were things to be told about the melons, the grapes and the tomatoes, which could only be told by word of mouth. Even Grandfather understood that. I promised that Grandmother should never know, never, that he had given me the money for my trip.

The Rue du Ranelagh has a garden in front of every house. Yellow climbing roses with red hearts which have survived into autumn and jasmine cling to pretty grey 'Number 52'. It is still early morning. The concierge received me in a friendly but patronizing way: 'Quite right, Monsieur Strindberg lives here.' She ought to know, since she waits on him. Politely and without contradiction but with a cautious restraint, she suffers me to inform her that I am Madame Strindberg. As a Parisienne, she does not believe in the marriage certificate of these Mesdames. Madame our predecessor, from whom Monsieur Strindberg took over the flat, was certainly not married — and the poor thing had a child too.

Oh, how he rejoiced to hear about the melons, grapes and tomatoes! Such a surprise for him! I was no longer expected — for three days Monsieur G. had sent Monsieur Langen's valet, in spotless livery and fine white kid gloves (servants are now wearing white and gentlemen lemon-yellow) with the carriage to meet the train, equipped with a huge bouquet of roses. Thank Heaven, they had given me up: the fine valet would have pulled a long face at the third-class passenger. Nor do we need flowers. I have brought a whole garden with me, two pots of our cyclamen, roses, clematis, as well as a melon and a pot of earth which he wanted and which contained some of his gold germs.

Our flat is attractively furnished, with a taste that betrays ripe culture, and it has a strikingly Austrian note. A painted Tyrolese coffer is particularly appealing. How did that happen to get here?

The drawings on the walls are astounding, all originals, old Masters, Boucher, Rubens, Leonardo. The bedroom is in a soft olive green (green, my favourite colour), a large couch serves as a second bed. In the dining-room there is a beautiful Cézanne in blue, green, brick-red and ochreous yellow. The ten youngest Strindbergs stand attendance on easels and chairs like well-behaved children awaiting their mother.

We go from the dining-room to the kitchen. I utter a discoverer's cry of triumph: 'Look, there is a pasteboard and a rolling pin. An Austrian woman has lived here. I can make noodles here and apple *strudel*.'

'Supposing we stay long enough.'

Strindberg thinks it would be best for us to look about for new rooms at once. Ever since he has lived here he has been wondering who the mysterious, invisible lady might be who has a Cézanne and a rolling-pin, and who exactly Monsieur G. himself may be. Strindberg dined with him recently at the Boulevard Malesherbes. G. had told him he occupied two stories in the house. It turned out, however, that the princely apartment in which he received his guests and played the host belonged, not to him, but to Albert Langen. G., however, had furnished it for him with connoisseurship, every room in a different style, the one in

Chippendale, the next in Louis XV, one in Gothic, another Renaissance; on the walls there spread a picture gallery big enough to supply any number of castles with an ancestry.

The food was good, the wine still better. G. occasionally mentioned, as a matter of course, that it came from his own vineyards near Bordeaux. Whether true or not, it was soon gone, and G. ordered the valet Antoine to go down to the lower story and ask Madame for another bottle. (So there existed still another Madame) — The valet is soon back, but he brings no bottle. Henry Becque, to G.'s obvious discomfiture, gets the amusing confession out of him — 'Madame thinks one bottle suffices for this evening'.

A general peal of laughter: 'Poor G. . . . so Madame has closed the Vineyard of the Lord for this night?' — G. wants to hide his confusion and joins in the laugh.

Strindberg, however, continues to wonder who is and what is this other Madame (no doubt also lacking a wedding-ring). . . .

And who and what exactly is Monsieur G.?

Evidently the halo of mystery is to be maintained. A day goes by, then another — I already possess the third lovely bouquet sent by Messieurs G. and Langen. But neither of them has yet put in an appearance. 'Is it delicacy of feeling?' I ask, laughing.

'Bluff. He wants to rouse your curiosity.'

'He — which he?'

'When the two are together, G. alone counts. Only when they are apart, do you notice Albert Langen.'

I was becoming curious now.

'You wrote that G. had talent. Is he a man of culture?'

'Hardly. He had never read Goethe's Theory of Colour. I had to tell him all about it and explain it. And yet he is a painter: but he has a quick wit and an independent way of

z   353

thinking. He had read my *Red Room* and no doubt had read it hastily all over again to refresh his memory before he paid his call. He had appreciated its finesse and thoroughly grasped its fundamental ideas. We chatted for a while like a pair of collaborators. And after an hour's talk I had conceived an idea for a humorous weekly, a new kind of *Journal Amusant*. G. was by no means a bad midwife and he hugged the new-born as excitedly as if it had been his own.'

And then G. and Langen and all new ideas and old money troubles and schemes are once more clean forgotten.

O, what a joy to ramble all over Paris with August Strindberg, to go up the Seine on a steamer, to see again the gardens, bridges, churches and the gay boulevards! To see them all as one had never seen them before, now that Strindberg has imbued them with his own spirit.

At last the two gentlemen announce themselves and pay their call. They are both quite young and quite good-looking, with bright, wholesome faces, dressed with a touch of dandyism. I never saw so much 'shine' as upon these two young heads, sleeked with brilliantine, and on these patent leather shoes.

They are both ingratiating. The two really seem complementary parts of one and the same person. They treat Strindberg with ceremonious deference and for the first time in my life I behold him playing the part of the Master. It would seem to be his natural role, touched with a little stiffness, with an imperceptible breath of distance; it may be interpreted: 'Bow down before me!' just as well as: 'touch me not!'

G. and Langen pay extravagant court to me. G. admires my handwriting and says Sardou recently praised it as the most beautiful woman's writing he had ever seen — and I know I write like a nervous hen. Langen wants to have French authors translated into German and acclaims my, hitherto undiscovered, famous translator's skill. He asks me to do Hervieu's *Peints par eux-mêmes* and offers a whole four hundred francs for it. He was about to say three hundred, but G. caught up the word as it left his lips and made four hundred of it. I rejoice so obviously that everybody laughs, even Albert Langen himself.

Then at a sign from G., Langen takes Strindberg on one side and begins to talk confidentially to him about Madame and Monsieur St. Cère. St. Cère is the almighty King-maker of the *Figaro* at the moment. The way to the paper's pages leads through his drawing-room. 'But,' — Langen's voice sinks to a whisper at this point.

G. entertains me meanwhile. He is good at it. He is a splendid *causeur*. He is not regularly good-looking, but he has *le je ne sais quoi*, beside blue eyes, strong white teeth and the figure of a sportsman. A pity that he is lame on one side and drags one leg after him by sheer force, like a defeated enemy. If he could dance as his talk dances, then his whole life would probably be different and he would not need to play the adventurer out of sheer overflow of vigour, love of combat and of danger.

Our talk darted here and there, has lighted upon Goethe. I can scarcely trust my ears when he suddenly says to me, patronizingly stern and almost rebuking:

'Do you know Goethe's Theory of Colour, Madame? Certainly not. No one does. But it is the most glorious of all Goethe's works . . .'

And almost word for word (the youth has a marvellous memory), he quotes to me Strindberg's opinions, which I know so well, on the prism, Newton, Goethe — all of which he had heard from my husband a couple of days earlier.

He takes my speechlessness for admiring awe and executes a rapid and satisfied departure.

'There you have Paris!' laughs Strindberg. 'But the rascal is talented.'

Langen in the meantime had secured Strindberg a commission: the *Figaro* wants an article. What subject could he suggest?

They come to terms at once. Strindberg is to write 'On Modernity'.

'Modernity at any period implies the art, the idea of expression best fitted to stir contemporaries.'

He had coined this definition long ago in Berlin. And now the words just leap down on the paper. We moderns want to economize our time, our nerves, anything and everything. This explains the one-act play and the three-act drama which have routed the many acts and scenes formerly employed, the new leader in the Press saying everything in two hundred lines and supplanting the old half-page affair, the one-man flying machine which is to supplement the idea of the airships.

He himself is a prestissimo of concentrated matter-of-factness, in which he sees the appropriate expression of our coming age.

Sometimes it seems to me as though the whole man already lived in the future and only walked here at my side by a strange miracle.

But I must confess, I myself failed the other day at my very first début as a great man's wife. Have I no talent for display?

The Divine Sarah had reserved the state box for us. G. had told her just as much as was wise — that I resembled her a little, seen in profile. As a result, during the interval, Maître Strindberg and I were to pay her our regards in her dressing-room. But I distinguished myself by absence — without even having sent an apology. I preferred strolling about the fortifications — a place where no decent body ever sets a foot. I shall never get anywhere.

They were playing the *Wife of Claudius* by Dumas. At the request of the *Figaro*, Strindberg had written about the play. The theme, 'Slay her!', appealed to him in this new version. Claude, the inventor, reckons up with his Messalina in a modern spirit. He shoots her down, like husbands of old, but not as an adulteress, rather as a thief. That is distinctly new. Besides, even before he kills her, he has already replaced her by another love, quite as advised by Stendhal.

Strindberg savours with a professional's gusto the efficiency of this procedure. 'Hun's blood!' I laugh. — But there is one passage in his article over which I do not laugh. Therein he complains of woman, who does not value the man's creative effort, but only his success. The passage seems strangely familiar and reminds me of Berlin days, when he ascribed base motives to my aversion to Sulphur, whereas I (to own it openly) simply had no faith in it.

'You misjudge me,' I am about to say in a pained whisper and then stop short as if on the brink of a confession — he has not been addressing me, but talking of Claudius' reptile, which ought to be killed as soon as it has been replaced.

Albert Langen had arranged for the publication of this article and the subsequent invitation to meet the Divine one, as publicity for Strindberg. This is all part of the conquest of Paris. Langen works out whole battle-routes. In his opinion, the author is only one-half of a success and his publisher the other half. He had also arranged for the most important journalists to visit the theatre that evening and meet Strindberg meeting Sarah.

Preceding the performance, he had given an exquisite little dinner at his home in our honour, with dishes served on gold plate or Meissner porcelain. Choice company: Hervieu, Henri Becque, Sven Lange, Pavlovsky and others.

Hervieu is good-looking, slender, dark and elegant: and he also wears the red ribbon of the Légion d'Honneur in his buttonhole. He represents the decorative element in Langen's publishing house. When G. and Langen entered a restaurant they always saw that Hervieu and the Legion of Honour entered first. But Henri Becque presents the most interesting personality. About fifty. A square skull, everything on it in rebellion, his dark stubble of hair, his stiff little moustache, his glittering eyes. Becque is reputed to be a genius, although he has not yet 'arrived'. He has so far written nothing but an anti-bourgeois drama, a Bohemian comedy and — as he laughingly emphasizes — just one good poem.

There are gorgeous flowers on the table. The talk sparkles lightly like the champagne. Only Langen and I verge dangerously near unpleasantness. He has a wonderful young Algerian dog and frightens him cruelly by throwing down burning cigarettes and forcing him to catch them. I caught one instead of the dog and put it out with slow enjoyment on Langen's well-manicured hand. It cost him a bit of skin. But even this did not spoil the good spirits for long. Champagne and *bons-mots* began popping again directly.

Then it is high time for us to be off to our box of honour. We take a hasty farewell.

'Je vous enverrai mon poème un jour!' Becque called after me.

We had been animated and gay and I was not a little startled to see the gloomy face my husband all of a sudden showed as we stood in the street and the manservant ran to get a carriage. Strindberg ignored the servant, he ignored the carriage, he ignored my evening shoes and I dared not make any protest, for merely to look at him frightened me. He had put on a regular Bluebeard expression. I took his arm in silence and secretly prayed that he might not put the command 'Slay her!' into practice even before the performance began. He distinctly had some plan or other. He did not continue along the broad, bright street that led to Sarah Bernhardt. He turned down suspiciously dark, narrow streets — until he and I were on the boundaries of the city by the fortifications. I do not know how far he would have gone if I had not uttered the saving phrase:

'*J'ai soif.*'

He laughed out loud and we entered a small café. Two minds with but a single thought. He ordered beer. Neither of us wanted anything finer at the moment. Until our fate overtook us. We had just smiled broadly at one another, but suddenly we were turned to stone. From all sides of the room, August and Freda Strindberg were grinning at us! Strindberg had a fantastic dislike to mirrors in restaurants and here, although it was a poor little place, they covered the walls in every variety of size and form. He sprang up as if he had seen an evil spirit, gulped down his Bock and vanished without a thought of payment. The guests had already begun to notice us. The waiter prepared to detain me, none too gently, by holding my arm — 'Lapin, ou non, ma fille — you'll have to pay me!' Luckily I had money by me.

In the street I found Strindberg. He was walking decorously the proper way back to town. After a while he said: 'Ten o'clock'. He meant: 'Too late for Sarah Bernhardt.' Now he was in the best of spirits, gay and sparkling, charming, everything went as smoothly as possible after this. We found brasseries without mirrors although these are rare. We found good, cheap wine, and the atmosphere of our bridal days. For the rest of the evening there was no question of 'Slay her!'

But Albert Langen looked sorrowful when he came to see us next day and would not hear of any excuse less weighty than that we both had the smallpox — or at least one of us — otherwise we should never be forgiven. 'You will not be likely to succeed in Paris at this rate!' he sighed sadly. He is beginning to calculate.

Everyone is calculating now. A letter from Mother has just arrived. Instead of my monthly one hundred gulden *apanage* (which I have passed on to Mother to pay for the nurse and the child), Papa says that from now on he will allow me only fifty florins. He is getting old, he needs his money himself: 'Since you can afford to live in Paris . . .'

Paris has not up to now made any such attempt to provide for us. Langen has disclosed himself as a regular man of business, in respect to me too. I have no objection, I would rather he demanded his pound's worth of work. Unfortunately Strindberg promenades up and down the room like an imprisoned lion behind bars, while Langen and I are translating. Langen has literary ambitions, he wants to put Becque's play *La Parisienne* into German with me. He brings me his version to perfect. I have endeavoured to secure a permanent position with him as a secretary. 'A literary social secretary' is exactly what he needs. Our own uncertainties would be at an end. I believe he would not be disinclined. But Strindberg is ready with a terrible utterance: 'Emancipation and prostitution are one'. 'Slavery and mutiny are one,' I answer him and for days neither of us so much as looks at the other.

'Very well then, I shall not translate with Langen any more. But the results will come of themselves,' I at last agree, weary of the struggle, and write an embarrassed letter to Albert Langen to tell him that he would not find us at home on the morrow, nor the following days, as . . . we had important business.

Strindberg puts this edict of banishment in his pocket, claps on his hat and departs to town to deliver it in person.

He leaves me alone all day — in spite of the sacrificing of Albert Langen. But in the evening he compensates me royally. We are to dine with the Fritz Thaulows.[1] The Thaulows are almost the only friends for whom he always had a good word. Their permanent address is Villa des Orchidées, Dieppe. This is remarkably practical, for from Dieppe they can get to London almost as quickly as to Paris. Strindberg is enthusiastic over the system of growing one's crops in the country and coming to town to market them.

Thaulow is a blond giant with bright eyes and an open countenance. The man radiates kindliness and when he stretches out his arm, you feel like running to him for protection. His wife is as tall as he is and smiles benignly. Both of them remind one a little of the sea.

It is a pleasant evening. I have never seen Strindberg so animated. He speaks in his native tongue, like a man released after being sentenced to silence. Now for the first

[1] Alexandra Thaulow described the first meeting with August Strindberg's second wife in *When Thaulow Painted* (Gyldendal, Oslo).

'On one of our cycling excursions to Paris, we met Strindberg one afternoon in the Café de la Paix. We meant to go back to Dieppe by train and invited him to dine with us before we left.

' "Thank you, I will, but I have my wife with me." Fritz proposed to take a carriage and fetch her from the house where they were staying.

' "She is rather malicious; she steals my thoughts and writes books. She is a devil."

'We had heard that he had married an Austrian and after such a description we were rather puzzled as to what she would be like.

'When we had arrived, Strindberg said: "I shall go up first and tame the wild animal".

'We waited patiently, prepared to see a most repulsive creature.

'We were no little surprised!

'With Strindberg came a poor, pretty, dark-haired little lady, her eyes red with crying. She did not look a day more than seventeen or eighteen. She had been sitting lonely waiting for him all day. Now she smiled radiantly, overjoyed at the prospect of an evening with him and his friends.

'She had heard of us from her husband and she was delighted to meet the only woman whom Strindberg respected and of whom he had never spoken with mistrust. She told me that she had a child. It was only a few months old. She had left it with her parents, for Strindberg had demanded that she choose between him and the child, in order to prove to which she was most bound—and now she longed so dreadfully for her little one.'

time I understand what a torture exile means to him. He enjoys the unhampered exchange of thoughts with all his heart and in his happiness permits himself a *poculum hilaritatis*, a cup of joy.

Past one a.m. when we break up. We have only twenty francs left in the world and beyond - *sans Langen* — is the void. But Strindberg has cast off his earthly cares for an hour or two and takes a carriage. The ride lasts ages. For the first time since I have known him, Strindberg is blissfully drunk. In the restaurant it was imperceptible, but the night air has set the little devils free. The scenery enraptures him as never scenery enraptured him before. Every five minutes or so the coachman has to halt. The fare gets out of the cab and stands for another five minutes lost in contemplation of the pitch-dark night. And — I have lost all sense of humour; I feel deeply wounded in my poetic sensibilities, become a well-behaved young lady. And when my husband presents the coachman with our last, our very last ten francs as a tip, besides the ten francs the ride has cost, I am frozen into a true *Hofrat's* daughter.

In our bedroom I reproach him with the fact that it is nearly four o'clock in the morning. He accuses me of having put the clock on — it cannot be so late, we do not need three hours for such a journey home. I insist the clock is right. He is no longer light-hearted. Without a word he takes his hand out of his pocket and clenches it at me. He raises it and takes aim; but at the last minute he lets it sink as if he had bethought himself for the better. His hand wanders thoughtfully back and then reappears clutching a huge pocket-knife. He fixes on the blade a meditative gaze. So do I — with one leap I am on the window-sill, with another in the garden below, garlanded round and round with climbing rose trails. He makes as if to follow me, but 'Something' paralyses his will and when at last he in his

turn has scrambled down, I have long since taken refuge
with the concierge.

Not until the following evening does the touching reconciliation take place. We decide to celebrate it solemnly with
a festival banquet — but it dawns upon us that we have not a
single franc between us and do not know anyone in Paris
whom we could ask for one.

The situation is worse than we are willing to acknowledge.

At this very moment, prompt at eight o'clock, enters
Albert Langen!

In his joy over meeting the Thaulows, Strindberg had
forgotten to deliver the fatal letter. Langen had no idea that
his banishment had been determined upon. He was hugging
his *Parisienne* MS. lovingly under his left arm and was much
too preoccupied with it to notice our confusion.

Another second and he had installed himself in place. I
took my seat beside him like a stern preceptress, Strindberg
barricading himself indignantly behind his desk. For two
hours I suppressed a desire to giggle, for the next two a
longing to yawn, and so midnight came. At the twelfth
stroke I asserted the rights of a working woman and demanded immediate payment. Langen actually turned pale,
Strindberg blushed: then we all went off laughing to supper
together . . . we breakfasted with Langen in the *Halles* and
went home to bed at daybreak, rightful owners of one
hundred francs.

*

We shall soon be leaving Passy. Willy G.'s poor lady
friend really seems not to have paid her rent, or for the
Tyrolese chest, or for the Old Masters — perhaps not even
for the rolling-pin. Two gentlemen came yesterday to view
the furniture; with dark looks they sized up all the treasures
around them. Strindberg, who always fears the worst,
trembled for his most sacred possessions and stood

protectingly in front of his 'Green Bag'. He might have spared any anxiety. Although I had bought a fine new covering (green again, of course) for the 'Green Bag' at the 'Samaritaine', the visitors merely give it a disdainful side-glance. 'Worthless' their glance says to the bag and to the Cézanne as well, which G. had recently purchased from the painter Gauguin. On the other hand, the two were very interested in the carpet, the sofa, the bed and the mattresses. I would gladly hire the furniture from the owner in order to facilitate things for her (although Strindberg wants to break off all connections), but am I certain that I would always be able to pay her?

We have one more reason for moving. The concierge can no longer conceal her dark fears for my future, since my leap out of the window in the small hours. She warns me all day long against marrying my husband. It is hopeless to contradict her, you cannot alter a concierge's idea of the world. At this address many others have lived before us and not any of them had a right to a wedding-ring, although they all called themselves 'Madame'. We must leave, or she will write to my mother. She is sure such a marriage will bring me no luck.

Albert Langen has gone away for some time. It causes me anxiety, on account of our funds.

*

Langen's literary adviser, the quiet, cultured Sven Lange, keeps us company on our last evening in the Rue du Ranelagh. Now at last Strindberg learns what he had pined to know. It might be a story by Balzac — Lange narrates it with the tolerant smile of a Parisian philosopher.

The name G. is a pseudonym. Willy Petersen belongs to a family of respected industrialists in Copenhagen. He had resolved to become a portrait-painter early in life and, in honour of a certain Greta, a Swedish girl he was in love with, he had assumed the name of G. But Art wants martyrs and priests. That was not his line. He finds it preferable to speculate in art, having increased his natural flair by dogged study. Through a German lady friend, G. makes the acquaintance of an Austrian baroness who has just inherited two hundred and fifty thousand gulden. A few weeks later, both lady and heritage are his. He scatters the money to the winds and sets *tout Paris* talking about him. He invests forty thousand francs in Severina, a beautiful Italian *demi-mondaine*. When his pockets are once more empty, he meets Albert Langen and becomes his Mentor.

Once more the banknotes fly. But under the cloak of thoughtless youth, Langen knows quite well what he is about. He gives up a part of his paternal fortune to G., but in so doing, he has definite intentions. His own rise is parallel with G.'s. Langen is soon the owner of a collection of paintings which excites connoisseurs to wild disputes; amongst old canvases which aspire very dubiously to Master rank, are pictures which are genuine masterpieces. G. is also buying quantities of Meissner porcelain for Langen. He puts advertisements in the papers. The market is suddenly full of nymphs and shepherdesses. Langen congratulates himself on having made his early purchases so economically.

Gradually and very cleverly, Albert Langen's publishing house is being founded, basing itself principally upon Knut Hamsun. G.'s instinct for the right thing extends also to literature, he recognizes Hamsun's importance. The publishing house is said not to be a business undertaking and therefore does all the better business. After Hamsun, the list soon swells. The names of Henri Becque, Anatole France, Brandes, Hervieu, have been added to it — and now we have come. Langen finds himself suddenly surrounded by a body of famous men. He is *en vue*; he is the lover of Polaire, the Kabyle dancer with the wasp waist. — All this would be a good return anyhow for the paternal sugar fortune, but he is already beginning to make money on the top of it.

'And what about this flat?' Strindberg asks our guest.

'It belongs to the Austrian Baroness F. It is doubtful whether it will be hers much longer. Her heritage has been dissipated. At the moment she is living . . .'

'On the first floor of the house in Boulevard Malesherbes,' finished Strindberg, proud of his detective sense.

'No,' Sven Lange gently shakes his head, 'she is living in a little cottage in the country. Severina is living in the Boulevard Malesherbes. She keeps a pretty tight rein on G. By the way, the vineyard belongs, of course, to Langen.'

AU QUARTIER

The little Hôtel des Americains, 14 Rue de l'Abbé de l'Epée, stands quiet and peaceful in the students' quarter not far from the Luxembourg. The Thaulows always stay here when in Paris, and have recommended it to us. 'You come here too. A cottage but mine own,' Thaulow had said.

Most of the guests of this hotel are Scandinavian artists. Hermann Bang lived here too. The place has an attractive Janus head and the frivolity of the neighbouring *Bal Bullier* is balanced by the solemn stillness of the Institute for the Deaf and Dumb across the street with its mighty ancient trees on which our windows look. We have two windows and a so-called room to each of them. Besides the window, each room has a bed, a table and a chair as well as a very smoky fireplace. It certainly has an effect of intimacy. Only one must not get out of bed too precipitately, or one hits the wall either with one's head or one's feet. There are also fine rooms in the hotel, but we had to be satisfied with what happens to be vacant.

Strindberg needs either the loneliness of a monastery or a city like Paris which is a whole world. Here, at the Observatoire, he will watch the stars. In the Sorbonne laboratory, he will continue his chemistry. In the library of St. Géneviève he finds the treasures of medieval wisdom. The newest achievements of modern thought in all countries appear and are sold in Paris. — Theatres and directors, book publishers, powerful newspapers — all at his call.

Soon the research work is under way again. He feels with every fibre in him that here he will be listened to. He sits up half the night and I — lying on my bed — watch him, see the flame glowing and flickering under the retorts and how he disintegrates and transmutes his materials. I see them changing from yellow to blue and red like the mysteries of a new earth in birth. It is all most weird yet wonderfully beautiful. If only I knew how it would end! The only tangible means of subsistence I can foresee is the translation for Albert Langen. I have reckoned that if I translate two novels a month I may thereby earn eight hundred francs. We can live well on that and the child too. For of course, baby must come here.

Strindberg is painting now, painting, painting — one picture after the other. He calculates our income per canvas, as I reckon it per page.

*

Langen's return, for which I am longing on account of the translation, is most painfully delayed. There has been a violent quarrel between him and G.

'What about — ?' I ask.

'The nymphs. Oh, the nymphs! — ' sighs Sven Lange.

'Polaire?'

'Why yes — why no — I mean, that's ancient history. Langen did not mind that. But this time it is worse, Polaire was a mere matter of prestige, this is a money matter. G. has been deceived about the nymphs. They are not yet legal age for old china, not one of them, they are quite young . . . new, I mean. Not one of them genuine, all of them faked! *Tout Paris* is laughing.'

I rush to Strindberg and complain that Langen will not come back on account of G.'s misbehaviour with the nymphs.

'What do the man's love affairs matter to you?' he rebukes me sternly. Sven Lange has some difficulty in explaining it to him. But gradually his brow clears. 'Langen was determined to get his money back,' the story proceeds. Even Strindberg finds this naive and smiles sceptically. But Sven Lange continues solemnly. 'The matter has been most satisfactorily settled. G. is a *grand seigneur*; he has *le beau geste*: he has given Langen a marvellous business idea to make up for his loss'. — 'Whose idea?' asks Strindberg, once more thoughtful. He receives no answer, for Lange does not know, though he may have his suspicions.

Sophus Clausen, a charming young Danish poet with flaming red locks, has offered to introduce us to Verlaine, who greatly admires Strindberg's work. Verlaine, however, is not reliable when his admiration for a man is limited to literature alone. On the appointed evening we are in the Procopé, his favourite haunt, but Verlaine is not. Well, we get to know a famous historical café with traditions going back to Racine and Corneille and a modern artists' cabaret. That interests us, Strindberg had planned to found with Litmanson, the violinist, a Scandinavian *Chat Noir* in Paris. Here Xavian Privas sings, a romantic, handsome, slim blond *chansonnier*. When he has finished, the thin, dark little Trimouillat enters and melodiously sighs 'Madelon, Madelon, — Madeleine!' I am delighted. But to imagine Strindberg on such a stage — no, that would be quite impossible.

Two elderly, unemployed professional dames cast disapproving looks at our table. They think that two gentlemen are too many for single me and that none is too few for them.

'I can understand anything, but how can men kiss them?' I ask naively, out of the pathetic voids of my convent education.

'The men are young and mostly drunk...' answers Strindberg, evasively.

'But could you ... at your age ...?' I pursue him, neglecting courtesy.

'I cannot talk philosophy with prostitutes,' he replies disposing of the question in his way.

'That was a bad evening,' said Strindberg abruptly, as we prepared for the night at home an hour later. — 'You ought not to go to such places. Ask a copper engraver, if he would let any third party spoil a fine plate, his work of art.'

'But one ought to see everything sometime.'

'One ought — ? Why do you want to study the craft's handiwork for copulation? It is useful knowledge for a cocotte. You do not need it. Do understand, whatever you see and take in, you experience. And if you have experienced all that — then what have I to do with you?'

Strindberg saunters through Paris with distended nostrils — Breathes new human beings here, new thoughts, new art. Art is the breath of life; it is the high mystery of spiritual human communion. It is the thing supreme between us all and over you and me.

Most of all, he and I love the book corner under the Odéon arches. There the books lie out on the stalls. Both of us could stand here for hours, reading, seeking laughingly, selecting ... and never noticing that all about us a cold autumn rain is beating on the grey pavement.

Is this one of the bonds that link us together, this searching for happiness and knowledge, this eternal thirst, this longing never satisfied? He will never again find the woman who shares his thought as I do — nor I the man of whom I should less tire — never tire in all eternity.

These last days of autumn are magically beautiful. Once more in the parks love and dreams build fairy castles for us on clouds crimson with sunlight above the canopy of the ancient trees. Once more the slim white bodies of the birches sway to and fro like houris in a paradise. They wear a mantle of golden leaves and strew them like destiny's final tribute at our feet. 'It cannot be difficult to make gold, one must only know how.' — August Strindberg's eyes are sparkling, he will soon know. Then we shall stagger the world.

And we both laugh. Thus children laugh before life begins in earnest — and gods perhaps when life ends.

The Luxembourg garden is quite near the hotel and we pay it a daily visit. We have friends there. Peaceful and dreamy is the *Fontaine des Médicis*. Here venerable and portly carp dwell at the feet of the pretty hapless shepherd and shepherdess, Acis and Galatea and the wicked jealous Cyclops under the glorious plane trees and they allow me to feed them.

'Galatea will come to a sad end,' says Strindberg suddenly one day and it sounds so prophetically woeful that I stare at him aghast, — 'Polyphemus will crush her lover under his rock!'

'The child must come here!' we had resolved. But the child obeys no orders. It commands. It does not want to come to Paris. I must go to Dornach; and at once. An emergency call lies waiting at the hotel when we return — a letter from Anna.

Grandmother, it seems, has 'insulted' her, accusing her of

'looking at men' in the street. Anna's blood is up and she gives me notice.

The next train leaves in the evening. We had been invited to dinner at Otto's (a Swedish photographer) — through the Thaulows. It is important for business reasons. Strindberg must certainly go. He will not have time to see me to the train. What does it matter, I shall soon be back, bringing him his child ... We have bought toys for her in the Printemps and now we embrace and kiss in the street in front of that big shop and say farewell and *au revoir* to each other without end. It is not the first time that we have parted hugging each other on the pavement of a foreign town. The first time had been in London and passers by had regarded us disapprovingly as lost souls. In Paris nobody thinks of objecting to us, but whoever sees us is now convinced — as was the good concierge in Passy — that we are not married.

Then he jumps on top of a bus, an *impérial*, he is already late. The omnibus moves on. We wave to each other as we had done in Dornach.

Over the heads of the people on top of the bus, his white fluttering handkerchief in his hand, half laughing, half crying, staring after me with all his eyes and waving, always waving his white kerchief — while the black crowds that fill the streets coil round me and carry me away — I see August Strindberg vanish.

XX

DIEPPE; PARIS, 14 RUE DE L'ABBÉ DE L'EPÉE; AND DORNACH

October — November 1894

DOCUMENTS

I

August Strindberg, Dieppe, to Freda Strindberg, Dornach

'Dear heart: I had left you on the crowded pavement island, with the 'Printemps' (shop) behind and autumn in front of us — and rushed off to the Otto dinner which I had completely forgotten. I secretly hoped I should be too late by now and should have missed it. I knocked at the door. Pang! Madame herself opened it. You can imagine that I regarded this as a punishment for my having left you.

'Now here I am in Dieppe! Glorious landscape, green hills and deep valleys — and the sea as a background. An old castle, picturesque houses. Thaulow lives in a delightful spot.

'Am told that four furnished rooms and a kitchen cost seventy-five francs a month, some can be had for even fifty francs. That is cheap — twenty-five Austrian gulden. I get excellent coffee with real cream and am therefore in good spirits at the moment.

'Must sleep here one more night, though, and reconnoitre a bit.

'Feel just a trifle lost, collect myself at my desk and wish you luck, you and the baby! Yours — August.'

2

From Alexandra Thaulow's Memoirs[1]

'After our stay in Paris, Strindberg came to see us in Dieppe. He had just permitted his wife to go home for a fortnight.

'But on the very first morning already, Strindberg inquired very uneasily and restlessly whether letters from her had come. This question he repeated day after day, and his uneasiness and restlessness went on increasing. On the sixth day he had come to a resolution. "Six days without a letter", he decreed, "that signifies divorce!"

' "But, Strindberg," I appeased him, "listen, are you sure you gave your wife your address? Does she know you are staying with us here?"

' "I did not. Am I under obligation to give accounts to my wife of where I stay?"

' "Then there will be a whole mount of letters waiting for you in Paris."

' "That cannot change my resolve. I have been through hell, not hearing." '

3

August Strindberg, Dieppe, to Freda Strindberg, Dornach

'Five letters without an answer. According to the *Code civil* of international politeness, this means that the correspondence is at an end and the acquaintanceship too.

'To-day I shall go to Paris and set myself up there as best I can.'

'He is mad!' writes my sister, 'Love and divorce within six days and all his own fault! He told you, did he not, that he would stay in Paris, and now he rushes off to Dieppe, most likely without leaving behind a forwarding address!'

[1] *When Thaulow Painted*, Oslo, Gyldendal.

'He is keeping his troth magnificently!' I answer. 'Has he not sworn to me that he would never bore me, that there should be no stagnation for us two . . . ?'

'No stagnation? — no rest, no peace . . . ' retorts she.

'Is there anything I could not pardon him? — Only if he loved me no longer and wanted me no more.'

LOVE'S HATRED

There had been much to do in Dornach, no time for letter-writing. Anna, the wet nurse had already taken leave, a whole day before I arrived. She was back in Vienna, offering her goods to other aspirants. Wonderful nourishment she had to give. The child was not to be recognized, so rosy and plump was she, and all from that unholy blessed human fount.

But she did not know me, stretched out her little arms full of distress for her vanished provider and would have nothing to do with me nor with a bottle. She was quite right. I kissed her quickly from head to toe, kisses from her father as well, and set off still more quickly for Vienna. I did not waste words, but gave the invaluable Anna five gulden as a plaster for her moral sufferings and offered her an extra five gulden raise of salary a month. For such a sum she was at once delighted to sacrifice her good reputation to Grandma Uhl's wicked tongue for ever and submit to be called 'Babylon' and 'Messalina' by Mother's sour twin-sister — it even sounded nice, quite ladylike, said she. We travelled home together in perfect harmony. It was good that I was sleepy and tired to death, or I should have been jealous at night — my husband in Paris and my child clinging to this hideous stranger.

It has become cold and empty here. Our friends, Lumpi and Pythagoras, are no more. During the moving, in our absence, they were both slaughtered for convenience's sake. Simply slaughtered, our two friends, because it was more convenient to leave the Hut deserted and not to lodge and feed them any more.

A land of ghosts. Autumn mists rise from the Danube, the river is once again broad and treacherous, yellow and savage and rolls along threateningly like a greedy lindworm of saga. The skies are leaden and rags of cloud hang low, hiding the shores. I have become a stranger here. I live where the child lives, in the Big House. They are kind now. But what is broken never grows whole again. Only a little while ago, I thought I could not be really bitter. But Strindberg is right. Nowhere do people devour one another as they do in families.

*

August Strindberg, Paris, to Freda Strindberg, Dornach

'Dearest: This cancels yesterday's angry note. Forgive me! Yours arrived only to-day. Am now home again — Rue de l'Abbé de l'Epée — *Que c'est triste* and hungry. Everybody gone. Shall probably go to bed without dinner — unfit even to eat alone. My position ticklish. What will happen now?'

'Dear One: Once more the sun shines! ... All we need, therefore, is patience, I shall presumably move to Asnières or to Pontoise one of these days. On the 15th we shall see each other again and then — and then all will be well!

'Your letters still travel *via Dieppe*. Why? I have written you a thousand letters and live in the *Rue Abbé de l'Epée, 14*. Our little one got a loving reply to her letter, why is the little darling angry? — Ye gods — no money! — in haste — August.'

(All Souls' Day)

'I do not know, but it seems to me as though the past alone were bearable, the living moment is always doleful. I

375

hated the *Rue Abbé de l'Epée* and now — I love the *Jardin du Luxembourg* and the carp; I love Passy, which is full of such mixed memories. Probably, most probably, my affection (love, eh?) for you, gilds all these indifferent things with its aureole. — Yes, Passy was good. The Quarter Latin was good — then. And now I cannot bear them and lament the past, good and bad.

'But I am in despair! Nothing moves.

'Therefore I have sold myself body and soul to Satan and promised to write on Henri Becque for *Zukunft*. I hope that in return he will support the publication of my articles in the *Journal* and write about the *Plea*. I am shamefaced and feel that this is a cheapening, that I am selling myself; this humiliation may drive me to flight.'

'I have no more illusions as to my finances. Everything has gone to pieces, in Germany, in Scandinavia, in Italy, in England. It is impossible to find new moorings; time is passing and we with time. To be truly modern means to tear and lose the connecting thread, only the epigones are winners at this game.

'Besides — I have done the work I had been called to and would have no more to add . . .'

'When are we to meet again? And where? Haven't I worked hard, what more can I do? Your youthful optimism will not provide us with eternally new courage, but plunge us into despair. A hideous dearth prevails just now in literature; academicians come to blows over their chances to get an article into a newspaper.

'But what is to be done?

'How is the feeling among the Danube folk?

'This time our parting threatens to be unwarrantably long. What do you think?'

'Dear Sun-Scarab: How fortunate that you too miss me a little, else I should be lost, for I am tied up tight. Horrid as it is, it seems that we are welded for all our lives! The bliss of blisses — and misery without end. Deep in your heart you hate me, just as I call down curses upon you; there can be no doubt of that. And we love each other, there's no denying it. Do you see how contradictory life is? And yet people write books about love as if it were a thing apart and separate from hatred.'

'I have lost my freedom and I loathe life. The mania of suicide attacks me. I cannot defend my independence in any other way, and I fear, I feel, that we shall not see each other again.

'Why otherwise did I experience such fierce joy when you went away? — to be then overcome at once by qualms of conscience and by longing.

'How strange! Failings and talents, virtues and vices! Pest upon it! I love just your alleged faults, your light-mindedness, your unconsciousness, your care-free heart, your almost plant-like response to your impulses!

'Explain it to me, do! For me, everything in our love is pure! You are scarcely gone before everything round me seems sullied. Our passion is pure, and that of the others soiled. The others! How dare they!

'Listen, little one, our marriage must be carried on in a perfectly modern fashion! Modern. Yes, we must go ahead of the times! Must subject the old institution to a wise process of evolution.'

'Dearest: Now your card just arrived, still *via Dieppe*. The books and the photographs of the hut! Oh, you mad girl! You have roused my homesick longings for the Danube all over again! Just as I wake up in you the nostalgia for the Rue du Bac, "*Au bonheur des Dames*", and for the street corner by the Pont Royal, where I emptied many a glass, large and small, during the Passy epoch.

'The Hut! Where I went through so much joy and so much sorrow. Oh, the unforgettable evenings before the satanic little angel arrived!

'And the garden! Is that really you, in the Japanese straw hat among my cucumbers — those *"concombres fugitives"* which, alas, were just as transient as the rest? The Hut! And in the background the sunset into which we have so often gazed, seeking the unknown, the great city which should give us wine and bread! The city, which is a mother and yet is so unmotherly!

'A dream that came true! Do you remember the morning sun when we set out, like two good students, the glorious morning in front of the Panthéon and the Bibliothèque de Sainte-Geneviève (she also had a wicked husband, had Sainte Geneviève — no doubt he was much too severe and particular about his breakfast coffee). You were dressed like a schoolgirl. Oh, I am a fool, an old fool!

'I will not believe it!'

'I gave you every freedom, because I believe you to be thoroughly decent, and not because I believe myself to be irresistible! My confidence is not an insult, it is proof of my respect for you. But never make your husband ridiculous. Once a husband is absurd, the wife soon becomes — doubtful and — so does the child! I never feel jealousy. But disgust, hatred and the spirit of revenge — I know what these mean!

'The Hut! Yes!

'Till to-morrow — your old and young August.'

'Dear Sun-Scarab: What a miserable existence. I detest crowds, but I cannot live alone. So now I am a prey to boon companions, alcohol, nights out, cabarets, headaches and all other sorts of aches — worst of all, paralysis. What have I to do in Paris? Nothing — My plays are produced just as well when I am not present, my novels are being translated whether I am on the spot or not. The newspapers are crammed anyhow — nothing doing there.

'Why do I want you to come? Would your presence give me courage, spur my energy? Perhaps. As long as you were here, we had money; you gone, I become indifferent to everything. . .'

'This Paris benumbs me. Would it not be wise to take a three months' rest and come back after the *Plaidoyer* and *Axel Borg I* have paved the way? In February or so? In the meantime you can translate anywhere and write book reviews anywhere too. In three months Baby will be better fit to travel, she will have a few teeth of her own by then and will no longer depend on a wet nurse's company. . .

'I do admit it, I am tired, nervous and times are hard. Have a little patience and we shall win the day. You won't? Then something must be done, for I cannot let it come to the pass that I must live by your work. . . .'

'Dearest: Well, Litmanson has been in town and we have 'planned to found a *Chat Noir* — or Procope-Strindberg. I shall decorate some café. Then I shall cut silhouettes and produce my *Keys of Heaven* as a shadow-play. The guitar will also come to honour. Litmanson will conduct a small orchestra in a new, original fashion. The audience . . . Scandinavian and other. Drachman will be called upon. In short, it will be the Ferkel all over again, with chronic alcoholism, etc. Well, such is life! Abase yourself that you may be raised up in order to live! The tavern in place of the family! *La joie de vivre!* Only a fortnight's bachelordom and already I am a wastrel. A lunch with Becque lasted six hours. With Litmanson I drank one whole day long from morning till late at night. With Loiseau, one evening and

379

half the night. To be sure, this is swinishness. But when I am alone in a great city, the tavern alone saves me from suicide; all the better, then, if someone drags me there!

'Tell me, can you form a resolution after reading all this *pêle-mêle*?

'We have been parted for a fortnight. You have the child and I . . .

'*Sunday afternoon!* Funereal atmosphere. *Saint Jacques* sounds with all his bells. No farewell! And when is the *au revoir*? All books received. Thank you.'

He wants a decision, a resolution — alas, is it not rather a solution which is expected of me — the solution of the quadrature of the circle?

Where shall we go!

The Hut cannot be heated in winter. The Big House has decreed: 'The Child: YES! — The Father: NO!' — And if we live elsewhere in the country where we know nobody, we are cut off and without help if we need food.

I dare not leave the child behind. It might mean my losing her. She is healthy by now, she blooms. But Mother and Grandmother are gradually shutting me out from the springtime she sheds. 'The child without a father,' the dream of the matriarchate! They have obtained it without giving birth.

A wave of ease has folded us in once more. If the sun does not shine, the fire burns bright. They feed nurse, they dance round the little one, they sing and laugh — my heart is heavy. I want to get away from their wealth, their joys. I want to fight at Strindberg's side, to starve with him, if need be. I want to be his woman, his child's mother.

But have I a right to rob the little one of a shelter?

Ah, but to solve the quadrature of the circle!

If only he would trust me, believe in me always, always. . . .

What can I do to gain his confidence?

August Strindberg, Paris, to Freda Strindberg, Dornach

'Dear Sun-Scarab (*Käre Nyckelpiga*): I have just been reading in my "Antibarbarus" printed and unprinted and now I understand the great disharmony in my existence: this is my real self and that other is not I.

'I fear death, because my work will gradually vanish. Science will stride on past me and I shall be wiped out.

'So we must publish. But where? And how get money?

'Lectures? They go against my grain. Impossibilities on every hand.

'Writing? Oh, I have written so much!

'Painting? I have painted so much.

'*Cabaret, Chat noir*, etc.

'A mountebank? No, I hate taverns. And I am sentenced to the tavern.'

(Continued, two days later)

'You want to keep me as a good comrade at the expense of the child? No, my beloved, I know that song and that is why I went off, after I had drunk to the dregs the humiliations put upon me by the rich family on the Danube.

'Just recently, here in Paris, I've been through it all over again. Then you wanted to persuade Herr Langen to pay me money for the sake of your pretty face. What money? Money he owed me. And when he suddenly gave up his eager visits, you were jealous of his mistress. I won't have charity. Did you not give me to understand that I had you to thank, whether the others owe me anything or not? Comradeship with a woman! We know all about that! I have had a marital song to sing once before, methinks.

'Nor do I see a chance of future happiness if you keep up your bachelor habits. A married woman who makes appointments with unmarried men and meets them is no longer a respectable woman. This is the naked truth. After our marriage I gave up all my platonic and non-platonic lady friends. But as soon as you resume your past habits, I shall also take up mine again.

'You do not notice that you are doing wrong, because you do not stop to think, but simply obey your impulses. You cannot make me jealous because I do not know the man whom I should envy. But if you continue to make me ridiculous, I shall take my *révanche*, then and there.

'I had to tell you this! For retaliation is a natural instinct with me. It is an irresistible one and plays the part of justice — an instinct which endeavours to restore the balance. And you know very well that I do not need to make any great effort in order to find comforters.

'That's enough! Enough! Think it over and do not forget it!

'Can you read my love behind my anger? Oh, yes, you do! But never imagine that my love is roused by that teasing of the sex-urge of other men, called coquetry. That affects me like perversity — it disgusts me. And that is all.

'Nay, it disgusts me so much that, as a good comrade, I feel that I could plunge into the mire myself, just to cause my little comrade to feel the same disgust.

'Why do you want to drive me to this?

'Stop! A curtain lecture!

'And why not? One must get to know the reefs. You know them now by heart. Paris is a great city and very beautiful, full of dangers for the women and the men of all ages and all dimensions, especially the fourth, which is much sought after — at any rate in the months which stand in the Sign of the Crab (see calendar).'

*

So it means battle.

The enemy has been coming nearer and nearer. Now he has disclosed himself. But I see only what hides behind him

— this human countenance, drawn with pain. I think only of this and of nothing else. Indeed I hear the unjust cry of hate, but it is the shout of a man in agony.

Loneliness has once more clutched him in its claws. Then lust to devastate comes over him, no matter what or whom. Now I suppose it will be me. That is bad for me, for I am powerless against the enemy — my opponent is not of flesh and blood. In Paris while watching his experiments at night, the flames under his retort often frightened me like visions of hell. Half-asleep, I fancied they were shooting out fierce little yellow, enviously venomous tongues at me — His science grudges him love.

A stifling fear takes hold of me and I cannot shake it off.

I needed something to read the other day and took up Balzac's *Le Lys dans la Vallée.* I found various passages underlined in red. This was one:

'*Il faut comprendre l'affreuse Nécessité où sont les amants de ne plus se revoir quand l'amour s'est envolé.*'

I had not noticed these marks before. He must have made them shortly before my departure from Paris. I had taken the book with me as the first thing that came into my hands, to read on the journey. It was lying on the table beside his bed — Why had he marked that passage? . . . If only the money from Langen would soon come . . . I must return to Paris, ask Strindberg — why?

*

August Strindberg, Paris, to Freda Strindberg, Dornach[1]

I do not know what is going on in me now, but I fear for our future.

'I have good-naturedly allowed myself to be deceived,

[1] Excerpts.

but there are limits which one does not exceed without punishment. And if I do not obey the urge to self-preservation, I shall be lost, sooner or later. You assault me again and again and I defend myself. But I no longer find any pleasure in these home battles . . .'

'You want to hire that man G.'s furniture. I rescind the order. You demand it back.

'After an endlessly long argument, you finally admit that Herr Langen has insulted me by his late visits; you promise me you will forbid him these visits, and yet I know that you yourself have asked him to read manuscripts with you until midnight. Four whole hours! From eight o'clock on! And this on the same day when you had sworn to me that it should not happen again. You suggest yourself to him as a secretary and are ready to go to him every forenoon!

'This whole edifice of lies and deceit is bound to tumble with a giant crash. It is better not to wait for this, but end the matter beforehand — and that at once.

'While I am writing these words, I have only one desire, to defend my honour, revenge myself and shake off everything which has disgraced me.

'Do you act consciously and with intention? In London your reputation is destroyed, now that you have shown yourself publicly at lunch with a bachelor! You — a young wife! You are well-known in Berlin and in Vienna too and you have made a good début in Paris!'

'What is the use of a comedy of love, since we hate each other? You hate me out of a feeling of inferiority; I am a superior who has done you nothing but good; and I hate you as an enemy, for you act like one.

'If I wanted to continue the fight against you, I should have to use the weapons of your decadent morality, but I will not do that. So I shall leave you and go, never mind where. No sooner will you be alone, deprived of the itch to humiliate me, than your energy will leave you too. Your strength roots in cruelty, you need an eternal victim to play the part of the eternal fool. I don't want the role any longer.

'Look for another man! Adieu!

'PS. My god-like insouciance has bewitched me into a marriage in which I have been treated like a beggar, worse than a serving-man, and have fallen so low that my children curse me. You beg me to have confidence in you — a lovely philosophy. We've heard that before already, I think, when you and Mr. Langen translated *La Parisienne*:

' "Confidence! That is the only system that is successful with us women!" '

*

All through this last week I had felt a cruel unseen danger stealthily creeping nearer and nearer. Dogs tremble and howl for days before a catastrophe in nature occurs. That was how I felt. I was weary and discouraged when the afternoon post was brought to me to-day. I had worked half through the night. Autumn was cold as winter, dismal and dirty. Outside the fog hung heavy over the river. I felt cold.

Then his letter came.

I am too benumbed to comprehend it altogether. Only fragments spring out and catch my eye.

Yes, my dearest is bidding me farewell . . . throwing me off. I sit hunched up as if someone had hit me on the brow with a club; I try to think, make a beginning and forget what I had begun to consider . . . stare at the letter and cannot see it any more.

No, this is no longer a misunderstanding that might be cleared up. This is brutal, intentional, a blow in the face . . . I cannot stand up against it. Where shall I begin to explain . . . how shall I ever make it clear to him that he is wrong?

I lose my footing on his accusations as on some slippery and treacherous surface. I know well enough that I am helpless against him if he does not believe me... does not believe me.

'I have readily allowed myself to be betrayed...' Oh, when did I ever betray you, and you know it well.

But I am grasping in the air, I cannot reach him — he does not want to be reached. Even if I stood before him now in Paris, close to him, I could not reach him.

'Look for someone else!...'

I will not think of it any more — will not think of it — it is like this: '*il faut comprendre l'affreuse Nécessité...*'

'Look for somebody else.'

Does he fear that I shall not go? The letter has a 'continuation'. It seems to have been written a day later. Compared to this, what went before seems only a harmless lovers' quarrel. In keeping with his already classic *Plea*, it contains a list of my supposed shameful doings and vices. It is a good thing I have read scientific works and have read the *Plea* — otherwise I should not understand a word of what he writes to me.

Am I, too, beginning to see visions in bright daylight? Or is there really someone creeping out between the hills of the Huns, rising up out of the yellow Danube fog, with lust of killing in his face, bearing down upon me? Has he come to see whether I am done for yet, come to remedy the matter, in case the blow of the day before did not suffice? Does he strike again, no longer taking much pleasure in it, but for the sake of thoroughness, with the first weapon that comes to hand?... This time I cannot escape his past, he has himself set it upon me.

Why has he done this thing to me...?

He says it in his letter, does he not: 'I do not kill, I replace ... you are replaced.'

Strange, how familiar that, too, sounds! . . . Where can I have read that before? Oh, now I know, it was in Paris . . . Sarah Bernhardt . . . 'The Wife of Claude' . . . *'Soyons modernes!'*

I am replaced.

Then all is very quiet, I do not weep, nor do I resist any longer. Even the old-fashioned shot in the last act could not make a more thoroughly dead thing of me.

I lie thrown forward over the table — my head buried in my hands. For hours. . . .

I did not hear the door open. A voice makes me start to my feet as if it were the Last Trump. It must be late, all the lights are already out on the opposite shore. Mother on her nightly rounds has come into my room. She waves an open Letter in her hand. Is there nothing but letters in the world to-day?

'From your poor father . . . there, read it!'

The letter falls on to my writing-table. It lies on Abel Hermann's frivolous *Carrière*, next to Strindberg's missile — a hellish trio — have I gone mad? — It is some time before I can realize the meaning of the lines.

*

Friedrich Uhl, Vienna, to Maria Uhl, Dornach

'Dear Maria: Enclosed a letter from the legal representative of the children with whose father your daughter is living in wedded community of bed and board. He seems to owe them a considerable sum. I would strongly recommend that the matter be attended to at once; the lawyer's report seems to stick to facts. August should have had more consideration for me. — F. Uhl.'

'August should have had more consideration for me. . . .'

'How delightful!'

But mother feels provoked. She is waging the battle for

the child, the clandestine battle going on all the time in this house against Strindberg and me, so unceasingly that the sweat of exhaustion often breaks out on my brow.

'Your poor father will be 70 years old next May 14th,' she says. 'He has worked for others all his life. Now he is tired, needs rest, and to be taken care of . . . And you may as well know it, Grandmama has now come to a decision. She does not want her inheritance dissipated one day by you two . . . Either you give up your husband or you leave to-morrow morning, along with the child.'

'You may as well know . . .' Mother begins again, as I remain silent — But her words trail off in bewilderment. I now have turned to her quietly — and smile.

'Don't excite yourself, Mama,' I interrupt. 'Everything shall be just as you wish. Everything will now go splendidly. I shall get a divorce from August Strindberg and entrust the child to you. If you pledge yourself to continue looking after Kerstin until she is grown up, then for my part, I renounce all right to inherit my grandparents' possessions. Grandmother can have it at once in writing and in legal form. But please leave me alone now for a little while. I shall be going early to-morrow morning . . . first to Vienna.'

My calm frightens her.

She leaves the room, honestly sorry and hesitating. She says no more. She would like to spare me, but she believes firmly that it is for the best. No doubt there is not room in the world for everybody.

It has become unnaturally quiet. I have locked my door. Everyone is asleep. Only I dare not sleep, even if I could, — my soul must search for light, now in the night.

So that is why he did it. That is why he cast dirt upon me, not believing in it himself.

Poor, poor man!

Everything evil is forgotten. Out of his letter only those

words stand out which at first I had not noticed at all, those heartbreaking words, a cry from the soul. . . .

'*My God-like insouciance has bewitched me into a marriage in which I have been treated like a beggar and in which it has come to this, that my own children curse me.*'

So that was it. — He had kept silence to me about it all these months to spare my feelings and out of shame. And now he is writhing in pain and hates himself and me.

No, love, I will not make the parting hard for you!

XXI

PARIS, 14 RUE DE L'ABBÉ, DE L'EPÉE; AND VIENNA

November — December 1894, January 1895

WHOM GOD HATH JOINED TOGETHER

GRANDFATHER owns eight or ten houses in Vienna. When he is in town to look after them, on the first of each month, he usually lives in the Althanplatz, facing the Franz Josef station. He occupies two rooms, the rest of the flat is tenanted by a cousin of mine. These rooms he has now put at my disposal. I am once more a bachelor girl and intend to remain one.

It is scarcely four weeks since Dr. Max Burckhard, the Lord Almighty of the Burg Theater, and I were sitting together, deliberating whether it would cost him his position if he introduced Viennese Society to August Strindberg's views on marriage, as expressed in his plays. Now we are once more deliberating how my own marital tragedy may be concluded. I could find no better legal adviser than Burckhard. He was a lawyer by profession, is one at heart, and only a humorous mistake of a typical Austrian high Court official made him director of the Burg Theater instead of making him director of a bank. The law that he is not familiar with does not exist. And he knows marriage to its bitter end; he, too, is divorced. When he is questioned about his wife, he beams with thankfulness and joy — that she is no longer his, or rather that he is no longer hers.

'I want to get a divorce,' I sombrely announce, without so much as an introduction.

'Not a bit surprised. I expect you have quite a number of

complaints. Which one do you intend to cite: adultery, ill-treatment, unconquerable aversion . . .?

'None of them fits, but even if they did, I would not use them. I do not want to put the blame on Strindberg. I want to take it upon myself.'

'For this you would get an Excellent at school, but not a divorce in court, dear lady. Sorry to say you cannot, as a Catholic, get a divorce anyhow. Only a separation. Without the right to marry again.'

'I shall never marry again. A separation will do for me.'

'It will be rather difficult to get one without giving reasons.'

'What shall I do?'

'Do not despair. This is Austria. Here everything can be arranged. The Catholic Church will not dissolve marriages but she is very willing to annul a marriage which she herself did not perform. Listen: Strindberg was married once before. Therefore, you, as a Catholic, had no right to marry him. The State of Austria recognizes Roman Church Law. In Austria your marriage was and is no proper marriage at all!'

'Wh - a - at?'

'Don't be horrified. You are perfectly respectable . . . legitimately, legally and lastingly married in every other country in the world. But not quite in Austria. Is it so painful?'

'If it is limited to Austria and not contagious, perhaps it is not painful. But the child . . .?'

'The law counts only in Austria. Other countries are more thorough. And even in Austria it applies only to your person and not to the child. The child is legitimate as long as the parents declare that when they contracted the void marriage they did not know that it would be void in Austria.'

'Austrian legislature is a wonderful thing.'

'It is quite unique, that is true.' And the Herr Hofrat laughs heartily. He has been a judge in Court. The stupidity of mankind is but a stage-play to him.

The day after, I pay a visit to Burckhard's confidential man, Dr. William Fuchs, a lawyer who lives in the Dom Gasse behind the old cathedral of St. Stephen. The whole neighbourhood is redolent of incense and medievalism. Dr. Fuchs is a quiet, kindly man, he has a tremendous opinion of Burckhard's legal knowledge.

'The Herr Hofrat is absolutely in the right. I will go over your case with him, madam. May I ask you for Herr Strindberg's address?'

The . . . address . . . August Strindberg's address . . .? Well, why should I not tell him the address, this kindly gentleman who is willing to set him free from me . . . why should I not betray the address?

Betray. Yes, that is the word. I feel like a traitress as I falter at last, reluctantly:

'Herr Strindberg lives . . . at number 14, rue de l'Abbé de l'Epée . . . in Paris . . . in the Quartier Latin, yes, opposite the Home for the Deaf and Dumb.'

I hardly know what I am saying. Dr. Fuchs throws me a pitying glance.

'Thank you, madam.'

Opposite the Home for the Deaf and Dumb, I repeat in spirit, opposite yon fine old garden of legend on which we used to look down every morning, he and I — the garden whose trees and birds we know so well — he and I — where children speak by a mute smile like flowers and where flowers are as eloquent as men. He lives in the rue de l'Abbé de l'Epée, where he and I lived together, not long ago, and where we were both happy, not long ago — he and I.

And now I have sent off the messenger, bearing the declaration of war. I have signed the power of attorney.

against my grain. If you will come and wipe out the bad impression by behaving well, you are welcome. Now you know the terms. Otherwise, adieu!'

'In spite of my protests the Strindberg banquet is being organized. Zola is to attend the first night of *Father*.

'If you can possibly scrape up the money for the journey, do come along! I cannot send you any! But make haste. A warm fire is waiting to greet you in your fine room. — August.'

'THE FATHER' IN PARIS

I could scrape up the money, I cannot scrape up the resolution. My love has not flown away, but its wings are broken.

The newspapers and letters tell me that success has come to him at last.

What a first night! Gala night. Paris flames in a glory of light. The streets are ablaze. The whole town goes on pilgrimage to August Strindberg, at the big Théatre Nouveau. The hall, which holds 1800 people, is crowded. Zola has said he would come, his disciples are present. Becque is to bring Sardou. The stalls point out the famous ones: Rodin, Porto Riche, Hervieu, Prévost. Mendès is there, Maurice Denis and Gauguin. The great critics, Sarcey, Fouquier, Henri Bauer and Henri Becque. The staff of the revolutionary review, *La Plume* — pen and poignard. St. Cère (of *Figaro*) glides through the hall, astonishingly alert, swimming in fat. Mme Rachilde (*Mercure de France*), Mme Adam (*Nouvelle Révue*) — whom does one not see? It is an evening of artists and of art.

Philippe Garnier, the star of the Théatre Libre, plays the Father, intellectual Lucienne Dorsy is Laure, Lugné Poë himself, the spirit of it all, embodies the pastor very finely and Louise France, the very soul of humanity, is the old nurse. The piece if preceded by a lecture by George Vanor, whose renowned speciality is the illumination of Nordic literature.

The production is a victory. 'Tremendous . . . gripping . . . terrific . . . superb,' are comments heard in the foyer. But one word sounds again and again and above all on their lips — 'Genius!'

The critics repeat it the next morning. They acclaim the great Swede, who hates Woman and knows how to tell her so in such impressive fashion. They invite him to stay and make his home in Paris — and warmed by his success, to become (as says the *Figaro*) '*a very gay sire*'.

Is it true that he hates woman?
No, it is not! Or if it is, there is nothing in the world true any longer — my gay Sire!

August Strindberg, Paris, to Lugné Poë, Paris

'Dear Sir: While expressing my gratitude to you, I beg you to excuse the stranger. My indisposition forces me to stay at home. Besides . . . what need is there of my poor self? You have my work.

'Do not consider me an ingrate, but a sick man, to whom retreat and solitude are necessary. Please convey my thanks to your artists to-night for me, I shall pay them a due *visite de reconnaissance* to-morrow during the day. The evenings I must spend indoors. — August Strindberg.'

August Strindberg, Paris, to Freda Strindberg, Vienna

'Freda: There rang a cry for help of such obvious sincerity in your last letter, that it leaves me no peace.

You are suffering from the parting, so am I; but I have trained myself to endure suffering, though I am unable to look on and see others pine. It seems to me that all is not yet over between us, otherwise you would not have written thus. You see, you would not have written at all, for one does not speak a serious farewell, one simply takes it.

'You believe that life now smiles upon me and that every thing is good and well on its way? So it is, to a certain extent, materially speaking, but all this is of no value to me, I must be no such great egoist after all! So-called fame gives me no pleasure unless I can lay the wreath at a certain person's feet.

'I must be a very healthy man, since nature drives me again and again to seek out unwholesome women and complement them with my strength and since I can find no interest in life without a woman.

'The consequences of my success here are more far-reaching than you imagine, but I cannot make the most of them, because everything disgusts me and leaves me indifferent. So indifferent that I refuse all invitations, am even countermanding the banquet and am now willing and prepared to allow them to put me (for my *Plea*) in prison in Berlin where I shall be able to educate myself to solitude.

'But if you will come here, to look after my truly considerable financial affairs for the child's sake and to inspire me to fresh work, you shall be welcome.

'You speak of insurmountable walls which you have erected between us? Have you ever seen a wall that I could not surmount? I have never broken the marriage vow which I took in Heligoland although I was obliged to bolt my door against certain women and to avoid other ladies' staircases! That is all.

'You wish my daughter to bear my name, and yet you sully my name in a court of law?

'But this does not matter; I have the eternally verdant bath tub and can cleanse myself! Again and yet again! Where is your divine insouciance gone to, child?

'Come soon . . . or never! Otherwise I am bound to end in a madhouse or go right off to Sweden, or far yonder into the Unknown!

'I shall not keep up this correspondence. You will find me alone in Paris, more alone than ever, for people are as shy of good fortune as of poverty and ill-luck! And envy is always awake!

'If you want freedom, let your marriage be annulled!

'In the hope of your coming, I do not send your portmanteau, which cannot be sent anyhow without a lock.

'I shall only open a telegram reply, no letter!

'In two months we can have the child with us!

'Decide your destiny for yourself, now!

'Do you not believe that love's hatred is hiding under our alleged hatred of one another?'

*

CHRISTMAS 1894

From August Strindberg's Diary — (Inferno), Paris

I had curtly declined the invitation extended to me by a Scandinavian family, where the atmosphere does not please me on account of its painful irregularity. On Christmas evening, however, I regret it and decide to go. We at once sit down to dinner and begin to eat it in tumultuously noisy fashion. The young artists are quite irresponsible.

Their speeches and gestures are unrestrained and a tone prevails which is out of place in the family . . . I feel irritated and displeased.

In the midst of all this, I fancy I see, as in a vision, my wife's peaceful home. The *salon* fades, a memory rises . . . the Christmas tree, the mistletoe, my little daughter, her deserted mother. . . . Pangs of remorse seize me, I get up, pretend that I am ill and take my leave.

The thought does not occur to me that this may be a punishment, the fatal result of a crime. I feel innocent in my own eyes, believe myself to be the victim of unjust persecution. The Unknown Powers have hindered me from pursuing my mission. The hindrances must be broken down before I can carry off the crown of victory. I have done wrong and yet I am in the right and shall be right in the end.

I slept badly on this Christmas night. A cold breeze passed several times across my face. And from time to time I was awakened by the sound of an Aeolian harp.

From Freda Strindberg's Diary, Dornach

Grandmother has invited me to spend Christmas with the baby. So I am back once more in the Big House. But the rooms in which he and I lived are locked up. I have brought the baby a tiny tree from Vienna. She holds out greedy little hands to it. Shouts with joy over the bright little lights, rings the tiny bell, squeezes the rubber dog, has a frill of white lace round her face and a white lace frock on.

The wee angel that sat waxen on the Christmas tree a year ago has come to life.

At night I steal her for myself. The nurse has made a heavy meal and drunk several glasses of wine and now she is sleeping the deep and contented sleep of the just. She does not notice me come and take baby out of its little bed. She does not know that I hold it in my arms the whole night long.

Over his empty bed still hangs his guitar:

> Swayeth my linden,
> Singeth my nightingale?
> Smileth my little child?
> Will my heart be glad
> Ever again?

Thy linden swayeth not,
The nightingale singeth not,
Thy daughter weepeth
By day and by night —
Glad shall thy heart be
Never again. . . .'

*

IF THY RIGHT EYE OFFEND THEE, PLUCK IT OUT!

Could the man from the Danube shores thrive in Paris?

He had put himself the question on arriving and now he knows, he cannot. The vultures know it too. They scent the prey. *Father* is taken by the actors away from Lungé Poë, goes on tour in Belgium with Garnier, triumphs: — for Strindberg not one franc. The papers, the magazines, the publishers, all are now there: the royalties are not.

His translator presents fraudulent accounts. Besides poverty, which creeps inescapably closer, there is the feeling of rage and shame at being duped. There are his nerves, overstrained from work, tortured by solitude, there is the aching heart — He has renounced the hearth to live for his mission: shall the grind for daily bread now rob him of it?

No! Once more, *vogue la galère!* Hail to the highroad, where monk and singer are as free as the vagabond.

Alas, he is no longer fit, even for the road. The fire on his hearth has scorched his hands when he held his phials over it, pursuing his chemical experiments.

All that is left for him is — as for Verlaine — the hospital!

August Strindberg, Paris, to L.L., Versailles

'. . . I could not explain it, but I have of late been living as though with Death with a distinct premonition of the end, such a trying time have I been through. Or is the end at hand? — I have sealed envelopes and torn them open again, have written fresh ones and again torn them open. I don't care a fig for the money, but to permit oneself to be cheated means renouncing one's sense of power and it was this which rekindled my interest in life and the fight.

'Now I have come to a decision. I shall give up money altogether. Then I shall no longer be a dupe, but only a beggar, that is less mortifying.'

'. . . For the present, I am going to the Hôpital St. Louis, to-morrow, Wednesday or Thursday. The Swedish colony with pastor and plenipotentiary has begged me a place there.'

'. . . I am going to the hospital because I am ill, because I am ruined and my translator Loiseau fobs me off with scraps of paper purporting to be bills and with minute loans. I borrow louis d'or from him, one at a time — *quoi!* to save myself annoyance and disappointment at sight of his accounts.

'I shall now become a mendicant. And the devil may henceforth swallow all future royalties and authorizations. From now on I voluntarily accept poverty. To Hell with the goods of this world, which are nothing but evil. But I shall not let my honour be stolen into the bargain.

'To-morrow I shall be interned in the *Hôpital St. Louis, Salle Gabrielle.* . . .'

'The doctor who looked at my bleeding hands, which can no longer button up a shirt, believed for a moment that they were leprous, that is incurable. Although this is not the case, they are very difficult to heal, after having undergone treatment by so many physicians for six years. And they torture and pain me. My nervous system is wrecked. I am paralytic, hysterical, full of tears I have not shed, the Devil knows! But I feel that humanity has treated me so swinishly that I weep over myself, out of sheer self-pity. Just as if I were watching another human being enduring the tortures of hell. I can see myself objectively, apart from my person; the he- and she-asses call that my subjectivity, which is supposed to be something bad.

'My cerebrum and my grey matter are intact. They work so subtly, so delicately! With but a little help, I could turn the earth on its axis, this earth which is now once more supposed to be standing still, as a pamphlet is trying to prove which has just been issued in Paris: *"Est-il bien vrai, que la terre tourne? . . . Non."*

'I have not read it, can you get hold of it? *Le Temps* published an article yesterday on the third component of the atmosphere.

'Think of that!'

'I am sad, unspeakably sad, Life is rotten.

'And if the best of all the rottenness — Love — also goes on the rocks, then there is nothing left but misery and despair.'

Attorney-at-law Wilhelm Fuchs, Vienna, to Freda Strindberg, Dornach

'Dear Madame: This morning a message from Mr. Strindberg arrived: the envelope enclosed merely two documents about his divorce and no comment. One of the documents was also forwarded in German translation and I see from it that Mr. Strindberg's first marriage has been legally dissolved. The second (Swedish) document I shall have translated. I presume that these are the papers which I had requested and as he sent them I further presume that he consents to your demand for a divorce, and that he will not oppose us with any difficulties. If I am now to start proceedings, I must beg you to let me have your own marriage certificate and the baptismal certificate of your little daughter. Believe me yours, W. Fuchs.'

XXII

PARIS, HÔPITAL SAINT LOUIS, AND VIENNA

January 1895

IN THE HOSPITAL

From Strindberg's Diary (The Inferno)

'The carriage takes me to the hospital of Saint Louis. On the way, in the rue de Rennes, I get out to buy myself two white shirts.

'A shroud for my last hour!

'I really do think of approaching death, I cannot say why.

'In the hospital I am forbidden to go out without permission; besides this, my hands are so bandaged up that it is impossible for me to do anything, so I feel like a prisoner.

'My room is abstract, naked, containing only the barest necessities, without a trace of beauty; it is next to the common room, where people are smoking and playing cards from morning to night. . . .

'The breakfast bell rings. When I sit down to table, I find myself in the midst of a frightful company, among the heads of the dead and dying. Here a nose is missing, there an eye; there a lip hangs down, here a cheek is rotting away. Two figures do not look ill, but their faces express trouble and despair. These are big society thieves, who have escaped prison on account of their high connections and live here as sick men.

'A vile stench of iodoform takes away my appetite. And as my hands are bandaged, I am obliged to accept my neighbour's help in cutting bread and pouring out. At this banquet of criminals and those condemned to death, the good Mother Superior, in her solemn nun's habit of black and white, goes her rounds and gives each of us his poisonous medicine. I drink to a death's head out of a beaker of arsenic and he responds with digitalis. This is horrible and yet one is supposed to be thankful; this makes me furious! To be obliged to be grateful for anything so low and so unpleasant!

'I am dressed and undressed and looked after like a child. The Sister of Mercy has taken a fancy to me, treats me like a baby, calls me "my child" and I call her "Mother".

'How good it is to utter this word "Mother" which has not passed my lips for thirty years! The old woman — an Augustine nun — she wears the robe of the dead because she has never really lived . . . is as mild as resignation itself and teaches us to smile at our sufferings as if they were so many joys, for she knows the virtue of pain. Not a word of reproach, neither persuasion nor preaching.'

*

I am always having breakfast in bed now, reading the papers. Breakfast with papers has ever been my most sybaritic habit. Grandfather's beds happen to be lovely. Viennese coffee also happens to be superior — as long as I myself do not prepare it. I have never been a cook.

Have I even been a housewife? Was I not right in warning Strindberg, when he proposed to me, that he had chosen the most unlikely mate in Europe? . . . He would not listen then . . . He loved me . . .

August Strindberg did!

But what is this . . . what does this paper which I am reading, say —

Once more news concerning me! I had learned from the newspaper that I was a fiancée . . . Am I to learn to-day that I may soon be a widow?

... Strindberg is ill ... is in hospital ... and I, his wife ... know it not!

The *Wiener Fremdenblatt* writes:

'A victim of Experiments: We hear from Paris that August Strindberg, an amateur chemist (a most enthusiastic one), contracted blood poisoning in consequence of his experiments with explosives and is now in hospital.'

Quick, my hat and coat — never mind which ... in my dressing-gown and slippers — what does it matter ... to my father. He must help me — I must go to Paris.

*

Father is still in bed, but already hard at work. The big sheets of yellowish blotting-paper with which he has papered the wall behind his couch so that he can blot his manuscripts quickly and conveniently, are full of fresh inkmarks. He must have written at least two articles early this morning. The candles which light him at his work are flickering deep in the socket. He looks tired, old, full of trouble. I have never seen him looking so tired.

He rebuffs me coolly. He hates outbreaks of feeling. Yes, yes, he had seen the paragraph. The paper containing it lies beside him on the chair. But he is too old a journalist to believe a newspaper notice unless he has done something to prove it. He does not credit this news of the injury just because it is in the paper. Even if it should be substantiated, it would not greatly excite him. He honours Strindberg as a critic honours a genius. The man in him cannot conquer the resentment he feels towards the man who has taken his daughter and to whom she now belongs. He does not greet me, but growls: 'I have sent to the *Fremdenblatt*. At my request they have wired at once to Paris. Perhaps it is a lie.'

'I want to go to him in any case.'

'He has already given you *congé* by post. If you also want him to give you *congé* to your face . . . then go. There is nothing to prevent you.'

'He is my husband.'

'Your husband! your husband! A father is nothing, is he — but a husband, *un mâle*, that is everything in the world to you women.'

Did he get that from Strindberg? If there is any answer I cannot utter it.

Tears choke me. Tears rise in my eyes. I dare not look up, or the tears will run down my cheeks, I turn to go. Father is ashamed of himself. His outburst of anger was nothing more than pity for my downfall. He calls after me gruffly:

'No money again, I suppose. Go to the cashier and ask him to advance you a hundred gulden. But wait for the answer from Paris before you leave. The answer will come in a couple of hours. I believe *you are not wanted there*.'

'Thanks.'

'Don't howl. Don't bring any more shame upon me, here in my own house.'

I nod silently. I have collected myself. The old man is right. He once travelled on foot from Poland to Vienna and worked his way up. It cannot have been easy for the penniless student to become the formidable Herr Hofrat. Now he lives in the Imperial Hofburg in Vienna, where the Emperor lives, and his influence is felt all over the country. I have no right to 'bring shame upon him' in his dearly bought stronghold and to display my troubles under his roof.

The power behind the pay-desk honours the daughter of the chief by servile bows. His whole countenance beams with reverence and willingness to oblige:

'A hundred gulden? Of course, immediately, madame. Shopping, no doubt? Madame no doubt forgot and left her purse at home?'

'Yes, I forgot my purse. It must be an organic failing of mine. I never think of my purse.'

'That doesn't matter. Herr Hofrat has plenty.'

But the tired old man up in his room who 'has plenty' lives imprisoned in these stone walls for eleven months of the year in order to preserve this power. Love of life and joy of life have bled to death there.

It is snowing in the Burghof. Pillars of snow are whirling along the Ring Strasse. Only the black iron staves of the garden railings project like repellent graveyard crosses out of the white desolation.

At four o'clock in the afternoon, the valet brings me a note from Father. It contains only one sentence:

'Tragics not needed . . . nor are you!'

The telegraphic report which the *Fremdenblatt* has just received from its Paris representative in answer to the inquiry is enclosed, with hearty greetings to Father:

'. . . Strindberg's condition need not give rise to any serious anxiety. It is only a question of a slight grazing of the skin, caused by chemical experiments. The hospital was chosen more as a place of recuperation.'

It is some time before my excitement subsides. Then my glance wanders again to the station clock, hungrily. . . .

> '*On s'exténue, on se ranime, on se dévore*
> '*Et l'on se tue, et l'on se plaint*
> '*Et l'on se hait —*
> '*Mais on s'attire encore.*'[1]

Becque has sent me his poem.

---

[1] We rend one another's vitals, devour and rack,
We kill and bewail our fate,
And we hate —
But we draw one another back.

'Freda: You asked me to write in your last letter; I did write then and write now again, because to-day I have been taken in at the Hôpital St. Louis to find a cure for my nerves and hands, and I do not know when I shall be able to touch a pen again. Yes, I am like a child and cannot dress myself alone, nor eat, nor handle a book.

'Thus it was to end; and with an appeal to the Scandinavian Society, for *The Father* only realized three hundred francs, in spite of ten performances — I don't know why. Yes, Freda, such a Christmas Eve as my last, and most of my other evenings — I could not send my children anything.

'Lonely, so lonely, that is solemn, but weird. Perhaps it would have been better never to have known the joys of life, since the memory of the happy hours is so cruel. And I remembered our last Christmas in Dornach with Mistletoe, which once killed Baldur; you gave me everything and I gave you nothing.

'I saw you last night in a dream. At first you were a tall lady in black and then you were your own little self and the black veil fell off and you smiled, but not with your sun-scarab smile which rejoices my heart so, but rather —

'I often ask myself whether you were consciously my enemy, and then I answer myself: "and what if it were so!" You were a bright, cheerful enemy, of whom I was so fond, although from long practice I was able to disguise that pretty well.

'Now I have a feeling as if I should not see you again, the same feeling that I had when we parted in Paris on the Isle of Stone, with the 'Printemps' behind and autumn in front of us, in the twilight and amidst the rolling of wheels.

'However that may be: write me a few lines about yourself and your child. Why should we part as enemies? Let us be modern. Treat me like a discarded lover, who is always more inoffensive than the legitimate one, and believe me that

I am chivalrous enough to let my lady love assume the role
of the victor.

'In a word, let me chat with you by post, for I am really
devilishly unhappy. My address is: *Hôpital St. Louis, Pavillon
Gabrielle, Paris.*

'Do not be angry about my keeping back the portmanteau:

'It is such a long story. It has so many aspects; the hope
that you would come back, inhibitions, vain search for a
locksmith who could make a key, etc. etc. To-morrow it
shall be sent off: forgive me and believe me that I had no
mean intention. I have no *laquai* malice.

'Where are you living, where is the baby, what are you
doing and what do you hope to get out of this wretched life?

'Oh God! "A Happy New Year!" That is what we wished
each other that time in Dornach. It is gruesome! It is
enough to make one weep! Weep, if you can. I still can,
alas!'

*

'Freda: It is not your money I want, and I shall return it
by the next post as I did before. Avoid useless scandal in
future.

'As soon as I saw that the ravens were coming to rob me of
the fruits of my success, which was greater than I had dared
to expect, and when my power of resistance collapsed, I made
up my mind and became a beggar.

'According to Swedish and natural law, the man who has
been robbed is no more guilty than the man born poor. I am
therefore not ashamed of my poverty.

'And I am glad you did not come. To be a beggar, that can
be endured, but to be a beggar with a wife — never! I have
no right to be married, no, and shall remain celibate.

'If you insist on providing money, I shall be the one to
demand a divorce.

'I have been three days in St. Louis and am being well

looked after. I have a *Mère* who gives me food and a *Soeur* who looks after me at night: have a doctor to bandage me up, and so on. What I was afraid of, was the swelling of the veins on the right arm. I feared blood-poisoning, but it was no such thing.'

*

'Freda: With still wet paws I hasten to scribble these *pattes de mouche. . . .*
The Theâtre de l'Oeuvre was a success in Sweden.

'Lugné was received in audience by the King of Sweden yesterday and invested with the medal *Pro Litteris* for promoting Scandinavian literature in Paris. I wonder what he is likely to confer upon me? We shall see.

'While *Father* was still playing, the Rector of Stockholm University called upon me. He was "up to the mark", ordered a Lucullian dinner at Voisin's, two *Couverts à sixty francs*. Told me that he had proposed me as professor of literature to the University! Fine! Perhaps the situation is not so bad and only my loneliness and your plaguiness, Madame, cause me to see things blacker than they are.

'We changed the diet to-day. Grand council of physicians. The disease is original and unique — just like its victim. Probably it will also be obstinate.

'Sad, sad, indeed! — Explosions with Loiseau! — Grander one still with Grétor.

'Did you get my picture in Maupassant's *Fort comme la Mort* that I sent to you?

'Where are you living? And the little one, who can never cease to be my child, in spite of your mad attempts to make her illegitimate . . . as you will always remain her mother. So we shall continue to be related, you and I.

'*Ma Mère* sends you greeting. *Ma Soeur* has vanished like a beautiful dream, she resembled you!'

'Freda: As a matter of fact, it is no cheerful matter to be ill, but it's better than the Rue de l'Epée without you . . .

'Now everything is in good order for my heirs, among whom your child also has her place. Take whatever you desire. I am about to leave.

'Why did my letter stagger you, as you write? Had you received spurious news, anonymous letters?

'In a week's time I shall depart from my hospital, incurable; then I shall disappear, somewhere here in France, where my suggestions have taken root and are beginning to sprout. Whoever cares to, may have the money! Let the ravens have it, and the foxes! I hate it and will never write another business letter. I have called off the banquet. I have a horror of people . . . not of life, though, for I still have things to revenge and shall have even more.

'What are you doing? A secret? Keep it well! I have emptied my cup of suffering to the dregs and do not want to begin afresh. I need no money, for I am a beggar and live on everyone's mercy, only yours I will not have.

'Life, fame and money be yours . . . take them! — August.'

*

'Freda: Set free for a moment, I write you my thoughts, just as the mood brings them.

'I do not know what I want. I suffer under our separation, but it is necessary. Poverty may be permissible for a lover, but not for a husband. Yet there are moments when I believe that your presence might give me a renewed interest in life and harden me for the sordid struggle for money. On the other hand experience has taught me that your light-heartedness tempts me to take things too easily.

'What do you want? Life for the sake of life, noise, fame, money? That is strength. And who knows that it will not be fulfilled even without and especially without me.

'You have all the potentialities of success.

'I am not happy. The two months since your departure have made me old and the bitter experiences have deprived me of my courage.'

'Here it is not exactly pleasant. A kind of prison. This morning the porter refused to let me out of the house without a permit signed by the director, who refused to sign one. Two *sergeants de ville* are quartered indoors in the evenings and the company (many of them minus a nose) is depressing. The doctor is a cynic and — I fear that the alms which have been promised me find their way into other pockets. (But not a word of this, or I am lost!!!)

'I have done everything possible to put some poetry into my present way of living — but without success.'

'Paris has caught fire over the "inferiority of woman". Three lectures on the subject are announced. The newspapers joke about it, but I do not read them.

'Everything is in full swing, except me.

'It is all our own fault. Mine, because I did not teach you Swedish in the course of last year. Oh, that beautiful winter in Dornach and that incomparable spring! I do not see how you can forget the way we painted the Hut between us and planted the cucumbers as fugitive as all the rest — and the thuya tree and the baby's walnut tree! The restful April evenings after Berlin.

'You have forgotten all of it!

'I have so often recalled it to my memory that it seems to me I must see it all again, to-day or to-morrow — perhaps in a dream. Just as I saw the baby in a dream a few days ago, her little jaw full of snow-white teeth. Does she talk? Where is she?

'Farewell.'

*

'My friend: The alms have also been stolen! This is really a fine new world and will soon be too clever for me!

'You know, one must not bring up children to be honest any longer, otherwise they will be ruined some day. I shall write a catechism for the coming generation.

'*First Commandment.*

'Lie! Else you're lost, for the others will abuse your confidence.

'*Second Commandment.*

'Cheat! Or you will be cheated.

'*Third Commandment.*

'Steal! Or you will be stolen from.

'*Fourth Commandment.*

'Kill! Or you will be killed. . . . and so on.

'Yes, it is true. I am not keyed acutely enough for this highly developed, acute modern life! Exploitation! Blackmail! Frau Marholm, Loiseau, Grétor . . . & Co.

'Shall you educate your child to be a sheep, her too, that she may be devoured by vultures and foxes? Think it over!

'Imagine, I sit down to meals with two thieves, who eat well here, drink well and play cards all day long, because they stole from the State and have been sentenced to penal servitude, but "serve" their "sentence" here, because they are rich (how did they get rich?). They receive visits from their wives and children, these fortunate thieves! . . . Let us be thieves!

'The German translator Wiecke says (a propos of thieves) that the Bibliographische Bureau has changed hands! Is that true? Then my money from the *Plea* is gone too. No written agreement. "Between men of honour" said Steinschneider.

'You must know that Madame Siri Strindberg holds a position as directress of a subsidized dramatic school for young ladies, so she is not without means of subsistence. Moreover, as a member of Women's Societies, she has a much better opportunity of cheating people out of their money than I have.

'Yesterday a Swedish woman told me that in Rome they are playing my dramas to full houses daily. Do you know about it?

'Well, and so I shall stay on here and let the Swedes do the paying. If I leave, I shall be swallowed by the Street. How does it come about that the Bibliographische Bureau will not pay for *Master Olaf?* — My hands seem to be incurable! August.

'Saint-Louis, 22nd January (my birthday), 46 years old, 1895.'

*

'Dear Sun-Scarab: So your letter came. Well then, no divorce, because you love me just a little. And so I send you the newspapers you wanted. The piece is well played, the success tremendous, it is sure to remain on the programme till May. Do you know Pontoise? It is a pretty village on the Seine, at the foot of a hill. No excursionists. Half an hour by express from St. Lazare Station. Or shall I look for something in St. Germain? If the money comes from the north, will you come back at once and do your translating here? It is not good to be parted too long. . . . Love to you and the child — August.'

*

'Dear Friend: I have just read your good letter, and went happily to the chemical expert to learn his opinion on the carbon in my sulphur. Ha! It was carbon! And it is carbon every time.

'To-morrow I go to him again. We shall see whether this will alter my destiny and give me a new interest in life, now that every other is dead.

'It worries me that the little one should still have no teeth, the front teeth usually pierce through between the fourth and seventh month. Very likely the wet nurses had the wrong food, meat cooked until all juice was gone. But she will be able to bite when we see each other again. Eight months old! However long have I been in Paris?

'I shall leave the hospital soon. It is unbearable and lacks the intensified emotions of a prison. Only *Ma Mère* inspires me with courage. She thinks I am respectable enough to suit a clerical career. I told her that I had started that way and should probably end that way.

'In three days I shall be free again, thrown upon the streets.

'My abstinence from alcohol makes me weak and sentimental; it does not seem to matter whether I drink or not. Too much sleep is not good, neither is too little.

'What do you want me to do? I must not leave Paris or everything will come to an end here. And as long as I am here, I have a feeling of power. Intellects are in flux, mock and scold, but that is fine. It is incredible how much they now discuss the woman question. There used to be a saying, "Le ridicule tue à Paris." Not a bit, if one has talent!

'Did you read about yourself in *Le Gaulois*?

'Let me have a portrait of you and the child (both of you together). And do not let the *Fuchs* (Fox) make away with my divorce papers. Otherwise I can never again make myself unhappy.'

*

'Dear one: A note just came from Wieck about *Master Olaf* and you were mentioned twice in it. It was a voice in the wilderness, anyhow. — But still as the grave are you now. And yet you have read my *Master Olaf*? And have discovered that at twenty-three I was already a misogynist and that Madame Olaf lived in a hell of which you could not dream, because you were not born then . . .

'Don't you think that this correspondence ought to come to an end soon and that a personal talk would best clear up the situation? You see that there is no lack of money, one only needs fingers to snatch it out of the fire.

'Is it so difficult? Or must one be a villain in order to live? It seems so and here in this country, poverty is a patent of nobility.

'In any case, I am afraid of the great void, and, worn out as I am now, I may fall into the hands of queer folk. I am so far already. Freda, let us make another try! Come and rescue me! Have we not suffered enough to become less careless? A little more serious.

'Everyone congratulates me, envies me, does me honour and calumniates me and above all, exploits me. Something great must be going to happen to me!

'But the atmosphere in which I live is rotten and my sickly condition saps my powers of resistance. I feel like a sheep that the vultures have already begun to attack and one of these days I shall be mixed up in revolting affairs. Come! or it may be too late.'

*

'Freda: The fight within me and between us is the eternal combat over the retention of personality, the ego. According to my experience, it is no use making compromises, it is a question of submission or severing ties.

'I take it that a part of my nature demands wife, child and family, and since I loathe any attempt upon my independence, I am an enemy of woman. And you . . . the same. I love you, otherwise I should not be married, and I hate this love, for my soul is in danger. I dream of the life of a hermit, but I cannot bear it. I should like to shut myself up in a monastery — but to see only men? I am not sure. The mere presence of this *mère* comforts and soothes me. *La douce chaleur du sein maternel*, as Baudelaire calls it (I think it was he), does me good. But it does not suffice.

'Your bringing-up stands between you and me, your ambition. This ambition can never be satisfied until someone tells you that your work is better than mine, which someone will certainly say sooner or later, without its necessarily being true. And the suspicion that it might not be true will make you unhappy.

'In spite of everything you will make your way upward, my enemies and those who envy me will smooth your path. But if you are honest with yourself, you will always realize that I am your creditor, even if I do not send in an account, and you will hate me with that savage hatred which you know so well.

'What shall we do? Get divorced? But suppose you are not successful? And if you then realize that you have sacrificed too much for the sake of a chimera?

'And if you are successful and we are married, then, then . . .

'I see no way out. You have eaten of the apple and will never more be at rest. What is still worse, the combat between us will never end. If we are parted, you will work with that one end in view of competing with me or being revenged upon me. There we have eternal Torture.

'Love vanishes, but hate never dies. How sad that is.

'Why do you seek to be revenged? Do you not know that revenge again in its turn calls forth revenge?

'Do not make me turn cruel, for that saddens and demeans me.

'I suffer when I do evil, particularly to those I love.'

XXIII

PARIS, 14, RUE DE L'ABBÉ DE L'EPÉE, AND VIENNA

February 1895

HIS MELODY

I HAVE finished the tortuous new translation for Langen which must pay my Paris trip and the first weeks of our stay there. I have begun to pack my books and my trunk is ready, as soon as Langen's money comes . . .

There can only be one answer to his letters — I must go to him. Perhaps Mother is right and I am not the right wife for him, or Father, when he says, 'the best thing is — no wife at all'. All I know is that he needs someone now — no matter who.

Langen has written that he is not seriously ill, just a harmless little skin trouble.[1] Quite so, but the mind . . .?

'Paranoia!' they all cry here. Only the blind and deaf past

---

[1] 'Dear Madame Strindberg. – Forgive me that only now I am answering – I believe as many as two – kind letters. First of all: Herr Strindberg leaves the hospital on Friday. I had begged him to let me know when it would be convenient for him to see me, I wanted to get a personal impression of his condition. Herr Strindberg, however, declines this as *"inutile"* and so I only know from people who have visited him. Anyhow, you will be aware that he is suffering from a purely external skin affection. To-day I spoke to M. Loiseau, who told me that he was much improved and would leave the hospital as early as next Wednesday.

'I have decided to call on Herr Strindberg to-morrow without previous notice, since I also have business to discuss with him. *Le plaidoyer d'un fou* comes out to-morrow and I believe it will be a success, which would give me great pleasure also for the author's sake, to whom I personally bear no grudge.

'Paris, 28.1.1895.

'With kindest regards,
'Very sincerely yours,
'Albert Langen.'

asks me, slyly cautious: 'Or does it happen *not* to be paranoia?'

Once I read a traveller's account of a world tour — the Southern Orient. A potentate gave a banquet and at its close he caused six elderly naked worthies with troubled countenances and long beards to be brought before him, mounted on a red-hot grid. The grid was hissing under their bare feet and the men hopped up and down like goats in a field and uttered the most comical cries. Later the traveller heard that prominent scholars had been specially chosen to contribute this entertainment. Their nerves being particularly sensitive, they were especially suited for such purposes.

Paranoia — when one is in eternal torment?

If he is mad, there is a method in his madness.

He has a mission. If it is not possible in the nineteenth century for a genius like Strindberg, with thirty books in print and a labour of twelve hours a day, to earn enough by working on his mission, then any other way of support must do. If medieval monks had lived on alms, why not he? Nothing shall step between him and his mission. 'Only he has a right to stride in the forefront who also has the courage to see himself ridiculed and despised,' he wrote in his *Master Olaf* when he was twenty-four years old. He has never walked but in the forefront ever since.

His Melody! He kept watch over its intactness. It was the voice of the Unknown in him.

Sweet and radiant with fragrance had been the summer night on the shores of the Danube that now comes back to me. The moon was pouring light upon the earth as out of a beaker of silver. Half laughing and half angry he had shown me a letter. He had sent his 'Leitmotiv' to Litmanson, asking him what he took to be its origin. Litmanson had sent it back, written up tidily in D minor, divided into bars. Strindberg raged, he would not be reduced to such simple formulas:

'School music, indeed! When it is a question of the Eternal between a man and that which has been and ever will be!'

'After my *Red Room*, a professor of music came to see me who had formerly been in the army. He wanted a libretto for an opera. I was already well known and made excuses. But he came again. I then led him direct. I put old requiems of our Swedish Middle Ages into his hands which I had just discovered and copied out. I presented him with bibliographical notes and took him to the Royal Library. That made an overpowering impression upon him! Two years later he gave concerts, reformed church music, received subsidies from the state and travelled all over the country. Now he has "reformed Swedish church music" — i.e. I have done so. Ah, that was power.

'When I had written the "Secret of the Guild" and that essay about the cathedral church in Upsala, I received a letter from the historian Nyblom, thanking me. A couple of years later he pushed through the scheme for restoring the cathedral church. Now it has been completed. Consciousness of power again for me!

'But do you believe any man can ever achieve it, if he falsify his own melody?'

Thus had the man of the Danube shore spoken to me not long ago, the same man who shelters to-day at public expense in a Paris hospital — my man. And, God knows, I was never prouder of him than at this hour.

There is a letter in which Strindberg asks whether I have read of myself in the *Gaulois*, an interview by our then preferred translator, Loiseau.

How I remember! Passy, sunshine. Soft noontide shadows in the garden. Foliage, luminous and mysterious like the nenuphar. The scent of the roses comes in at the window, creamy climbers with red hearts. Everything is dozing a little, having been happy.

Loiseau had just arrived in Paris after his holidays. He measures Strindberg with his eyes, up to now he had only known him from pictures. Paris sees at a glance who's who. Loiseau is satisfied now with his author's prospects.

We had asked him to lunch. I had gaily cooked it myself. Now the gentlemen were resting agreeably in easy chairs, drinking coffee and puffing clouds of blue cigarette smoke. Loiseau, I noticed, was surprised that I should sit perched on the arm of Strindberg's renaissance chair. It was not a comfortable seat. But I had a continual fear of losing him and the nearer I could get, the better I felt. Our talk turned upon a successful play treating of the marriage failure of an *Amoureuse*.

It had stirred me. I had partly found myself in this woman, who will recognize nothing outside love, whereas the man has other gods. The talk turned from this upon love's hatred. Loiseau jubilated. Here was his story! I shall never forget his surprise when Strindberg confirmed to him his reputed misogyny in the mildest and friendliest manner and when I smiled in duet from my perch. It was as if we were merely voicing our opinion on quite impersonal matters which could not touch us — not him and me.

Yes, and now Loiseau describes how free the interviewed author was from the old bitterness. Loiseau expresses his hope and his belief that the gentle hand of the new love will smooth away dark memories. 'Unless, indeed . . .' he says: 'Unless . . .!'

No, there shall be no 'unless . . .' There can be only that one answer to his letters: I must go to him.

The money from Langen has come.

Why, if there is only that one answer, does the answer not go off?

I am no longer sure that he does want it.

They have succeeded in unleashing the jealous furies of the *Amoureuse* in me.

Brother Weyr was here yesterday. He is fond of me. Wishes me ten husbands if it would make me happy, does not approve of that one. He came to say good-bye. Or did he come, so that I should not go away?

He had received a letter from Paris. He would not tell me its contents, he has his manly delicacy. But he gave it to me to read. That was his duty; he would not guarantee its truth, but he did not feel it right to keep silent. I read it and flung it into the stove. 'How can you bring such verminous matter into my house?'

It was the poison of a little journalist in Paris, who had at one time 'adored' me and was now busy telling my family that August Strindberg was frequenting the loose Gauguin and Molard set, alcoholic Bohemia, and was considered the acknowledged lover of a young English or rather Scottish sculptress, with a big plumed hat, and who sang Yvette Guilbert piquancies. The writer had seen the sculptress. Fancy, she resembled me!

Brother shook his head, half amused, half pitying: 'Is that really necessary, child?'

They all want to part us. And they are here, are always present, at any time of day or night, while he——

Why is he not coming?

He — to me?

*

He does not write about the sculptress, but he writes about my 'old friend' again. He has handed his sulphur samples to an expert chemist of the Boulevard Magenta. Now he sends me the analysis, because he thinks I would not believe in it otherwise, and a copy of it he sends for my incredulous grandparents.

Eureka! His sulphur contains carbon! — says the expert chemist. But if the chemist be mistaken?

My deaf and blind poet friend arrives that night as on every evening.

'How are you getting on with Strindberg to-day?' is his regular greeting.

'We shall come to a decision now,' I say. 'He has had his analysis of sulphur examined. Sulphur is not an element. Tell me — do you believe it? Everything now depends upon it, whether Strindberg will be forgotten as a genius overcome by darkness, or will live on as the genius who had visions in the night of that which others do not yet see. . . Do you think that August Strindberg is right in believing in unity, in the possibility of transmuting everything material and finally matter itself, into energy?'

'I think August Strindberg is wrong — and right. The unity of all things as well as the law of transmutation — even the reality and invincibility of the Ego and the Culture of the Ego — have every chance of becoming dogma some day. For the time being, he will not convince the world. And so long, he is wrong.

'But, devil take it, to-morrow he will be right. It would be more honourable to stand with him in the gutter, begging, than to sit in the academy with the laurelled sages. Which does not prevent its being very easy to catch a cold and die in the street.'

'I shall go to him to-day.'

'Out of love for him or for yourself? What were you telling me the other day about this one-man flying machine of his? Did you not say that he was not interested in group flight?'

'No. He wants to build a one-man flying machine which should carry, not only the man, but his personality. The man and his machine should be but one body, a thing ideal, divine, an improvement on God's work — I saw the flame blaze when he spoke. Such a triumph would the airman feel, pinions on body and soul! — reaching the heavens in immensities of azure . . . so near the sun, so near! And hand in hand with this went danger that too was joy! Every moment it must be overcome. Every moment was a deadly combat and a victory. It was this which fascinated him.'

'Oh, now I know what you mean — one doesn't soar into the clouds with one's respectable family.'

'He dreamt of a one-man flying machine! You cannot hold him back from the pyre, dear lady — you can only hold him back from his heavens!'

It is late at night. The station clock stares at me with its round, dim face. I am writing, page after page — without a stop, without hesitation, driven by anguish, bitterness and jealous passion. I am writing to him for life, his and mine.

Now we shall see whether he wants me. Now he may choose.

*

He has chosen long ago.

The form does not matter, the farewell letter he sends me is a repetition of the horrid letter of November. Can one get used to anything? Does hate become a technique like love? The letter causes me no pain, does not rouse me to indignation, it only creates an infinite, hopeless weariness. The same man who taught me to worship flowers now treads me into the mud in wild hatred, because he would be free of me and the common clay. That is his highest command, he can do no other. The same man who trembles before the lightning, who hides away from a storm, who will not look in mirrors in brightly-lit rooms and cannot endure to see his

own face — this same man goes out into the world and flings
it a challenge, he starves and is cold, fears naught and minds
naught.

He can do no other.

Semele, Semele,
Who has enticed you, beloved.
To look your love in the face?
The Gods will not spare the wilful
Who do not stoop to beg grace.

Semele, Semele,
Your lover came in his glory
Of lightning and leaping fire,
Bride's wreath is wreath of a victim,
You perish, a blazing pyre.

AUGUST STRINDBERG

XXIV

PARIS, 12, RUE DE LA GRANDE CHAUMIÈRE, AND DORNACH

March — June 1895

AS HE SEES IT, AS THE OTHERS SEE IT, AND AS I SEE IT

ONE month has passed since my alternative and his rebuke. It has parted us. How weird! — A correspondence ceases — and the void sets in.

I have left town and sought refuge in Dornach with the child. I feel uprooted. It is impossible to live with August Strindberg, but worse to be without him.

All of a sudden, news. Mother and I sit and idle. The child comes toddling in. It is a bright afternoon, she has been for a walk with gaily garbed nurse, they have met the postman. Proudly and joyfully, she brings me a big white envelope. She rings three little bells on a silver bow which grannie has given her and intimates — laughing with dimples in her rosy cheeks — that she is a little lamb out at pasture.

Little lamb — stop ringing your bells — they fit not with this horrid news.

The message comes from Adolf Paul in Berlin. It has two enclosures, one a newspaper clipping from the Danish journal *Politiken*, the other a letter to Paul, from Knut Hamsun, now in Paris. The paper publishes an appeal signed by half a dozen famous Scandinavians there on behalf of August Strindberg. The letter:

Here are both of them.

From 'Politiken'   *Copenhagen*
   'August Strindberg has been ill for some time in the St. Louis Hospital, Paris. We know that his convalescence does

not permit him to work and that he has exhausted his last resources. Those about him are deeply concerned. They feel that he is going through a crisis which in this helpless condition might be fatal to him. He feels a profound urge to return to his native country and it might be of decisive importance for his recovery to fulfil it.

'It is therefore beyond doubt a duty for all Scandinavian compatriots of this man of genius to lend him a helping hand.

'Much as opinions may conflict about his tendencies, all must acknowledge his supreme importance in the intellectual life of the northern lands and should hasten to his assistance, both as a fellow being and a compatriot.

'Jonas Lie, Allan Osterlind, Sven Lange, Albert
Edelfelt, Anders Zorn, Knut Hamsun.'

*

The Friend (Knut Hamsun, Paris, to Adolf Paul, Berlin)

'Strindberg is very badly off. I have succeeded in getting an appeal for him into the press. But I do not know what will result. The Swedish newspapers to whom the appeal was sent did not publish or even mention it. He lives here on a most insecure basis, writing an article now and then, which perhaps some paper prints and perhaps not. He is badly paid — he was paid only forty francs for his last article on sulphur; his translator kept twenty francs, so that only twenty francs was Strindberg's share. He is in debt and has been living on credit the whole time and does not know how long he will be able to remain where he is.

'He lacks clothing. Now, in winter, he goes about in a light green summer suit and he is embarrassed. He feels he cannot call on anyone, not even on publishers, in his present state.

'I thank you personally, for being willing to intervene on his behalf in Berlin. You tell me he has a grudge against you. But I scarcely know anyone against whom he has no grudge. He does not like me either, he says my personality is too strong for him. It is hardly possible to have anything to do with him. But I do not mind and I see that you don't either. In spite of everything, he is August Strindberg.

'It ought to be made possible for him to live as he chooses. If he wishes to write masterpieces — all right. If he wants to dabble in chemistry, all right. If he wants to dabble in alchemy, all right. If he wants to do nothing at all, all right. The man has done so much good work and is of such importance that he ought to be allowed to occupy himself according to his own desire.

'We were to dine together one evening and were looking for a place. We had stopped in front of a little restaurant which made no particular pretensions and where other people went in who were also poorly dressed. But Strindberg said: "No, here it is too well-lighted for me, here it is too bright. Let us go somewhere else." He did not say it in a complaining tone, he only stated it as a fact. "Here it is too bright for me!" — And yet it was no other than August Strindberg! I cannot forget the impression it made upon me! Do something for him if you can — Knut Hamsun.'

I [*from Freda's Diary*]

Little lamb, why do you cry? Have I frightened you with my outburst? That it should always be those who love us best who hurt us!

Don't cry now, we must act.

Bless your words, Knut Hamsun, I never heard any more beautiful — Thanks to you all, you, Lie, and you, Zorn, and you, Sven Lange — but are you sure he really wants great Sweden and not this little maiden at my side? Do you know him, do you even see him while your eyes behold him? Do you realize, he leads a double life, the man of sorrows lowered to the profoundest depths of humiliation, while the

Unknown, the mysterious king in him, reaches radiantly out for the heights?

No, little lamb, you must write to him — you!

What shall we say to make the sun shine? We must not know of this appeal, mind! I am certain they published it without his knowledge and he resents it bitterly. He would not want me to tell you, and I never shall. Well then, let us write — that you are good — and are growing plump and strong and bright — that you love to play on his guitar and already have your own unruly melody, you too — that your little turn-up nose is as disrespectful a challenge as his own, and that your eyes are getting quite unwarrantably dark, like violets in the shade ... That you are such big friends with all those nice cows ... That we are waiting now for summer to bring back the melons, the tomatoes and the cucumbers ... And would he come back too ... ?

Can that save August Strindberg?

*

He (August Strindberg, Paris, to Freda, Dornach)

'Freda. — I received your letter, postmarked "Saxen". What! You are in Dornach? If lack of money has driven you there, I am heartbroken! But you never tell me anything about yourself!

'You also seem not to have received my last letter or the French newspapers, which would have informed you of my position and my hopes. My hopes! Tell me once again, tell me honestly, is it really true, are you really going to leave me? In your last letter you mentioned the possibility of a "friendly solution".

'It was this hope which gave me strength to master my nervousness, leave my retirement and grasp at the prize which was mine by right. Give me a final answer. Do you mean to stay in Dornach all the summer and would you think it all right if I took up my quarters at Schlipitzka's Inn there?

'If your answer is "Yes", I promise you to give the lecture on sulphur and display the experiments, some time before May 15th, in a hall of the Sorbonne. Think it over and write to me about it.

'Keep my luggage for the present. I shall only send you yours if you write and give me your address.

'If I had the means, I would ask you to come to Paris. Your being here would give me the courage and interest in life which I now lack.

'I fancy I see signs in your last letter that you have again begun to believe that I am called upon to solve problems of a high nature. . . .

'So you have seen our little home again and our garden? How do you manage with the baby? Can she walk already? And has she any teeth?

'Write to me soon. Sans adieu — August Strindberg.

'PS. — Is there no picture of our child you could send me some time or other? It might help me to recognize her, supposing chance should ever make us meet. Anyhow it would be a souvenir of my second marriage and the month of April (*Germinal*).'

The Friend (Knut Hamsun, Paris, to Jonas Lie)

'Strindberg will not receive me, so that I cannot talk to him.

'I still got on quite well with him last winter. I suspected no evil therefore and scented no danger when I called on him on April 2nd, to hand over some money which had arrived for him. He happened to be out of town for a couple of days; so I left my visiting card, on which I had scribbled a message explaining things. A few days later, I sent him a couple of lines by post, repeating that I had some money for him. In answer I received a postcard on April 6th, saying: "Keep the thirty pieces of silver and let us be done with one another for the rest of our lives."

'I did want to punish him a little for this rudeness and sent him a postcard in return in which I wrote that if he did not fetch the money from me within two days I should return it to the sender. Besides — said I — a man who had become such a big fellow that he could fling away thirty pieces of silver should first of all pay his debts! And I reminded him that he had borrowed money from such a pauper as I.

'I received no answer to this and I concluded that he must be away. I did not return the money to the donor, but forwarded it care of the *Göteborg Journal*.

'Frankly, I did not feel eager to pay Strindberg another personal call, but in the end, I did. There I heard the bad news that he has not been away at all, but up in his room. I wrote on my card: "It is a matter of a thousand francs!" and I sent up this message. The servant came back with the answer — "not at home".

'The position is now this: I cannot get audience of the man, that one fact I have ascertained to-day. And so I know no more about him than anybody else. All the same, I should advise against more money being sent to him. He is now adequately supplied. He can go home any day, as far as his fare is concerned. But he does not go.

'His reasons seem to be of a private nature.

'But it is a pity about him in his confusion. It would really have been a relief to me if, let us say, I could have taken August Strindberg to the train and put the thousand Swedish crowns in his pocket, wishing him a happy journey. As things stand, I must be excused, he will have nothing to do with me — Knut Hamsun.'

He (August Strindberg, Paris, to Freda, Dornach)

'. . . Is it possible that enemy hands have intercepted our correspondence?

'I often ask myself whether it is really you who desire our

separation, or whether it is others who desire it? Whether you are not the victim of an illegitimate revenge?

'Our child's birthday is drawing near — and I cannot remember the date. Kiss her for me and tell her that I am working for her when I build up my future.

'To-day I solved my problem and accomplished my mission in the Sorbonne Laboratory. Now I am considering going to Rouen to look for a position, no matter what.

'In one of your last letters, you had invited me to come and see my child. I replied that I should not mind staying at Schlipitzka's for a while. In answer, you bade me a farewell for all eternity!

'Please tell me where you are, what you are doing, how the child is. Is that asking too much?

'I am not happy, in spite of the success of my researches. And you?

'The frightful winter is over. It is spring and the summer will pass by, to make room for another winter.

'How stupid life is! And we? August.'

'. . . Since we have now got so far, I would beg you to undertake nothing before May 1st, the position being as follows:

'I have just come back from Rouen, where an engineer named Dubose is approaching the representatives of the Rouen chemical products in his name and mine.

'We hope to obtain money enough by this to continue the experiments needed to make my sulphur discoveries, which are admitted by Paris chemists to serve industrial purposes.

'While we await results, I shall continue to work in the laboratory of the Sorbonne, so as to keep matters alive. It is no longer the question: "Is Strindberg right?" Emulation has started in and now people ask, "Who among us Frenchmen was the first to say so?"

'I beg you, therefore, to wait, with a little patience and a little faith, and then it will be revealed whether I am not at last to exploit my own work, my own self. The hope of rejoining my family will give me nerve to pluck the fruits of my labours.

'PS. — I am determined to be near my child during the summer, you cannot prevent that. I want nothing of you. You need not translate me, for my works are already translated and on offer. I shall not interfere with your affairs and you need not fear the constraint which my personality seems to inflict upon you.

'I will live by myself without inconveniencing your household and if I can help you and the child, you can rely upon me.

'I have not broken my marriage vows and will conduct myself in your vicinity so that my presence will bring no disgrace upon you.

'And the little one! I often see her in my dreams. Tell her that after cruel suffering, her father stands on the threshold of a door opening on to a beautiful future for his child.

'Do send me your address, or rather Kerstin Strindberg's address this summer. Otherwise you will cause me expense and trouble, for I will find out where she is.

'I beg you, send me the address without metaphysics and circumlocution — August Strindberg.'

'*Two more words in haste:* We really are no longer children and I beg you to keep my luggage, because my brother does not want to take charge of it. I intend to spend the summer in some hostelry between Dornach and Grein. People have got together money for me (a donation) so you need not fear, and your family need not fear, that I shall run into debt and compromise you. Get your divorce, if you are determined upon it. I want to see my child every day. As for what is proper, Good Heavens, propriety — and you! On the road beside the Danube there stroll worse vagabonds than I.

'Tell Kerstin I am glad for her sake that I have succeeded in making iodine out of the by-products of coal; it is certain to cause a revolution. I am publishing a report in the *Temps* some time this week. Now I am preparing for my journey to the Danube without asking permission first. I shall bring your things along myself.

'I give you full liberty and I do not demand to see you in Dornach and will not annoy you by the sight of me. You will never as much as catch a glimpse of me.

'If our marriage is annulled in Austria, let it be annulled; no one can nullify the child. — August Strindberg.

'Please write what I can bring Kerstin from Paris. And give her my picture (enclosed) as a souvenir.'

*

I [from Freda's Diary, Dornach]

Le Temps had published his article on iodine, and it had roused the interest, not only of the experts, but also of the public at large. Behind his scientific effort stood his moral and social one to liberate Knowledge from the frigid *'L'Art pour l'Art'* principle and make it serviceable to humanity. This time he was dealing with the production of iodine from the angle of industry. He aimed at a complete revolution of the latter and nothing less.

There is magnetism in the man, so there is magnetism in the idea. More than a hundred newspapers reproduced the article and their readers commented on it. Many attacked him, many felt enriched. They are no optimists, they know they cannot yet see the fruit, but they feel the fecundation — it is spring once more.

He is sending me three of the letters he received. Gold, industry and the occult are all courting him. He asks me to return or keep the missives — I am publishing them here.

They show the jarring contrast of the life led by the man, and that led by the king the man beareth within.

Gold (H. Massman, Paris, to August Strindberg, Paris)

Quinquinas,   *16 Rue Parc (Marais),*
Sels de quinine-Mercuriaux   *Paris, le 24 Mai, 1895.*
Produits chiniques et
Pharmaceutiques, H. Massman.

À M. August Strindberg: I have read your article on iodine with the greatest interest. As the representative of the largest manufacturer of *Iodures Hydroquinines* in the world, it would give me particular pleasure to have a talk with you on the subject.

With my best compliments, yours faithfully — H. Massman.

Industry (A. Dubosc, Rouen, to A. Strindberg, Paris)

Dear M. Strindberg: Many thanks for kindly sending me the *Temps*. Would you empower me to write a paper on your discovery for the Société Industreille de Rouen? If so, could you oblige me with a few supplementary details?

In friendship — André Dubosc, Engineer.

The Occult Sciences (Paul Sédir, Paris, to August Strindberg, Paris)

To August Strindberg: Hail! You are a God of the Dawn. — Now the origin of all things earthly will soon be revealed. Consider the periods of geology. The origin is Silurian, then Cambrian, then Pre-Cambrian. So do the schools teach at present. But our ripe spirits have departed from this teaching. The granite period did not open the Book of Life, it was, on the contrary, the penultimate chapter. — We have you to thank, you and the others, that you have laid bare the genesis of the albuminoids. You will show us the oceans of Chaos and the Spheres where the Monsters of Eld did battle, before the Spirit moved upon the Face of the Waters.

Let all answer to this writing be forbidden. But hasten the day on which the hospitable city of Paris shall throw open its doors that the Faithful may perceive the Master and hear his Words.

Health, Courage — forwards! — Paul Sédir.

The last letter startles me. The signature had been rendered almost illegible by Strindberg, but it is that of Paul Sédir, the favourite disciple of Papus, the acknowledged master of the occult sciences in France.

Gold had been the quickest to get in touch.

M. Massman followed up his communication at once. He suggested that Strindberg should take out a German patent for his synthetic iodine; the two of them would soon be rich! But Strindberg did not see it that way. He lived in such a tiny place, he said, that there was no room in it for wealth.

M. Massman returned to the charge. If Mr. Strindberg's home was too small to hoard up wealth, he himself had ample room for it. He seemed to be a gentleman of fortune already! He brought with him a nice, neat cheque for one hundred thousand francs!

Strindberg refused the cheque, even more energetically. He had never been on good terms with money — why should it thrust itself upon him so suddenly? It could certainly not be with honest intent. In any case, if his chemistry were worth anything, it belonged to humanity and not to himself at all. Should he drive a bargain over something which had been given him by God?

This was not even a temptation — the whole idea was so far removed from him.

And this is the man who for my sake should once more be sacrificed to the rule and spirit of the Big House?

He (*August Strindberg, Paris, to Freda, Dornach*)

'Beloved Sheep: First you write me a regular love-letter — a very model of its kind. You even talk of my non-existent beauty which is visible to none but your beautiful eyes. You tell me that we were made for each other and so on. And then you send me this hellish lawyer of yours and let him threaten me!

'That is just as characteristic of my Sheep as everything else she does!

'And now you ask me — can I forget? You can ask that! — Have you yourself forgotten how good I used to be at forgetting?

'But do not forget one thing: what one forgets out of love, one remembers later out of hatred, so well, oh, so well!

'And then you ask me whether I believe that it is still possible for us to live together?

'I can only say this: Let us see each other again! And if we find ourselves overcome by an unconquerable dislike, good, then we shall part! Is that all right?

'But sheepskin should not play with the fox (Fuchs). One fine day he will snap, because the lion has already snapped. Here is my hand, the hand once reached out to take yours in Heligoland. It is black with work, but unblemished and raised in the sacred vow which I have never broken.

'Do not play with happiness, child! For love is happiness, and gilds dirty old life with its radiance! And a good conscience is a fine thing, too!

'It's not every day that you will find someone you could love and who will love you as I do. Is it all right? Have we quarrelled enough and shed enough tears? Oh, this black winter! Is it over? Yes, I feel it. And now I have earned you and the child by toil and trouble, haven't I?

'I have been successful with my iodine and the future seems to be ours — August.'

'Freda: What a method of writing letters! It takes three to answer one of yours!

'To put an end to it, I am handing over your trunk, this last souvenir of you, to the concierge at Passy. The lock was repaired when she called, the key was made, all in good order.

'Do you think the little one will cry when she first sees me? That is what I am afraid of. But as a rule, children love me instinctively.

'It is a year now since she came into the world. It was a gruesome and yet a blessed year for me.

'When I have done with iodine, I shall return in summer to botany. I have made progress and this I owe to my friends, who have presented me with a splendid microscope and with books. *I have succeeded in proving that plants have nerves.* I am now occupying myself with astronomy. Two astronomical societies have elected me a member and quite a number of people are waiting for a man to come who will have courage enough to put an end to the supposed mad whirling round of the old earth in the void without losing its atmosphere. Do not have me locked up behind iron bars if I continue to work at my coelestography and all the rest of it.

'It is possible that during the summer I shall write a work of fiction as well as pursue my botanical studies. This is to be my farewell to worldly life, for I am preparing myself to enter a cloister in autumn. You are laughing? Laugh! — August.

'PS. — For the last time: Keep my luggage! By all that's holy, I shall turn up on the shores of the Danube in a fortnight's time at the very latest.'

August Strindberg, Paris, to Robert Fuchs, attorney, Vienna

'Sir: This seems to me the moment to terminate the comedy which your lady client is making you play.

'First she demands a divorce and I do not refuse it. Then she announces that she wants to visit me in my Paris home. Then she invites me to come and see the child, which lives with her and I accept, since she also writes that the child has rickets. But I have scarcely started preparations for the journey when I get a lawyer's letter — yours — threatening divorce. I am only surprised that this divorce has not yet come about after four months' efforts on your part. And I was still more surprised recently to read in a letter from your client (while you are conducting the case) that "she and I are made for one another, etc.", in short, a letter which proclaims the exact contrary of what she makes you write.

'Forgive me, therefore, when I refuse to go on with this correspondence which seems to me better fitted for the intimacy of the home than for publicity, and when I permit myself to follow the dictates of my conscience and of common sense. Believe me to be, my dear Sir, Yours very truly — August Strindberg.'

The Friend (Knut Hamsun, Paris, to Jonas Lie)

'A thousand thanks for the fifty francs you sent me for Strindberg and for all your kind help.

'It is difficult to handle Strindberg. The nuisance is that people are addressing their contributions to him direct. He must have received about a thousand francs these days, and that was not the idea. He has quite gone under, borrows a louis d'or here, a louis d'or there, has debts in his hotel, debts in his restaurant. When he first heard what we had done for him, he thanked me most heartily and begged me above all to convey his gratitude to you. But no sooner does it rain money, than dear Strindberg carries his head up high and no longer cares a button for you and the Committee. I had sent a kind of report about his condition to Berlin, and the actors of the Deutsches Theater planned a special perforance for his benefit. Well, he took the lead into his own hands and wrote to Berlin as would some Prince — Charity performance? Much obliged. But as far as he was concerned, he did not want the money; if any should come in, it might be sent to his child in Vienna. Now it is highly unlikely that a performance will be given for this child, which is the grandchild of a Court councillor and rich man.

'In the same tune he has written yesterday to Swedish, Norwegian, Finnish papers; there has been an appeal published without his knowledge, and if donors felt desirous, would they kindly send their contributions to his children in Finland? Nobody just then was interested in his Finnish children, though, and I much fear that the papers will stop collecting.

'Strindberg came to see me only to-day. I had been ill in bed these last three weeks and therefore on receipt of your wire had sent him a telegram. He told me what he had written to the papers and thought it fine. 'Strindberg must teach them!' He is as childish as a babe. But I am much afraid that he has killed this collection. I don't know what can be done — most likely nothing. One thing, however, has been gained. I am glad for him. A Swedish physician has invited him for the summer. He wants to go there. That means a shelter even if the whole collection should go to the dogs. Money for his fare he has: he complains quite openly about the disturbance the many orders cause him which he must cash at the post office. I questioned him as to how much he had received altogether. But he immediately grew mysterious: I must not take him for such a fool. And then he smiled. All the same, he has received as much as five hundred kronen from one single person and many a one-hundred marks from Germany. I estimate him therefore at a thousand francs or more.

'I had been warned that he is more eccentric than ever. But his condition staggered me and that is why I have begged Sven Lange to call on you. Now I thank you once more for your help. Strindberg is sure to get to Sweden and that is what he has been longing for — Knut Hamsun.'

*

I (from Freda's Diary, Dornach)

My lawyer, Mr. Fuchs, has sent me Strindberg's letter. He asks me what are my feelings on the subject. I will tell him the whole truth.

Yes, dear Mr. Fuchs — I shall say — it is so. I hate the idea of parting from August Strindberg and I abhor the idea of any interference, even yours — above all, of the law and the law-courts. I feel a constant burning urge to return to August Strindberg: he has become part of my own self and it will cost blood and the rending of flesh to tear us from one another. But what is the use?

Fate. — When an animal stands in the slaughter house, it must put forward its head and it puts it forward. Why it does it, nobody will ever know. But every animal, like its fellow, stretches forth its head when it is ordered. It simply is my turn now. Let the executioners do their duty by me and Strindberg then. Do yours. Please do it quickly. The more quickly, the better. Don't let us suffer long. It hurts.

No, I have not been play-acting, not even to myself. Everything came about as it must, and must at last come to an end. This seems the given moment. One suffers less at parting in the night when one already sees the dawn. He is now on the road to success. He will find it easier to do without me now — it was harder a little while ago.

What had impelled me to write again to Strindberg was

that appeal in the paper. I wanted to comfort and help. Love awoke anew. It had not been dead, anyhow, and I suppose it will never quite die. But he and I cannot come together any more . . . It often seems to me as if this marriage must pass by in order that some of our love can go on and persist untarnished through the ages. But you must not tell them so in court.

I do not know where my new exchange of letters with Strindberg might have led us if the dream had not been suddenly rent. It was. Something happened. It caught me by the shoulders and shook me awake. I realized that marriage with me was not a comfort and a help to him, but that it had been, at this time of his life, a hindrance and would be his ruin, if it continued.

His reply to the appeal in the press brought me back to crude fact. He begged that the money that would come in for him from a Berlin benefit performance to save him from want and destruction, should be given to our child!

'That was manly and fine!' I can hear you say.

So it was, it showed me the extent of my responsibility.

My father did not see it that way. His indignation was indescribable. Such a public insult, just as he had celebrated a pompous seventieth birthday on May 14th![1] He had been honoured and celebrated all over town and country as an influential personality, a distinguished man of letters, a prominent critic, a connoisseur and an art collector. Now, all of a sudden, spiteful and reproachful side-looks were shot at him everywhere in Vienna: a charity performance was to be given for his daughter's child. Was this Strindberg's retort — he asked me, foaming with rage, because he had not planked down on the table the money for the other Strindberg children when it was demanded of him?

---

[1] F. Uhl's birthday (May 14th) was to be Strindberg's day of death (1912). Strindberg's birthday, January 22nd (1849), became for Friedrich Uhl his day of Death (1906).

The public scandal does not touch me, nor father's wrath, although I am sorry for him. I have become detached, even from my own father. But father was quite right, it was Strindberg's answer — only in quite another sense. It was not revenge, but the salvaging of his honour. The man who in his penury could refuse riches because his science and his writings belonged to humanity at large and not to himself alone, thought that he, in his turn, had the right to expect of humanity that it should provide for his children. Had he not, like Epaminondas, given to the world two immortal daughters, Leuktra and Mantinea, his battles and his victories?

I see him before me, radiant with pride as he wrote his letter to the newspapers. What a breath of relief he must have drawn at being able to show his father-in-law that one can leave more to one's children than a mere cheque-book. 'A failure then — and now perhaps a victory' — he had written the words from *Faust* as a dedication in Father Uhl's copy of 'Antibarbarus'.

'And now perhaps a victory' . . . can Strindberg speak thus of himself? I do not know, but sometimes I see him before me, already far from us on the spiral pathway — high above! To try to hold him, to pull him back from his creator's life into the choking air of domesticity and the humdrum of a battle for daily bread, would be murder! Even if it draw blood and hearts must break. . . . *Il faut comprendre l'affreuse nécessité —*

It must be. I must write and tell Mr. Fuchs that the divorce proceedings must go on. August Strindberg cannot live in shackles. If I do not relieve him of his chains, he himself will tear them asunder some day. But then his hands will bleed — bleed!

'Dear Mr. Fuchs,' I write, 'I stand in the slaughter-house now, because I must . . . I am nothing but an ordinary, everyday animal . . . Never mind me . . . it doesn't matter

about me . . . but be merciful . . . Strindberg is different . . .
don't touch him . . . strike only me . . . I am stretching my
head forward . . . Take care . . . Don't hurt August Strindberg —'

The Bard (Drachmann, of Denmark, to Strindberg, of Sweden)

Restless one, Thou!
Who in Sweden, where everyone sings, thy harp in pieces
    didst shatter,
Plaiting its strings into scourges, beating all, beaten by all;
What shall I say unto Thee, who in every dangerous matter
Sprangest into the breach when I, weary, the weapon let fall?

Storm weather, Thou!
Worn with woe is the brow and the brain with pangs rent
    asunder,
When one, Sunday and weekdays, must fight the battle
    undying;
Only Thee I know with a heart unfailing, a wonder,
Whom Thy folk will acclaim, Thy corpse on the battlefield
    lying.

Pledge of the Future!
Thou — in Sweden, where every singer that grasps at the
    roses,
Tears but the flowers and the petals fall from his hand,
Thou hast woven a wreath, now torn, but the future discloses
Brother, to-morrow shall see Thee crowned with the Masters
    stand.

*

EPILOGUE

Autumn 1895

ASCENT

From August Strindberg's occult diary (The Inferno)

In spite of everything, I count the summer and autumn of the year 1895 among the happiest times of my storm-tossed life. Whatever I attempt is a success; unknown friends bring me nourishment, like Elijah's ravens. Money pours in upon me. I can buy books, instruments, among them a microscope, which reveals to me the secrets of life.

Dead to the world, since I had renounced the idle joys of Paris, I remain in my own quarter, where I visit the dead in the churchyard of Montparnasse every morning and then walk down to the gardens of the Luxembourg to bid my flowers good morning. Sometimes a tourist countryman of mine calls to invite me to lunch with him on the other bank of the Seine and go to the theatre.

I deny myself this pleasure, since for me the right bank is forbidden ground, it is the so-called 'World' — the world of the living and their vanities.

Although I cannot formulate it in words, a kind of religion has grown up in me. It is rather a state of soul than a point of view founded upon teachings — a maze of sensations which condense more or less into thoughts.

I have bought myself a Roman Bible and read it meditatively. The Old Testament comforts and disciplines me in a strange way, whereas the New Testament leaves me cold. This does not prevent a Buddhistic book from having a

447

greater influence upon me. It places actual suffering higher than mere abstinence. Buddha has the courage to repudiate his wife and child while in full possession of his manhood and the joys of married life, whereas Christ simply shuns the contact with the sanctioned pleasures of this world.

Otherwise I do not ponder over the feelings which arise in me. I am indifferent to them and let them have their way, for I allot myself the same measure of freedom which I allow to others . . .

*

From Freda's Diary, Dornach

I am alone on the meadow behind the little hut . . . All around me are signs of spring. Two years ago we were bride and groom in May, he and I. On that white veranda in Heligoland, under the first blossoming tree.

One year ago the child was born. I cried out loud in anguish, as though I were combating death. It was the nativity of a young life and neither of us knew whether my cry was of suffering or of joy — one year ago.

To-day two wide baby eyes are looking up at me, a little daughter of Man sits near me on the grass in her little white frock and plays with profound earnestness, as children play.

The heavens are as wide and blue as they were on the day of our marriage, when he stood on the outermost edge of the cliff and stretched himself up towards the sun as though he were borne on the air . . . longing to knead Matter into a more perfect and beautiful thing, and see Creation and Created happy, born without pain, living without suffering and dying in a mute bliss.

Wide and blue are the heavens now once more, as if they were open to everyone who had the courage to soar up to them. It must be possible to fly right in. The sun is so warm, everything smells sweet.

I lift my head and gaze into that open, radiant sky.

Have I merely thought the words, or did I speak them —

'Fly — fly!'

*

LOOKING BACK

WHAT did our marriage mean to him and what to me — loss or gain?

There are questions that sear the soul and go on burning until they find an answer.

In those days there were hours of despairing bitterness in which I asked myself again and again: 'Why was the marriage wrecked — the marriage which brought me so much happiness, which he would not give up, nor I? Why did he forsake me and I him, nevertheless?'

But only time could give the answer. And time did give it me.

As long as I lived at August Strindberg's side, I was the enemy of the Unknown and he was mine. The Unknown piled up the pyre and blew up the flame of the sacrifice in which the man I loved was consumed and my fragment of earthly happiness reduced to ashes. He was the spirit, and the misty substance of the body shut him in — I, again, was no saint, no martyr, no philosopher, no pearl of wisdom — not even a quiet, intelligent, gentle human being. I lived tempestuously only according to my feelings and they had been cruelly hurt. Something within me did warn me that behind reality there was a deeper truth which was other than the robe of deed and word. But I was too young to comprehend.

'One must be able to lose oneself in order to find oneself,' Strindberg had once said to me. I did not lose Strindberg by parting from him. I found him.

Each of us went our own way. But my longing was always calling after him and I lived through no experience without telling him of it in spirit at night and looking at it from his standpoint. I followed the news of him in all countries. I became a nomad. I stayed nowhere long. I was driven on and on, restlessly, relentlessly, away from the one and from all, in order to follow his soul's pilgrimage from a distance, until I should be able to comprehend him entirely.

Thus I saved what was best in me.

In Copenhagen, in 1896, I met Georg Brandes, who had been paid a brief visit by Strindberg not long before. Strindberg had made a most painful impression upon Brandes. He had spoken mysteriously of his latest weird occult experiences and of the magical power of human will and thought. Brandes, Taine's intellectual disciple, had his brain much too fast in the iron claw-grips of relationalism to have any appreciative understanding of such a mixture of Knowledge Eternal and an erratic poet's fanciful mind. To him, Strindberg the occultist was a tragi-comic figure, evoking ridicule instead of fear and pity.

He told me of some of the occult experiences Strindberg had confided to him. There was that ancient practice of black magic of which Stanislas de Guaita, contemporary French occultist, had recently been accused, on the occasion of the death of that ill-famed modern sorcerer, Huysman's Abbé Bouillant. If one of the adepts had enemies, he might destroy them by the force of his will and with the help of a simple pin, which he must run into the heart of a waxen effigy of the doomed men.

Strindberg had recommended him this practice.

Georg Brandes fell silent. Silently he and I walked together through the Copenhagen streets. The twilight was sinking as we came to the harbour. There hundreds of ships from all countries lay at anchor. Small fishing barques and great liners rested contentedly and like comrades side by side. All had come back to port and were ready to set forth anew.

What Brandes had just told me had made a profound impression on me, but one different from what he had probably expected. It was impossible for me to feel horrified and it was impossible for me to laugh. I had too often experienced in Strindberg's sayings and doings the deep sense in non-sense, while his thoughts shaped gradually into being. In this whole thing there was certainly a streak of amused mockery which had escaped the concerned Brandes' notice. But parallel with this I felt sure that Strindberg was creatively engaged upon some new work. The ashes and the dead lava must be hurled out by the mountain, before the pure flame could ascend.

Ere he arrived at Truth, he had to traverse superstition.

The work then in being was the *Inferno*. With it began his life's second and richest harvest. He broke with his human past prior to our marriage. Woman was no longer uniquely the destroyer; he had seen her endure and love. The disastrous ravines of old suffering in him had been flooded over by more powerful currents of grief, which swept away the poisonous prior memories. The poet once more rose. With bold defiance he started to build a bridge between the visible and the invisible world. He became the Chronicler and Poet of the Occult — *on his way home to his native soil.*

It seemed strange to me that Georg Brandes, with his fine feeling for a finished work, should seem to know nothing of the act of birth and that the creative spirit in its travail should so elude him.

Of course, I could not say such a thing to Brandes. So I began hesitatingly to speak of Strindberg, of his personality and his genius, of his astounding versatility, his winged intuition, his sensitive, kindly spirit ... I do not know for how long I spoke. Suddenly I came to myself as I caught a kindly but mocking smile.

'I never knew a virtuous, firmly married wife who spoke so enthusiastically of her lord and master. And in spite of this you parted from Strindberg?'

I remember still how I stared at him without comprehension and then replied hesitatingly:

'Yes . . . to be sure . . . not in spite of that . . . just because of that . . .'

The darkness closed in about us. The ships, great and small, had sunk into sleep. Brandes went on putting questions:

'Strindberg told me he attributed the failure of your marriage to the battle between himself and you to maintain your personalities.'

'Yes, that's what he said.'

'Do you regret that you left August Strindberg?'

'No.'

'You would not marry him a second time?'

'Oh yes. I would marry him again, without a moment's thought or doubt. At any price.'